MW00648708

THE GLUTEN-FREE GUIDE TO ITALY

Maria Ann Roglieri, Ph.D.

©2015 Mari Productions, LLC
www.gfguideitaly.com

Copyright 2015 by Maria Ann Roglieri

Seventh edition

All rights reserved. Printed and bound in the United States of America. No part of this book may be reproduced, stored in a retrieval system or transmitted in any form without written permission from the publisher.

Published by Mari Productions, LLC
63 Fremont Rd
Sleepy Hollow, NY 10591

Visit www.gfguideitaly.com for updates and additional publications.

1.Health 2.Travel 3.Gluten intolerance 4.Italy 5.Tuscany 6.Celiac Disease 7.Gluten-Free 8.GF 9.Senza Glutine 10.Celiac 11.Venice 12.Rome 13. Florence14. Sicily15. Sardinia

ISBN 978-0-9835409-1-5

Mari Productions, LLC gratefully acknowledges the Italian Celiac Association, known as Associazione Italiana Celiachia (AIC) for having granted permission to use and reformat information presented on the website www.celiachia.it. The efforts of the AIC to promote awareness of celiac disease and to help and organize restaurants to provide gluten-free food to their celiac customers are extraordinary and serve as a model for other celiac groups around the world.

We would also like to thank our friends who contributed photos: Susan Amatangelo, Amy Smith, Daniel Frost, David Impastato, Anna Komorowski, Elvira DiFabio, Sarah Wolozin, Luca Riccò, John Lubin, Gerald Friedman, John Roglieri, David Kraushaar, Julie Kelly, Ulla Benninger, Carly Caneparo, and Joe Coyne.

Maria Roglieri is a professor of Italian at St. Thomas Aquinas College in New York. She got her MA and Ph.D. in Italian from Harvard University, and her BA in Italian from Columbia University. She and her daughter, Sara, have both been gluten-free for years. In addition to authoring *The Gluten-Free Guides* series, she has authored *Dante and Music: Musical Adaptations of the Commedia from the 16th Century to the Present* (Ashgate Publishing, 2001) and numerous articles and chapters on Dante and music, and Dante and Ovid.

The Gluten-Free Guides

The Gluten-Free Guide to Italy
www.gfguideitaly.com

is part of the series which also includes:

The Gluten-Free Guide to France
www.gfguidefrance.com

The Gluten-Free Guide to Spain
www.gfguidespain.com

The Gluten-Free Guide to New York
www.gfguideny.com

The Gluten-Free Guide to Washington, D.C.
www.gfguidedc.com

To purchase these guides or to find out
about upcoming publications, see

www.theglutenfreeguides.com

TABLE OF CONTENTS

This book is dedicated with love
to my wonderful family,
Daniel, Sara, David and Julia Friedman

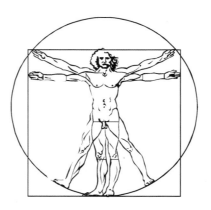

INTRODUCTION

As an Italian professor, a musician and an Italian-American, I have traveled all over Italy; I have even been lucky enough to occasionally spend long periods of time in my favorite Italian city, Rome. The country, the people, the art, the history, and the culture are fantastic. The food in Italy is a delight, a feast of the senses.

Ah, l'Italia: il paese della pasta (the land of pasta) . . . Most people imagine it to be a daunting destination for gluten-free tourists. To my surprise, as I have learned through extensive research, **Italy is a GF (gluten-free) paradise!**

Anyone on a GF diet can get GF croissants (known as *cornetti senza glutine*) in the local hotels and bakeries for breakfast; GF pizza for a mid-morning snack; GF lasagna with fresh-made GF bread for lunch; gelato with a GF cone in the afternoon; and if you still have room for dinner, three or four courses of anything you want GF for dinner. (Save room for the GF tiramisu for dessert!) Your biggest problem in Italy is going to be deciding what to eat first and trying not to gain 30 pounds from eating all the *delizioso cibo italiano* (delicious Italian food)!

Everyone in Italy knows about celiac disease. When you ask restaurant staff about GF food, they automatically respond, *Lei è celiaca?* (You have celiac disease?) This is because all Italians are tested for celiac disease at an early age. The many who test positive receive great services: a monthly stipend from the government for GF food as well as extra vacation time to shop for and prepare GF food. In addition, the Italian Celiac Association (AIC), the Italian government and a few major Italian companies that sell GF products have all worked to promote awareness and understanding of celiac disease. As a result, restaurant owners, managers, chefs, and waiters are well-informed.

While writing this book, I contacted the Italian Celiac Association and spoke to hundreds of restaurant owners, managers, and customers in Italy. Sometimes, restaurant owners said that they could not provide me a GF meal. But much more often, they said things like "Of course, Madame, with pleasure. Would you like gnocchi or tagliatelle? They are both GF and were homemade this morning.)"; and even "I am also a celiac and so I prepare everything here GF." Music to my ears!!!!

This book is presented as a service to the gluten-intolerant community, in the spirit of "celiacs helping celiacs." It offers lists of hotels, inns, B&B's, restaurants, caterers, pizza places, ice cream stores, bakeries, health food stores, and pharmacies that serve the GF community all over Italy. It lists all of the above by region. The establishments that are participating in the Italian Celiac Association program (more information about this in the opening pages of the book) are marked with AIC.

Let the reader be forewarned that *these lists are fluid*: restaurants come and go. It is a good idea to call first; for virtually all restaurants in this guide, phone numbers are listed. The list of restaurants *does not represent a guarantee* that food served at any restaurant is GF. Remember that it is always important to communicate with the chefs as to your own special dietary needs. For help with this, check out the Gluten-Free Italian 101 section which includes "Questions for the chef", food vocabulary, as well an extensive multilingual glossary section.

Enjoy your trip to Italy, and especially enjoy the food! Revel in your new-found gluten-free paradise.

Buon viaggio e buon appetito!

HOW TO USE THIS BOOK

The first part of the book offers information that is useful before you go to Italy. The second part of the book offers extensive vocabulary help for ordering gluten-free (GF) food in Italy. The third part of the book presents 4000 GF venues all over Italy. The venues are those that have been either personally contacted by the author of this book, recommended by fellow celiacs, sponsored by the Associazione Italiana Celiachia (AIC), trained and supplied by DS Food, or those listed by Dr. Schaar (a leading gluten-free food product company in Italy) as selling gluten-free food products.

The book is divided into **chapters** that represent each **region of Italy**, i.e. Sicily, Veneto and Tuscany. The chapters are divided into **provinces** and then into **cities and towns** within each province. The provinces are identified in bold print.

The following venues are identified in each chapter in this order:

- hotels and B&B's
- pizza places
- supermarkets and pharmacies that carry GF food products
- restaurants
- gelato places

The following information on each venue is provided:

Name   type of venue   price range
address   phone number   website (if any)
specialized notes such as days closed, etc, and, for the major cities, neighborhood location.

EXAMPLE:
Cammillo   trattoria   €€*, AIC **
Borgo S. Jacopo, 57   tel. 055.212427***   www.cammillo.it
Notes: closed Tuesdays and Wednesdays. GF pasta available.****

*price points are provided when possible for a main course for one including tax and service and are categorized as follows:

price range	symbol
Under €17 €	
€18-€24	€€
€25-€32	€€€
Over €32	€€€€

** AIC = sponsored by AIC (Italian celiac society)
*** phone numbers provided are from *within* Italy and do not include codes to dial out of the country of residence or the country code for Italy (which is 39).
****GF= gluten-free

WHAT YOU NEED TO KNOW

BEFORE YOU GO

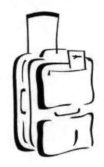

GETTING TO ITALY:THE FLIGHT

There are a number of airlines that will provde a gluten-free meal on the flight to Italy (see list below). It is very important to notify the staff that you need such a meal well in advance. You can do so via their website or in person on the phone.

Air Canada	Air France
Alitalia	American Airlines
Austrian Airlines	British Airways
Cathay Pacific	Continental Airlines
Delta Airlines	El Al
Eurowings	Finnair
Iberia	Iceland Air
LAN Airlines	Lufthansa
Luxair	Malev
Olympic Airlines	Qantas
SAS	SATA
Swiss International Airlines	TAP Air Portugal
Turkish Airlines	United Airlines
US Air	Virgin Atlantic

GETTING TO AND AROUND ITALY: THE CRUISE

Many of the major cruise lines are able to serve customers gluten-free meals with advance notice:

- Carnival Cruise Lines (tel. 800 438- 6744, www.carnival.com)
- Celebrity Cruises (tel. 800 647-2251, www.celebritycruises.com)
- Costa (tel. 800 288-6006, www.cruises.com/promotion/costa-cruises.do)
- Disney Cruise lines (tel. 800 951-3532, http://disneycruise.disney.go.com)
- Norwegian Cruise lines (tel. 866 234-7350, www2.ncl.com/)
- Princess Cruise lines (tel. 800 774-6237, www.princess.com)
- Thompson Cruise Lines (England: tel. 08712314691, www.thomson.co.uk/cruise.html)
- MSC Cruises (www.msccruises.com)

Your best bet is to book on one of two major cruise lines: Costa Cruises and MSC Cruises. The Italian Celiac Society (AIC) works directly with these two cruise lines to ensure a careful choice of GF food products, and a special GF menu.

WHEN YOU'RE THERE: FOOD OPTIONS

BREAKFAST

When you stay in a hotel, make sure to phone ahead and asked them if they can serve you a **gluten-free breakfast** ("colazione senza glutine"). Most hotels and B&B's serve a complimentary continental breakfast; with advance notice, they can order gluten-free food for you from a pharmacy or make it themselves. You can have, as I did, warm gluten-free croissants (called "cornetti senza glutine"), breads and little cakes for breakfast.

If your hotel says they cannot provide you a gluten-free breakfast, you can go to any pharmacy and buy some GF products to bring to the hotel breakfast. You can also buy gluten-free bread there and use it for lunch with some fresh cheese and cold cuts (when you walk into any food store in Italy, they will tell you which cold cuts are gluten-free and most of them are).

WHERE TO FIND PREPACKAGED GF PRODUCTS:

You will find gluten-free products in pharmacies, *farmacia* and in supermarket chains such as Carrefour and Conad. We have listed the biggest of these venues alongside our list of restaurants for each region (see the section "Italy by Region".)

AN ITALIAN STAPLE: PIZZA

If you're looking for gluten-free pizza ("pizza senza glutine"), you're better off looking for it at *night* instead of during the day because Italians tend to have a bigger lunch and a smaller dinner. A lot of places don't even make gluten-free pizza during the day. In addition to the restaurants and pizzerias that participate in the Italian Celiac Society program (see next page), there are a number of restaurants and pizzerias that offer gluten-free pizza under the tutelage of a commercial venture, DS. This is a brand of the Dr. Schär group that provides restaurants with all the right cooking tools, gluten-free foods and ingredients and the training operators need to prepare meals safely. The restaurants that participate in this program are called DS Pizza Points. The "DS Pizza Points" are clearly indicated in this book

ANOTHER ITALIAN STAPLE: GELATO (ICE CREAM)

You can't go to Italy without sampling the delicious ice cream but be careful. Just as in the US, gluten is thrown into things you wouldn't expect, in Italy it is thrown in as well.

Obviously you need to stay away from flavors that have cookies in them, but additionally, to be absolutely certain there is no cross contamination; you should go to the designated ice cream stores that serve GF ice cream. There you can often get a gluten-free ice cream cone ("cono senza glutine"). All *gelaterie* that are indicated in this book have guaranteed GF gelato, since they are sponsored by the Italian Celiac Society.

You can also get pre-prepared ice cream in bars or restaurants just about anywhere if you look for this poster:

A NOTE ABOUT CALLING AHEAD

Some restaurants close in winter, and those that are open in winter will often have different hours from the summer hours. Also, restaurants open for dinner much later than in other countries; 9 pm is a typical dinner hour. Finally, restaurants can go out of business very quickly. Make sure to call ahead before you go to any of the recommended restaurants.

ASKING FOR GLUTEN-FREE FOOD IN RESTAURANTS

Keep in mind that when you inquire about getting gluten-free food in a restaurant, the first response might be "no". In this case, ask again in a different way! Here's the deal: the Italians have a national, very well-coordinated celiac society (AIC) that works closely with restaurants to serve GF food that has been prepared in a completely uncontaminated environment. The restaurants are equipped with a separate "laboratory" with a separate oven, stove, utensils, and cookware to prepare GF food. The restaurants' special labs are inspected every six months. If there are any violations of the food preparation rules, the restaurants are taken off the GF restaurant list until the violations have been remedied. This keeps restaurant owners hyper-vigilant about the GF food they prepare and serve.

So if you go to a restaurant that is not working directly with the Italian Celiac Society, the owners/managers may automatically say that they are "not prepared" or "not set up" to serve you a GF meal. This is just a way to indicate to you that they don't participate in the program. You can still get an excellent meal at this restaurant because odds are they have GF pasta stashed away for their regular clients, and they're already well familiar with celiac disease and gluten-free food. Even if they don't have GF pasta stashed away, they can still easily prepare you a "second piatto," that is, a meat, chicken, rabbit, veal, or fish dish that is gluten-free. So you should let them know that you understand they don't participate in the Italian Celiac Society program, but that you would love to have a GF "secondo" at their restaurant.

GLUTEN-FREE ITALIAN 101:

REQUESTING A
GLUTEN-FREE MEAL
in italiano

CELIAC IDENTIFICATION CARD
FOR THE CHEF AND WAITER

Sono celiaca e devo mangaiare cibo SENZA GLUTINE. <u>Posso mangiare</u> il cibo che ha riso, mais, patate, ortaggi e qualsiasi frutta, uova, formaggio, latte, carne, pesce, purchè non sia stato preparato con farina, pangrattato, o salsa che contiene frumento o glutine. <u>Non posso mangiare</u> il cibo che contiene farine di grano o di cereali (kamut, spelta, duram, semola, e bulgar), segale, orzo, o glutine. Grazie per il Suo aiuto.

TRANSLATIONS:

(E) I have celiac disease and I have to eat food WITHOUT GLUTEN. I can eat food that has rice, corn, potatoes, vegetables and any fruit, eggs, cheese, milk, meat, fish, as long as it has not been prepared with flour, breadcrumbs or sauce containing wheat or gluten. I can not eat food containing wheat flour or cereal (kamut, spelt, duram, semolina, and bulgar), rye, barley, or gluten. Thank you for your help.

(D) Ich habe Zöliakie und ich muss Lebensmittel OHNE GLUTEN essen. Ich kann Reis, Mais, Kartoffeln, Gemüse und Obst, Eier, Käse, Milch, Fleisch, Fisch essen, solange sie noch nicht mit Mehl, Paniermehl oder Sauce mit Weizen oder Gluten zu bereitet sind. Ich kann nicht Lebensmittel mit Weizen Mehl oder Getreide (Kamut, Dinkel, langsamer, Grieß und Bulgarisch), Roggen, Gerste, oder Gluten essen. Vielen Dank für Ihre Hilfe.

(S) Tengo la enfermedad que se llama celiaca y tengo que comer alimentos SIN GLUTEN. Puedo comer alimentos que contienen arroz, maíz, papas, vegetales y cualquier tipo de fruta. También, puedo comer alimentos que contienen huevos, queso, leche, carne, y pescado, siempre que no hayan sido preparados con harina, pan, salsa o que contengan gluten de trigo. No puedo comer alimentos que contengan harina de trigo o cereales (kamut, escanda, duram, sémola, y bulgar), centeno, cebada, o gluten. Gracias por su ayuda.

(F) J'ai la maladie coeliaque et je dois manger des aliments SANS GLUTEN. Je peux manger la nourriture qui a le riz, le maïs, les pommes de terre, de légumes et de fruits tout, des oeufs, du fromage, du lait, la viande, le poisson, tant qu'elle n'a pas été préparée avec la farine, la chapelure ou de la sauce contenant du blé ou du gluten. Je ne peux pas manger des aliments contenant de la farine de blé ou de céréales (kamut, épeautre, duram, semoule, et bulgar), le seigle, l'orge ou du gluten. Merci pour votre aide.

QUESTIONS FOR THE CHEF OR WAITER

D=Deutsch
Sp=Spanish, Fr=French
Italian in bold

Is this dish breaded or dusted in wheat flour before it is cooked?

(D) Ist das Gericht paniert mit Weizenmehl, bevor es gekocht wird?
(Sp) ¿Está este plato preparado con pan rallado o harina de trigo?
(Fr)   Est-ce que ce plat est pané ou préparé avec de la farine avant sa cuisson?

È questo piatto impanato di farina di frumento o molliche di pane prima che sia cotto?

Is this dish preseasoned or cooked in broth or bouillon?

(D) Ist das Gericht gewürizt oder gekocht in Brühe oder Bouillon?
(Sp) ¿Está sazonado o cocinado el plato con caldo?
(Fr)   Est-ce que ce plat est cuit ou préparé avec du bouillon?

È questo piatto condito o cotto in brodo o bouillion?

(E) If it is preseasoned or cooked with boullion is there any wheat, rye, barley, or gluten in the mix or in the boullion?

(D) Wenn Sie verpackt Gewürze oder Brühe oder vorgefertigten bouillion, gebrauchen gibt es eine Weizen, Roggen, Gerste, oder Gluten Mischung?
(Sp) Si utilizó condimentos envasados o caldo, ¿ contienen trigo, centeno, cebada, gluten o una mezcla de estos ingredientes ?
(Fr)   Si vous utilisez des assaisonnements emballés ou préemballés avec du bouillon, y at-il de blé, du seigle, de l'orge ou du gluten dans le mélange?

Se si utilizzano condimenti confezionati in imballaggi o brodo o bouillion, non vi è alcun grano, segale, orzo, o glutine nel miscuglio?

Is this dish fried in the same fryer where wheat dishes are fried?

(D) Ist das Gericht gebraten in der gleichen Friteuse, wie die speisehaus Weizer?
(Sp) ¿Se frió este plato en la misma sartén en que se fríen platos que contienen trigo?
(Fr)   Est-ce que ce plat frit dans la même friteuse que des plats frits avec la farine?

È questo piatto fritto nella stessa friggitrice dove i piatti di grano sono fritti?

Is this dish thickened with flour?

(D) Ist das Gericht mit Mehl verdickt?
(Sp) ¿Se ha espesado el plato con harina?
(Fr)   Ce plat est-il épaissi à la farine?

Questo piatto è ispessito con farina?

Do you have gluten-free pasta?

(D) Haben Sie glutenfreie Nudeln?
(Sp) ¿Tiene usted pasta sin gluten?
(Fr)   Avez-vous des pâtes sans gluten?

Avete la pasta senza glutine?

Could I please get this dish without the pasta?

(D) Könnte ich bitte dieses Gericht bekommen ohne die Nudeln?
(Sp) ¿Podría usted servirme este plato sin pasta?
(Fr)   Pourrais-je obtenir s'il vous plaît ce plat de pâtes sans accompaniment?

Posso ottenere questo piatto senza la pasta?

Could you please substitute rice for pasta in this dish?

(D) Könnte ich bitte Reis anstatt Pasta für dieses Gericht haben?
(Sp) ¿Podría usted traerme arroz en vez de pasta?
(Fr)   Pourriez-vous s'il vous plaît echanger le riz pour les pâtes dans ce plat?

Potrebbe sostituire il riso per questo piatto?

ESSENTIAL ITALIAN FOOD VOCABULARY

Senza glutine (gluten-free)	Posso parlare con il cuoco, per favore? (May I please speak to the chef?)

MEALS AND COURSES IN ITALY

antipasti   appetizers

primo piatto   first course (pasta or risotto)

secondo piatto   second course (poultry, meat, fish)

contorno   side dish, such as vegetables

dolce   dessert

breakfast **colazione**

lunch **pranzo**

dinner **cena**

TYPES OF RESTAURANTS IN ITALY

ristorante—trattoria—osteria Traditionally, ristoranti are more expensive and more upscale, while trattorie and osterie tend to be more homestyle and family- oriented.

pizzeria---pizza a taglio--ristorante-pizzeria The pizzeria are similar to pizza places we have here. The pizza a taglio places sell pizza by weight, where you determine how big a slice you would like. The restaurant pizzerias are more like restaurants that also serve pizza.

tavola calda is a kind of fast food place where all dishes are preprepared. Celiacs are advised to stay away from these types of establishments.

gelateria --caffé—bar A gelateria is strictly an ice cream parlor, while a café or bar serves just about everything including ice cream and alcohol. People go to cafés or bars for breakfast and lunch and anytime for a drink (alcoholic or coffee) or ice cream.

enoteche—bacari (wine bar) is a place to go for wine and cheese. They often offer elaborate menus that describe which cheeses would complement particular wine.

agriturismo agricultural tourism has become increasingly popular in Italy. Accommodations vary quite widely from luxury apartments to farmhouses, but they are all generally on a working farm or a vineyard.

Italian	English	Spanish	French	German
pesce	fish	pescado	poisson	fisch
carne	meat	carne	viande	fleisch
legumi	beans	frijol	haricots	bohnen
verdura	vegetables	vegetales	legumes	gemüse
frutta	fruit	frutas	fruits	obst

SAFE AND UNSAFE INGREDIENTS

UNSAFE INGREDIENTS

Italian	English	Spanish	French	German
farina	flour	harina	farine	mehl
frumento	wheat	trigo	blé	weizen
amido di frumento	wheat starch	fecula de trigo	amidon de blé	weizenstärke
farina di frumento	wheat flour	harina de trigo	farine de blé	weizenmehl
orzo	barley	cebada	orge	gerste
segale	rye	centeno	froment	roggen
pane	bread	pan	pain	brot
pane grattugiato	breadcrumbs	pan rallado	chapelure	paniermehl
semolina	semolina	sémola	semoule	grieb

SAFE INGREDIENTS

Italian	English	Spanish	French	German
avena	oats	avena	avoine	hafer
riso	rice	arroz	riz	reis
amido di riso	rice starch	fecula de arroz	l'amidon de riz	reisstärke
farina di riso	rice flour	harina de arroz	farine de riz	reismehl
patate	potatoes	papa	pomme de terre	kartoffel
fecola di patate	potato flour	harina de papa	farine de pommes	kartoffel- mehl
mais	corn	maiz dulce	maïs dous	mais
amido di mais	cornstarch	de maicena	fécule de maïs	maisstärke
farina di tapioca	tapioca	harina de tapioca	farine de tapioca	tapioca mehl
farina di castagne	chestnut flour	harina de castaña	farine de châtaigne	kastanienmehl
farina di mandorle	almond flour	harina de almendra	farine d'almande	mandel-mehl
farina di soia	soy flour	haina de soja	farine de soja	soja-mehl

ICE CREAM IN ITALY

Italians love *gelato* (ice cream)! Their ice cream is relatively low in fat, often fruit or nut-based and is sold in *gelaterie* and bars. You can eat it in a cone or cup and enjoy whipped cream on top! All *gelaterie* that are indicated in this book have gluten-free ice cream and many have gluten-free ice cream cones. Be sure to be clear and ask for a *cono senza glutine* when ordering.

How to Order

cono – cone
coppa (or *coppetta*)- cup
granita -a flavored iced drink
panna - whipped cream (*con* = with, *senza* = without)
piccolo (small)

cono senza glutine – GF cone
gusto - scoop, flavor
frappe -a milkshake

medio (medium)   *grande* (big)

Sample of Gelato Flavors *(gusti)*

bacio - double chocolate and hazelnuts
caffè - coffee
fragola - strawberry
melone - cantaloupe
panna - cream

cioccolato - chocolate
limone - lemon
giunduia - chocolate hazelnut
nocciola - hazelnut
vaniglia - vanilla

risotto - cream with honey, rice, cinnamon and chocolate.
Spumoni - a blend of 3 flavors (e.g. zuppa inglese, pistachio and gianduia)
stracciatella – chocolate chip   *mora* - blackberry
tiramisu - Mascarpone cheese, lady fingers, Kahlua
lampone - raspberry
zabaione - Egg yolks, marsala, and fresh cream
pesca - peach
zuppa inglese - fruits and marsala, and cream

COFFEE IN ITALY

Italians love their coffee! They drink **espresso**, and in many variations:

caffè ristretto is extra-concentrated espresso.
caffè lungo is espresso with extra water.
caffè corretto is espresso "corrected" by a shot of liquor (i.e. Sambuca or Amaretto).
caffè macchiato is coffee "spotted" with milk.
cappuccino (or **cappuccio** for short) is a good morning drink, consisting of espresso with a "hood" of steamed milk. This drink was named for the Cappuccine monks who invented it; their hoods were "cappucci."
doppio is a double serving of espresso.
zucchero is sugar.

FOOD WORDS DICTIONARY IN MULTIPLE LANGUAGES

- **ITALIAN TO ENGLISH AND GERMAN**
- **ITALIAN TO SPANISH AND FRENCH**

ITALIAN	ENGLISH	GERMAN
abbacchio	lamb	lamm
aceto	vinegar	Essig
acqua	water	Wasser
acqua minerale	mineral water	Mineralwasser
affumicato	smoked	geräucherte
aglio	garlic	Knoblauch
agnello	lamb	Lamm
al forno	baked	gebacken
al sangue	very rare	sehr selten
albicocca	apricot	Aprikose
alla griglia	grilled	gegrillt
alla milanese	battered with eggs and bread crumbs and fried	mit Eiern und Semmelbrösel und gebratene panierte
alla parmigiana	with Parmesan cheese and tomatoes	mit Parmesan-Käse und Tomaten
alla tartara	raw with lemon and egg	Roh mit Zitrone und Ei
alla valdostana	with ham and cheese	mit Schinken und Käse
amido di frumento	wheat starch	Weizenstärke
amido di mais	cornstarch	Maisstärke
amido di riso	rice starch	Reisstärke
ananas	pineapple	Ananas
anatra	duck	Ente
anguria	watermelon	Wassermelone
aragosta	lobster	Hummer
arancia	orange	Orange
aringa	herring	Hering
arista	pork roast	gebratenes schweinefleisch
arrosto	roasted	geröstet, geschmort, gebraten

ITALIAN	ENGLISH	GERMAN
avena	Oats	Hafer
banana	Banana	Banane
ben cotta	well done	durchgebraten
bevanda	Drink	trinken
bibita	Drink	trinken
bicchiere di . . .	a glass of . . .	Ein Glas. . .
biscotti	Cookies	kekse
bistecca	beef steak	Rindersteak
bistecca a media cottura	medium steak	Steak-fast durdgebraten
bistecca al sangue	rare steak	Seltene blutig
bistecca ben cotta	well done steak	steak-gut durdgebvatenes
bistecca molto al sangue	very rare steak	Sehr selten sehr blutig
bottiglia	Bottle	Flasche
burro	Butter	Butter
caffè	Coffee	Kaffee
calamari	Squid	tintenfisd
cameriere/cameriera	waiter/waitress	Kellnerin/kellner
caraffa	Carafe	Karaffe
carota	Carrot	Karotte
cavolfiore	Cauliflower	Blumenkohl
cavolo	Cabbage	Kohl
celiaca	Celiac	Celiac
cena	dinner	Abendessen
cervella	brain	Gehirn
cetriolo	cucumber	Gurke
chiara/scura	light/dark	hell /dunkel
ciliegia	cherry	Cherry/kirsche
cinghiale	boar	Wildschwein

ITALIAN	ENGLISH	GERMAN
cioccolata calda	hot chocolate	Heiße Schokolade
cipolla	onion	Zwiebel
colazione	breakfast	Frühstück
con ghiaccio	on the rocks	On the rocks
con latte	with milk	mit Milch
con seltz	with soda	mit Soda
coniglio	rabbit	Kaninchen
coperto	cover charge	kosten für das Giedeck
coppa gelato	cup of ice cream	eisbecher
cornetto/brioche	croissant	Croissant
cozze	mussels	Muscheln
crema di . . .	cream of . . .	Sahne. . .
crostata	pie	Pie/pastete
cuoco	chef	Küchenchef
datteri	dates	Termine
di stagione	in season	der Saison
extra	extra fee/charge	Zuschlag/zusatzkosten
fagiano	pheasant	Fasan
fagiolini	green beans	Grüne Bohnen
farina	flour	Mehl
farina di castagne	chestnut flour	Kastanienmehl
farina di frumento	wheat flour	Weizenmehl
farina di mandorle	almond flour	Mandel-Mehl
farina di riso	rice flour	Reismehl
farina di soia	soy flour	Soja-Mehl
farina di tapioca	tapioca flour	Tapioka Mehl
fecola di patate	potato flour/starch	Kartoffel-Mehl/ Stärke
fegato	liver	Leber

ITALIAN	ENGLISH	GERMAN
fichi	figs	Feigen
focaccia	flat bread	Pfannkuchen
fragola	strawberry	Erdbeere
fritto	fried	Fried gebraten
frumento	wheat	Weizen
frutta	fruit	Obst
frutta fresca	fresh fruit	Frisches obst
frutta secca	dried fruit	Trockenfrüchte
frutti di mare	seafood	Meeresfrüchte
funghi	mushroom	Pilz
gelato	ice cream	Eis
granchio	crab	Krabbe
grazie	thank you	danke
hot dog	hot dog	Hot dog
in carpione	cold, with vinegar	Kält, mit Essig
insalata	green salad	Grüner Salat
la birra	beer	Bier
lamponi	raspberries	Himbeeren
latte	milk	Milch
lattuga	lettuce	Kopfsalat
limonata	lemonade	Limonade
limone	lemon	Zitrone
liscio	straight	geradeaus
lista dei vini	wine list	Weinkarte
macedonia di frutta	fruit salad	Obstsalat
mais	sweet corn	Mais (Mais)
mandarino	tangerine	mandarine
mela	apple	Apfel

ITALIAN	ENGLISH	GERMAN
melone	melon	Melone
menu	menu	Menü
merluzzo	cod	Kabeljau
minestrone	vegetable soup	Gemüsesuppe
mirtilli	blueberries	Blaubeeren
more	blackberries	Brombeeren
mousse al cioccolato	chocolate mousse	Mousse au Chocolat
nocepesca	nectarine	Nektarine
omelette / frittata	omelette	Omelett
orzo	barley	Gerste
ostriche	oysters	Austern
pane	bread	Brot
pane grattugiato	breadcrumbs	Paniermehl
paste	pastries	Gebäck
patata	potato	Kartoffel
patate	potato	Kartoffel
patatine fritte	fries	Pommes frites
pâté	pâté	pâté
pepe	pepper	Pfeffer
per favore	please	bitte
per piacere	please	Bitte
pera	pear	Birne
pesca	peach	pfirsich
pesce	fish	Fisch
piselli	peas	Erbsen
pizza	pizza	Pizza
pollo	chicken	Huhn
polpo	octopus	Krake

ITALIAN	ENGLISH	GERMAN
pomodoro	tomato	Tomate
pompelmo	grapefruit	pompelmuse
porro	leek	lauch, porree
pranzo	lunch	Mittagessen
prezzo fisso	fixed menu	bestehendos, uorgeschriebenes menü
prosciutto	ham	Schinken
prugna	plum	Pflaume, zwetschge
prugna secca	prune	Pflaume
rafano	radish	Rettich
ribes	red currant	Rote Johannisbeere
ribes nero	black currant	Schwarze Johannisbeere
ripieno	stuffed	gefüllt
riso	Rice	Reis
sale	salt	Salz
salmone	salmon	Lachs
salsa	sauce	Sauce
scampi /gamberi	prawns / shrimps	Garnelen / Shrimps
segale	rye	Roggen
semolina	semolina	Grieß
senape	mustard	Senf
senza glutine	gluten-free	glutenfrei
sidro	cider	Apfelwein
sogliola	sole	Scholle
sorbetto	sherbet	Limonade
specialità di casa	specialty of the House	Spezialität des Hauses
specialità locale	local specialty	Lokale Spezialität
spuntino	snack	Snack/zwischenmahlzeit
succo d'ananas	pineapple juice	Ananassaft

ITALIAN	ENGLISH	GERMAN
succo d'arancia	orange juice	Orangensaft
succo di mela	apple juice	Apfelsaft
succo di pomodoro	tomato juice	Tomatensaft
tasse	tax	Steuer
Tè	tea	Tee
torta	cake	Kuchen
trota	trout	Forelle
Un pezzo d'agnello	lamb chop	Lamm-Kotelett
Un pezzo di maiale	pork chop	Schweinekotelett
uva	grape	Traube
uva passa	raisins	Rosinen
verdura	vegetables	Gemüse
vino amabile	sweet wine	lieblider Wein
vino bianco/rosso	white wine/red wine	Weißwein/rotwein
vino secco	dry wine	Trockener Wein
vitello	veal	Kalbfleisch
vorrei	I would like	Ich möchte
yoghurt	yogurt	Jogurt
zuppa	soup	Suppe
zuppa di pesce	fish stew	Fisch-Eintopf

ITALIAN	SPANISH	FRENCH
abbacchio	Cordero	agneau
aceto	Vinagre	Vinaigre
acqua	Agua	Eau
acqua minerale	Agua mineral	Eau minérale
affumicato	Ahumado	Fumé
aglio	Ajo	Ail
agnello	Cordero	agmeau
al forno	Al horno	Baked
al sangue	Crudo	Très rare, rouge
albicocca	Albaricoque	Abricot
alla griglia	A la parrilla	Grillé
alla milanese	Batido con huevos y pan rallado y frito	Battues avec des œufs et des miettes de pain et frit avec
alla parmigiana	Con queso parmesano y tomates	Du parmesan et des tomates
alla tartara	Crudo con limón y huevo	Crus avec du citron et l'oeuf
alla valdostana	Con jamón y queso	Avec du jambon et du fromage
amido di frumento	Fecula de trigo	Amidon de blé
amido di mais	De maicena	Fécule de maïs
amido di riso	fecula de arroz	L'amidon de riz
ananas	Piña	Ananas
anatra	Pato	Canard
anguria	Sandía	Pastèque
aragosta	Langosta	Homard
arancia	Naranja	Orange
aringa	Arenque	Hareng
arista	Cerdo asado	Rôti de porc
arrosto	Asado	roti

ITALIAN	SPANISH	FRENCH
avena	Avena	Avoine
banana	Plátano	Banane
ben cotta	Bien cocido	À point ou bien cuit
bevanda	Beber	Un verre
bibita	Bebida	Une boisson
bicchiere di . . .	Un vaso de. . .	Un verre d'. . .
biscotti	Galletas dulces	Cookies
bistecca	El sector de la carne de bistec	Steak de boeuf
bistecca a media cottura	Filete mediano	Moyen steak
bistecca al sangue	bistec crudo	A point steak
bistecca ben cotta	Filete bien cocido	un steak bien cuit
bistecca molto al sangue	Bistec bien crudo	Très rare steak
bottiglia	Botella	Bouteille
burro	Mantequilla	Beurre
caffè	Café	Café
calamari	Calamar	calamars
cameriere/cameriera	Camarero/camarera	serveur/serveuse
caraffa	Jarra	Carafe
carota	Zanahoria	Carotte
cavolfiore	Coliflor	Chou-fleur
cavolo	Repollo	Chou
celiaca	Celiaca	Coeliaque
cena	Cena	Dîner
cervella	Cerebro	Cerveau
cetriolo	Pepino	Concombre
chiara/scura	Claro/oscuro	Clair / foncé
ciliegia	Cereza	cerise
cinghiale	cerdo	Sanglier

ITALIAN	SPANISH	FRENCH
cioccolata calda	Chocolate caliente	Chocolat chaud
cipolla	Cebolla	Oignon
colazione	Desayuno	Petit déjeuner
con ghiaccio	Con hielo	Avec de la glace
con latte	Con leche	Avec du lait
con seltz	Con soda	À la soude
coniglio	Conejo	Lapin
coperto	Cargo de entrada	Couvrir les frais
coppa gelato	Copa de helado	Tune coupe de glace
cornetto/brioche	Croissant	Croissant
cozze	Mejillones	Moules
crema di ...	De crema. . .	la crème de . . .
crostata	Pastel	Tarte
cuoco	cocinero	Chef
datteri	Fechas	Dates
di stagione	En la temporada	Dans la saison
extra	Suplemento / cargo	Supplément / charge
fagiano	Faisan	Faisan
fagiolini	Judías verdes	Haricots verts
farina	Harina	Farine
farina di castagne	Harina de castaña	Farine de châtaigne
farina di frumento	Harina de trigo	Farine de blé
farina di mandorle	De harina de almendra	Farine d'amande
farina di riso	Harina de arroz	Farine de riz
farina di soia	Harina de soja	Farine de soja
farina di tapioca	Harina de tapioca	Farine de tapioca
fecola di patate	Harina de papa o fecula	Farine de pommes de terre ou amidon
fegato	Hígado	Foie

ITALIAN	SPANISH	FRENCH
fichi	Higos	Figues
focaccia	Panqueque	Crêpe
fragola	Fresa	Fraise
fritto	Frito	Frit
frumento	Trigo	Blé
frutta	Frutas	Fruits
frutta fresca	Frutas frescas	Fruits frais
frutta secca	Frutos secos	Fruits secs
frutti di mare	Mariscos	Fruits de mer
funghi	champinon	champignons
gelato	Helado	glace
granchio	Cangrejo	Crabe
grazie	Gracias	Merci
hot dog	Perro caliente	Hot-dog
in carpione	Fría, con vinagre	Froid, avec du vinaigre
insalata	Ensalada verde	Salade verte
la birra	Cerveza	Bière
lamponi	Frambuesas	Framboises
latte	Leche	Lait
lattuga	Lechuga	Laitue
limonata	Limonada	Limonade
limone	Limón	Citron
lista dei vini	Carta de vinos	Carte des vins
macedonia di frutta	Ensalada de frutas	Salade de fruits
mais	Maíz dulce (maíz)	Maïs doux (maïs)
mandarino	Mandarina	mandarine
mela	Manzana	pomme
melone	Melón	Melon
menu	Menú	Menu

ITALIAN	SPANISH	FRENCH
merluzzo	Bacalao	Morue
minestrone	Sopa de verduras	Soupe aux légumes
mirtilli	Arándanos	myrtilles
more	Moras	Mûres
mousse al cioccolato	Mousse de chocolate	Mousse au chocolat
nocepesca	Nectarina	Nectarine
omelette / frittata	Tortilla	Omelette
orzo	Cebada	Orge
ostriche	Ostras	Les huîtres
pane	Pan	Pain
pane grattugiato	Pan rallado	Chapelure
paste	Pasteles	Pâtisseries
patata	Papa	Pomme de terre
patate	Papa	Pomme de terre
patatine fritte	Papas Fritas	Frites
pâté	Pate	pâté
pepe	Pimienta	Poivre
per favore	por favor	S'il vous plaît
per piacere	Por favor	S'il vous plaît
pera	Pera	Poire
pesca	Melocoton	pêche
pesce	Pescado	Poisson
piselli	Guisantes	Petits pois
pizza	Pizza	Pizza
pollo	Pollo	Poulet
polpo	Pulpo	Pieuvre
pomodoro	Tomate	Tomate
pompelmo	Pomelo	Pamplemousse
porro	Puerro	Poireau

ITALIAN	SPANISH	FRENCH
pranzo	Almuerzo	Déjeuner
prezzo fisso	Menú fijo	Menu fixe
prosciutto	Jamon	jambon
prugna	Ciruela	Prune
prugna secca	Pasa	Pruneau
rafano	Rábano	Radis
ribes	Pasas rojas	groseille
ribes nero	Pasas negras	Cassis
ripieno	Con relleno	Farcis
riso	Arroz	Rice
sale	Sal	Sel
salmone	Salmón	Saumon
salsa	Salsa	Sauce
scampi /gamberi	Camarones / gambas	Crevettes / crevettes
segale	Centeno	froment
semolina	Sémola	Semoule
senape	Mostaza	Moutarde
senza glutine	Sin gluten	Sans gluten
sidro	Sidra	Cidre
sogliola	Lenguado	sole
sorbetto	Sorbete	Sorbet
specialita' di casa	Especialidad de la casa	Spécialité de la maison
specialita' locale	Especialidad local	Spécialité locale
spuntino	Merienda	Snack
succo d'ananas	Jugo de piña	Jus d'ananas
succo d'arancia	Jugo de naranja	Jus d'orange
succo di mela	Jugo de manzana	Jus de pomme
succo di pomodoro	Zumo de tomate	Jus de tomate
tasse	Impuesto	Taxes, impots

ITALIAN	SPANISH	FRENCH
te	Té	Thé
torta	Torta	Gâteau
trota	Trucha	Truite
Un pezzo d'agnello	Chuleta de cordero	Côtes d'agneau
Un pezzo di maiale	chuleta de cerdo	côtes de pore
uva	Uva	Raisin
uva passa	Pasas	Raisins secs
verdura	Vegetales	Légumes
vino amabile	Vino dulce	Vin doux
vino bianco/rosso	Vino blanco/vino tinto	Vin blanc/vin rouge
vino secco	Vino seco	Vin sec
vitello	Ternera	veau
vorrei	Me gustaría	Je voudrais
yoghurt	Yogur	Yogourt
zuppa	Sopa	Soupe
zuppa di pesce	Guiso de pescado	Ragoût de poisson

GLUTEN-FREE
ITALY
BY REGION

ROME AND LAZIO

PLACES IN ROME TO BUY GLUTEN-FREE FOOD PRODUCTS, BY NEIGHBORHOOD

BEYOND CITY CENTER
L'Altro Alimento Gluten Free Shop
Via Antonio Zotti, 122 (In Ostia.)

ESQUILINO
Farmacia Brocchier   Via Orvieto, 33
Farmacia Merulana   Via Merulana, 185

NOMENTANO.
Celidoc   Via Livorno 27

PRATI
Celiachiamo.Com   Via Giulio Venticinque, 32

SAN GIOVANNI
CeliaMagic   Via Latina 162

SPAGNA
Farmacia Europea   Via Della Croce, 10

STAZIONE TERMINI
Conad   Piazza dei 500-Stazione Termini
Farmacia Indipendenza Dott   Via S.Martino Battaglia, 10

TESTACCIO
Farmacia De Angelis E C   Via Marmorata, 133

TRASTEVERE
NaturaSi'   Via Oderisi da Gubbio, 66
Trastevere Bio   Via di S. Dorotea 11

VATICAN
Farmacia Cola Di Rienzo   Via Cola Di Rienzo, 215
Farmacia Eredi Vincenti   Piazza Della Rovere, 2/C
Farmacia Fabio Massimo   Via Massimo Fabio, 78
Farmacia Mannucci   Via Andrea Doria, 35

PLACES IN ROME TO GET GUARANTEED GLUTEN-FREE GELATO
(SPONSORED BY ITALIAN CELIAC SOCIETY),
BY NEIGHBORHOOD

APPIA ANTICA
Gelateria Labate - Golden Ice   Via M. Menghini, 24

BEYOND CITY CENTER
Il Pinguino   Via Silvestri, 224

BEYOND CITY CENTER (PIAZZA TRIESTE)
Gel'Istria   Piazza Istria, 14

BEYOND CITY CENTER (TUSCOLANO)
Gelateria Greed   Via Vestricio Spurinna, 97
Gelateria Petrini   Piazza Dell'Alberone, 16/A
Grom Tuscolana   Via Tuscolana, 1370

CENTRO STORICO
Grom Giubbonari   Via dei Giubbonari, 53
Grom Maddalena   Via della Maddalena, 30A

CORSO (PIAZZA VENEZIA)
Vacanze Romane   Piazza D'Ara Coeli, 9/10

EUR.
Grom EUR Roma 2   V.le Oceano Pacifico, 83

MAZZINI
Fata Morgana 3   Via Giovanni Bettolo, 7

MONTI
Fata Morgana   Via Lago Di Lesina, 9/11

NAVONA
Grom Navona   P.zza Navona 1

NOMENTANO
Bartocci   Via Alessandria 145
Gel'Istria   P.zza Istria, 14
Cremeria Alpi 2   Via degli Equi, 42

TERMINI
La Romana   Via XX Settembre 60

VATICAN
Al Settimo Gelo   Via Vodice, 21/A

TRASTEVERE
Fata Morgana 4   Via Roma Libera, 11

PRATI.
Gelarmony   Via Marcantonio Colonna 34

ROME B&B'S AND HOTELS LISTED ALPHABETICALLY
(AIC = participates in the Associazione Italiana Celiachia program)

B&B's

Acquedotti Antichi   B&B   AIC
V.le Anicio Gallo, 196/c2   tel. 0645555635 www.acquedottiantichi.com
Notes: Beyond City Center (Along Appian Way). S € 50 D € 70 T € 95

B&B Bio   B&B   AIC
Via Cavalese, 28   tel. 3485500942   www.bedandbreakfastbio.com
Notes: Beyond City Center. S € 55. Located in residential area in Monte Mario Park. Close to Auditorium Music Hall, Maxxi National Museum of Art, Olimpic Stadium (soccer), the Flaminio Stadium, Tennis Centre Foro Italico.

B&B Roma Centro San Pietro   B&B
Via Giorgio Scalia   tel. 0645433333   www.bedandbreakfastromacentro.it
Notes: Vatican. GF breakfast provided upon advance request.

Bed-and-breakfast Roma Centro San Pietro B&B
Via Giorgio Scalia, 39   tel. 0645433333   www.bedandbreakfastromacentro.it
Notes: Vatican. Near the Vatican walls.

Capricci Romani   B&B
Via di Porta Castello, 33   tel. 0668802684   www.bebcapricciromani.com
Notes: Vatican.

Kosher & Gluten-free B&B My Guest Roma B&B
Viale 21 Aprile   tel. 0686324590   www.myguestroma.com
Notes: Bologna. GF breakfast provided upon advance request.

La Papessa   B&B   www.lapapessabb.it
Via del Corso, 241 (corner of Vicolo Sciarra, 61)   tel. 0645439953
Notes: Corso. Walking distance from: Trevi Fountain, Spanish Steps, Colosseum, Pantheon, Vatican Museums. Will provide GF breakfast with advance notice.

My Guest Roma   B&B
Viale XXIAprile, 12   tel. 686324590   www.myguestroma.com
Notes: Provincie. Can do gluten-free and kosher breakfast.

Residenza Piccolo Principe   B&B   €€€€
Via Giovanni Giolitti   tel. 3206993110   www.bbpiccoloprincipe.it
Notes: GF breakfast provided upon advance request.

Town House Fontana di Trevi   B&B
Via de Crociferi, 41   tel. 3336832012   www.bbfontanaditrevi.com
Notes: Spagna. GF breakfast provided upon advance request.

Zaccardi   B&B   , AIC
V.le di Vigna Pia, 40   tel. 0645445503   www.zaccardi.info
Notes: Beyond City Center (In Portuense). Near Trastevere.

HOTELS

Best Western Hotel President   hotel
Via Emanuele Filiberto, 173   tel. 06770121   www.hotelpresidentrome.com
Notes: Colosseo. GF breakfast provided upon advance request.

Dei Consoli Hotel   hotel
Via Varrone, 2/D corner Via Cola di Rienzo   tel. 0668892972
www.hoteldeiconsoli.com
Notes: Vatican. GF breakfast provided upon advance request.

Delle Province	hotel
Viale delle Provincie, 103	tel. 0644292670	www.hoteldelleprovince.it
Notes: Tiburtino. GF breakfast provided upon advance request.

Excel Rome St. Peter	hotel
Via Catone, 34	tel. 0639735082	www.excelstpeter.it
Notes: Vatican. GF breakfast provided upon advance request.

Franklin Feel the Sound Hotel	hotel
Via Rodi, 29	tel. 0639030165	www.franklinhotelrome.it
Notes: Vatican. GF breakfast provided upon advance request.

Gigli d'Oro Suite	hotel
Via dei Gigli d'Oro, 12	tel. 0668803579	www.giglidorosuite.com
Notes: Navona. GF breakfast provided upon advance request.

Holiday Inn Parco dei Medici	hotel	€€€€, AIC
Via Castello della Magliana, 65	tel. 0665581	www.holidayinn-eur.it
Notes: Beyond City Center (In Eur District).

Hotel Alexandra	hotel
Via Vittorio Veneto 18	tel. 064881943	www.hotelalexandraroma.com
Notes: Veneto.

Hotel Claridge	hotel
Viale Liegi, 62a	tel. 6845441	www.hotelclaridgerome.com
Notes: Borghese.

Hotel Diana	hotel, restaurant	€€€-€€€€, AIC
Via Principe Amedeo, 4	tel. 064786681	www.hoteldianaroma.com
Notes: Esquilino.

Hotel Fori Imperiali Cavalieri hotel	AIC
Via Frangipane, 34	tel. 6.6796246	www.hotelforiimperialicavalieri.com
Notes: Centro Storico.

Hotel Melià - Rist. La Sughereta hotel, restaurant	€€€, AIC
Via degli Aldobrandeschi, 223	tel. 06665441	www.solmelia.com
Notes: Beyond City Center (Near Airport).

Hotel Mozart	hotel	AIC
Via dei Greci, 23	tel. 06.360019151	www.hotelmozart.com
Notes: Flaminio, Centro Storico.

Hotel Nord Nuova Roma	hotel
Via G. Amendola, 3	tel. 064885441	www.romehotelnord.it
Notes: Termini.

Hotel Rimini	hotel
Via Marghera, 17	tel. 064461991	www.hotelriminirome.com
Notes: Termini.

Hotel Spring House (Best Western) hotel	AIC
Via Mocenigo, 7	tel. 0639720948 www.hotelspringhouse.com
Notes: Mazzini.

Hotel Teatro di Pompeo	hotel
Largo del Pallaro, 8	tel. 0668300170 www.hotelteatrodipompeo.it
Notes: Pantheon. Will provide GF breakfast with advance notice.

Hotel XX Settembre	hotel
Via del Macao, 6	tel. 064467215	www.hotelventisettembre.com
Notes: Veneto.

Holiday Inn Parco dei Medici   hotel (Italian)   €€€€, AIC
Via Castello della Magliana, 65   tel. 0665581   www.holidayinn-eur.it
Notes: Beyond City Center (In Eur District).

Hotel Alexandra   hotel
Via Vittorio Veneto 18   tel. 064881943   www.hotelalexandraroma.com
Notes: Veneto. GF breakfast provided upon advance request.

Hotel Claridge   hotel
Viale Liegi, 62a   tel. 06845441   www.hotelclaridgerome.com
Notes: Borghese. GF breakfast provided upon advance request.

Hotel Diana   hotel, restaurant (Italian)   €€€-€€€€, AIC
Via Principe Amedeo, 4   tel. 064786681   www.hoteldianaroma.com
Notes: Esquilino.

Hotel Melià - Rist. La Sughereta hotel, restaurant (Italian)   €€€, AIC
Via degli Aldobrandeschi, 223   tel. 06665441   www.solmelia.com
Notes: Beyond City Center (Near Airport).

Hotel Mozart   hotel
Via dei Greci, 23   tel. 0636001915   www.hotelmozart.com
Notes: Spagna. GF breakfast provided upon advance request.

Hotel Napoleon Rome   hotel
Piazza Vittorio Emanuele II   tel. 064467282   www.napoleon.it
Notes: Vittorio Emanuele. GF breakfast provided upon advance request.

Hotel Nord Nuova Roma   hotel
Via G. Amendola, 3   tel. 064885441   www.romehotelnord.it
Notes: Termini. GF breakfast provided upon advance request.

Hotel Rimini   hotel
Via Marghera, 17   tel. 064461991   www.hotelriminirome.com
Notes: Termini. GF breakfast provided upon advance request.

Hotel XX Settembre   hotel
Via del Macao, 6   tel. 064467215   www.hotelventisettembre.com
Notes: Veneto. GF breakfast provided upon advance request.

Hotel Spring House (Best Western) hotel   AIC
Via Mocenigo, 7   tel. 0639720948   www.hotelspringhouse.com
Notes: Mazzini.

Hotel Teatro di Pompeo   hotel
Largo del Pallaro, 8   tel. 0668300170   www.hotelteatrodipompeo.it
Notes: Pantheon. Will provide GF breakfast with advance notice.

Imperium Suite Navona   hotel
Vicolo della Palomba, 19   tel. 064880628   www.imperiumsuitenavona.com
Notes: Navona. GF breakfast provided upon advance request.

Luana Inn Airport   hotel, restaurant   €€
Via Monte Forcelletta, 23   tel. 3396933742   www.bbluanainn.it
Notes: Airport. Restaurant caters to celiacs. GF breakfast too. Very close to airport.

Radisson Blu Es H.Roma   hotel   AIC
Via Filippo Turati, 171   tel. 06444841   www.radissonblu.com
Notes: Esquillino.

Residence Il Vittoriano   hotel   AIC
Via Giulia, 141   tel. 6.98381849   www.residenceilvittoriano.com
Notes: Campo.

Rome Cavalieri Waldorf Astoria hotel
Via Alberto Cadlolo, 101   tel. 0635091   www.romecavalieri.it
Notes: Monte Mario.

San Carlo Suite   hotel
Via del Corso, 112   tel. 0668392055
Notes: GF breakfast provided upon advance request.

Sheraton Golf Parco de' Medici   hotel, restaurant (Italian)   €€€-€€€€, AIC
V.le Salvatore Rebecchini, 39   tel. 0665288   www.starwoodhotels.com
Notes: Beyond City Center (Autostrada Airport). Two restaurants. GF breakfast too.

Sunrise Hotel   hotel
Via Cilento, 3   tel. 0682011093   www.sunrisehotel.it
Notes: Sempione. GF breakfast provided upon advance request.

The Duke Hotel Rome   hotel
Via Archemede 69   tel. 06367221   www.thedukehotel.com
Notes: Borghese. GF breakfast provided upon advance request.

SUMMARY INFO: RESTAURANTS IN ROME LISTED BY NEIGHBORHOOD WITH PRICES

Appia Antica
O' Masto   L.go Salinari, 8/16   €€€

Appio
Antica Hostaria Dei Liberti – Ristorante Via Appia Antica, 87   €€-€€€€

Aurelio
Da Arturo   Via Aurelia Antica, 411/413   €€€

Beyond City Center
Circolo Ippico Tor S. Giovanni Via Tor San Giovanni, 245   €
Pomodori Verdi Fritti   Via dei Pescatori, 495   €€
Villa Grant   Via Pratica di Mare, 181   €€€€
Zen Fusion   V.le Eritrea, 69   €€-€€€
V Hugo   Via Cristoforo Colombo, 90   €€-€€€
Millennium   Via Tor Tre Teste, 35   €€€
La Piazzetta   Piazza dei Visconti, 8   €€-€€€

Campo
Da Sergio   Vicolo delle Grotte, 27   €€-€€€
Ditirambo   Piazza della Cancelleria, 74   €€-€€€
Il Sanlorenzo   Via dei Chiavari, 4/5   €€€€
Voglia di Pizza   Via dei Giubbonari, 33   €€

Casolino
La Nduja 2   Via Michele Tenore 21/31   €€-€€€

Centro Storico
Albrecht   Via Rasella 52   €€€
Ciao Checca   P.za di Firenze, 25   €€
Grano Frutta e Farina   Via Della Croce 49A   €€€
Il Vineto   Via Vittorio Veneto 6   €€
Quattro Spicchi   Via della Pisana, 51   €€
Settimio all'Arancio   Via Arancio 50   €€€
Taverna Barberini   Via Delle Quattro Fontane 160   €€
Toto   Via delle Carrozze 10   €€€
Osteria del Pegno   Vicolo di Montevecchio 8   €€€

Colosseo
Ai Tre Scalini   Via SS. Quattro, 30   €€€

Esquilino
Agata e Romeo   Via Carlo Alberto, 45   €€€€
Il Veliero   Via Albalonga, 46   €€
Taberna Recina   Via Elvia Recina, 22   €€€

Ghetto
Al Pompiere   Via Santa Maria dei Calderari, 38   €€-€€€
Sora Lella   Via di Ponte Quattro Capi, 16   €€€

Historic District
Pantharei   Via della Minerva, 18   €€-€€€

Monte Mario
La Pergola   Via Alberto Cadlolo, 101   €€€€

Montesacro/Talenti
Lanificio Cucina   Via di Pietralata, 159   €€

Monti

F.I.S.H.	Via dei Serpenti, 16	€€€€
Ristorante Tema	Via Panisperna, 96/98	€€€€
Sehgal Sanjiv Kumar Ristorante Indiano Maharaja Via Dei Serpenti, 124		€€€€
Zia Rosetta	Via Urbana 54	€€

Navona

Etabli	Vicolo delle Vacche, 9/a	€€€
La Scaletta Degli Artisti Srl	Via di Santa Maria dell'Anima	€€-€€€
Osteria del Gallo	Vicolo di Montevecchio, 27	€€-€€€
Ristorante Bibliothè	Via Celsa, 4	€
Trattoria Pizzeria Fiammetta	Piazza Fiammetta, 10	€€

Nomentano, Pinciano

Ops!	Via Bergamo 56	€€

Ostia

Biorestaunt ZenZero	Viale della Pineta di Ostia 30	€€€

Ostiense

Antico Casale La Carovana	V.le di Vigna Pia, 33	€€-€€€
Hopside	Via Francesco Negri 39	€€
Insomnia	Via Portuense, 469	€€€
Potter Pizza	V.le dei Colli Portuensi, 346	€

Piazza Venezia

Birreria Peroni	Via di San Marcello, 19	€

Pantheon

Armando al Pantheon	Salita de' Crescenzi, 31	€€-€€€
Il Piccolo Mondo	Via delle Coppelle, 16/a	€€€€
La Rosetta	Via della Rosetta, 9	€€€€
La Scaletta	Via della Scala	€€€
Osteria dell'Ingegno	Piazza di Pietra, 45	€€-€€€

Pigneto

Al Country	Via Teano, 243/245	€€
Casa Mangiacotti	Via Gentile da Mogliano 180	€€

Pinciano

Larys Restaurant Rome	Via Basento, 54	€€-€€€

Prati

Da Angelo alla Cupola	Via Aurelia 50	€€€
Dal Toscano	Via Germanico, 58/60	€€€
La Fiorentina	Via Andrea Doria, 24	€€€€
La Soffitta Renovatio	Piazza del Risorgimento 46A	€€
La Pilotta da Mario	Via Porta Cavalleggeri, 35/37	€€-€€€
Taverna Angelica	Piazza A. Capponi, 6	€€€
Baiamonti Lounge Bar	Via Baiamonti, 12	€€
Cesare	Via Crescenzio, 13	€€€

Quirinale

Tullio	Via San Nicola da Tolentino	€€€-€€€€

San Giovanni

Vintage Bistrot	Piazza Tarquinia 4A	€€-€€€

San Lorenzo

Fiorita	Via Bari, 11/B	€€€
Il Bello della Pizza	Via di Portonaccio 33/a	€

Spagna

Caffè Romano dell'Hotel d'Inghilterra	Via Borgongna, 4M	€€€€
Dal Bolognese	Piazza del Popolo, 1	€€€€
El Toulà	Via della Lupa, 29/b	€€€€
Gioia Mia Pisciapiano	Via degli Avignonesi 34	€
Margutta Vegetariano	Via Margutta, 118	€€-€€€

Termini

Mamma Angela's Trattoria	Via Palestro, 53	€€

Trastevere

Alle Fratte di Trastevere	Via delle Fratte di Trastevere	€€
Da Sandri	Via Roma Libera 19	€€-€€€
Il Maggiolino	Via Alessandro Cruto, 9	€-€€
Il Tulipano Nero	Via Roma Libera, 15	€
Jaipur	Via di San Francesco a Ripa, 56	€€
La Gensola	Piazza della Gensola, 15	€€-€€€
Mama.Eat	Via di San Cosimato, 7	€€
Ripa 12 Ristorante	Via San a Franceso Ripa, 12	€€€
Romolo	Via di Porta Settimiana, 8	€€€
Z'Imberto	Piazza San Giovanni della Malva	€€€

Trieste

Mangiafuoco Pizza & Grill	Via Chiana, 37	€€

Tuscolano

Il Portico	P.zza Aruleno C. Sabino, 89	€€-€€€

Vatican

Ad Hoc	Via di Ripetta, 43	
La Veranda dell'Hotel Columbus	Borgo Santo Spirito, 73	€€€-€€€€
Renovatio La Soffitta	P.zza Risorgimento, 46/a	€€€

Veneto

Alex Cafè	Via Vittorio Veneto, 20	€€€€
Hard Rock Cafe	Via Vittorio Veneto, 62	€€-€€€
Il Viaggio	Via Isonzo, 14	€€-€€€
Papá Baccus	Via Toscana, 36	€€€€

Villa Borghese

Al Ceppo	Via Panama, 2	€€€€

Vitinia

Pizza City 2	Via Sant'Arcangelo di Romagna, 55/57	€€

Zona Est

Le Tre Lune a Roma Est	Via di Lunghezzina 75	€€-€€€

Trevi Fountain (D. Frost)

ROME RESTAURANTS AND BAKERIES
LISTED ALPHABETICALLY
(AIC = participates in the Associazione Italiana Celiachia program)

ROMA

Ad Hoc   restaurant   €€
Via di Ripetta, 43   tel. 063233040   www.ristoranteadhoc.com
Notes: Vatican.

Agata e Romeo   restaurant   €€€€
Via Carlo Alberto, 45   tel. 064466115   www.agataeromeo.it
Notes: Esquilino.

Agrit. Torre Sant'Anastasia   agritourism, restaurant, pizzeria   €€-€€€, AIC
Via Torre Sant'Anastasia, 83   tel. 0671350361   www.torresantanastasia.it
Notes: Beyond City Center. Also B&B. Closed Monday-Thursday.

Agriturismo Pallotta   agritourism
Via delle Selve di Pallotta 2   tel. 06 9486833   www.agriturismopallotta.com

Ai Tre Scalini   restaurant   €€€
Via SS. Quattro, 30   tel. 067096309   www.aitrescalini.org
Notes: Colosseo. Closed Mondays. Limited selection but will do GF.

Al Ceppo   restaurant   €€€€
Via Panama, 2   tel. 068419696   www.ristorantealceppo.it
Notes: Villa Borghese. Reservations essential. Closed Mondays.

Al Country   restaurant   €€, AIC
Via Teano, 243/245   tel. 0621704704   www.ristorantepizzeriaalcountry.it
Notes: Pigneto.

Al Pompiere   restaurant   €€-€€€
Via Santa Maria dei Calderari, 38   tel. 066868377
Notes: Ghetto. GF pasta. Delicious Jewish dishes. Closed Sundays.

Gluten-Free Italy by Region

Albrecht restaurant €€€
Via Rasella 52 tel. 06 4880457
Notes: Centro Storico.

Alex Cafè restaurant €€€€, AIC
Via Vittorio Veneto, 20 tel. 064823618
Notes: Veneto.

Alle Fratte di Trastevere restaurant €€
Via delle Fratte di Trastevere tel. 065835775 www.allefratteditrastevere.com
Notes: Trastevere. GF pasta. Many GF options.

Antica Hostaria Dei Liberti - Ristorante restaurant €€-€€€€
Via Appia Antica, 87 tel. 065132888 www.anticaroma.it
Notes: Appio. Outrageously good food and lovely ambience.

Antico Casale La Carovana restaurant, pizzeria €€-€€€, AIC
V.le di Vigna Pia, 33 tel. 065577758 www.lacarovana.info
Notes: Ostiense.

Armando al Pantheon restaurant
Salita de' Crescenzi, 31 tel. 0668803034 www.armandoalpantheon.it
Notes: Pantheon.

Autogrill Aeroporto di Fiumicino autogrill €, AIC
Via dell'Aeroporto di Fiumicino tel. 6.65957477
Notes: airport.

Autogrill Corso autogrill €, AIC
Via del Corso, 181 tel. 6.76789135
Notes: Centro Storico.

Autogrill Stazione Termini autogrill €, AIC
Via Marsala, 25 tel. 6.47823106
Notes: Termini.

Baiamonti Lounge Bar pizzeria, bar €€, AIC
Via Baiamonti, 12 tel. 0637351954 www.baiamontiloungebar.it
Notes: Prati (Mazzini). Closed Sundays.

Bar Napoleoni bar, restaurant €€, AIC
Via Appia Nuova, 592 tel. 6.7804727 www.barnapoleoni.it
Notes: Tuscolano, Appia Antica.

Biorestaunt ZenZero restaurant €€€
Viale della Pineta di Ostia 30 tel. 06 5621293 www.ristozenzero.it
Notes: Ostia.

Birreria Peroni restaurant €
Via di San Marcello, 19 tel. 066795310 www.anticabirreriaperoni.it.
Notes: P.Zza Venezia. Closed Sundays at Saturday at lunch.

Caffe Da Claudia café, restaurant €€€
Piazza Della Rotonda 14A tel. 06 68806127
Notes: Centro Storico.

Caffè Romano dell'Hotel d'Inghilterra restaurant €€€€
Via Borgongna, 4M tel. 0669981500
Notes: Spagna. Already have GF pasta and bread. Still, reservations preferable.

Casa Mangiacotti restaurant, wine bar €€
Via Gentile da Mogliano 180 tel. 392 4319477
Notes: Pigneto.

Celiachiamo.com   bakery   €, AIC
Via C.Caneva, 40   tel. 6.64260188   www.celiachiamo.com
Notes: Prati.

Cesare   restaurant   €€€
Via Crescenzio, 13   tel. 066861227   www.ristorantecesare.com.
Notes: Prati (S.Pietro). Can make many things gluten-free. Preferable to call ahead.

Ciao Checca   tavola calda, gastropub   €€, AIC
P.za di Firenze, 25   tel. 6.68300368   www.ciaochecca.com
Notes: Centro Storico.

Circolo Ippico Tor S. Giovanni   pizzeria   €, AIC
Via Tor San Giovanni, 245   tel. 0687120537   www.circoloippico.com
Notes: Beyond City Center. DS pizza point. Closed Mondays.

Croquembouche   bakery, ice cream, chocolates   €€€, AIC
Viale Dell'Arte, 42   tel. 6.64651062   www.croquembouche.it
Notes: EUR.

Da Angelo alla Cupola   restaurant, pizzeria   €€€, AIC
Via Aurelia 50   tel. 6.39377133   www.angeloallacupola.it
Notes: Prati.

Da Arturo   restaurant, pizzeria   €€€, AIC
Via Aurelia Antica, 411/413   tel. 066623408   www.ristorantearturo.it
Notes: Aurelio. Closed Mondays.

Da Sandri   restaurant, pizzeria   €€-€€€, AIC
Via Roma Libera 19   tel. 6.5816469   www.daisandri.it
Notes: Trastevere.

Da Sergio   restaurant   €€-€€€
Vicolo delle Grotte, 27   tel. 066864293
Notes: Campo. Closed Sundays. Some choices that can be made GF.

Dal Bolognese   restaurant   €€€€
Piazza del Popolo, 1   tel. 063222799
Notes: Spagna. Closed Mondays. Reservations necessary and mention GF.

Dal Toscano   restaurant   €€€
Via Germanico, 58/60   tel. 0639723373   www.ristorantedaltoscano.it
Notes: Prati.

Ditirambo   restaurant   €€-€€€
Piazza della Cancelleria, 74   tel. 066871626   www.ristoranteditirambo.it
Notes: Campo.

El Toulà   restaurant   €€€€
Via della Lupa, 29/b   tel. 066873750   www.toula.it.
Notes: Spagna. English spoken. Reservations required for dinner. Closed Sundays.

Esquilino   bakery   €€€
Via Carlo Botta 21   tel. 06 70453930   www.pasticceriacipriani.com
Notes: Esquilino.

Etabli   restaurant   €€€
Vicolo delle Vacche, 9/a   tel. 066871499   www.etabli.it
Notes: Navona. Seeveral dishes are already GF. With notice, will do GF pasta as well.

F.I.S.H.   restaurant   €€€€
Via dei Serpenti, 16   tel. 0647824962   www.f-i-s-h.it.
Notes: Monti. Reservations essential.

Gluten-Free Italy by Region

Gioia Mia Pisciapiano restaurant, pizzeria €
Via degli Avignonesi 34 tel. 064882784 www.hoteljulia.it/imgioiamia
Notes: Spagna.

Grano Frutta e Farina sandwich shop, desserts, pizza €€€
Via Della Croce 49A www.granofruttaefarina.it
Notes: Centro Storico. They have some GF prepackaged products.

Hard Rock Cafe restaurant €€-€€€
Via Vittorio Veneto, 62 tel. 06420304 www.hardrockcafe.com
Notes: Veneto.

Hopside pub, hamburgers €€
Via Francesco Negri 39 tel. 06 69313081 www.hopside.it
Notes: Ostiense.

Il Bello della Pizza pizzeria €, AIC
Via di Portonaccio 33/a tel. 6.43253144 www.ilbellodellapizza.com
Notes: San Lorenzo.

Il Maggiolino restaurant, pizzeria €-€€, AIC
Via Alessandro Cruto, 9 tel. 065574484 www.ilmaggiolinosrl.com
Notes: Trastevere. DS pizza point. Closed Mondays.

Il Piccolo Mondo restaurant, bar €€€€
Via delle Coppelle, 16/a tel. 0668392065 www.ristorantepiccolomondo.it
Notes: Pantheon. Closed Sundays and month of August.

Il Portico restaurant, pizzeria €€-€€€, AIC
P.zza Aruleno C. Sabino, 89 tel. 0671582828
Notes: Tuscolano.

Il Sanlorenzo restaurant €€€€
Via dei Chiavari, 4/5 tel. 066865097 www.ilsanlorenzo.it.
Notes: Campo. No lunch Saturday-Monday.

Il Tulipano Nero restaurant €
Via Roma Libera, 15 tel. 065818309 www.tulipanonero.biz
Notes: Trastevere. GF pasta.

Il Veliero restaurant, pizzeria €€, AIC
Via Albalonga, 46 tel. 6.77209731 ilvelierobar.blogspot.in
Notes: Esquilino.

Il Viaggio restaurant €€-€€€, AIC
Via Isonzo, 14 tel. 0697997043 www.ristoranteilviaggio.it
Notes: Veneto.

Il Vineto restaurant €€
Via Vittorio Veneto 6 tel. 06 466617
Notes: Centro Storico.

Imperium Suite Navona hotel
Vicolo della Palomba, 19 tel. 064880628 www.imperiumsuitenavona.com
Notes: Navona.

Insomnia restaurant, pizzeria €€€
Via Portuense, 469 tel. 0655389376 www.insomnia.roma.it
Notes: Ostiense. Closed Sundays and at lunch.

Jaipur restaurant €€
Via di San Francesco a Ripa, 56 tel. 065803992
Notes: Trastevere. Closed Mondays.

La Cannoleria Sicilia   bakery   €
Via di Monte Brianzo, 66   tel. 0668806874   www.lacannoleriasiciliana.it
Notes: Navona.

La Creperie Di Testaccio   crêperie   €€€
Via Galvani 11   tel. 06 5743814
Notes: Testaccio, Ostiense. They also do take out.

La Fiorentina   restaurant   €€€€
Via Andrea Doria, 24   tel. 063737019   www.lafiorentina.net
Notes: Prati.

La Gensola   restaurant   €€-€€€
Piazza della Gensola, 15   tel. 065816312   www.osterialagensola.it
Notes: Trastevere. GF pasta or pizza, but plenty of dishes can be made GF. Reservations preferable.

La Mimosa Fiorita   restaurant, pizzeria   €€€, AIC
Via Bari, 11/B   tel. 0644291958
www.facebook.com/pages/La-Mimosa-Fiorita-Roma/167048666667644
Notes: San Lorenzo (Or Tiburtino). Closed Wednesdays. Special GF menu with many options.

La Nduja 2   restaurant, pizzeria   AIC
Via Michele Tenore 21/31   tel. 6.25210654   www.landuja.com
Notes: Casolino.

La Pergola (in Rome Cavalieri/Waldorf Hotel) restaurant   €€€€
Via Alberto Cadlolo, 101   tel. 0635091   www.romecavalieri.it
Notes: Monte Mario.

La Piazzetta   restaurant, pizzeria   €€-€€€, AIC
Piazza dei Visconti, 8   tel. 0666014164   www.giancarlone.com
Notes: Beyond City Center (In Trionfale). DS pizza point. Closed Mondays.

La Rosetta   restaurant   €€€€
Via della Rosetta, 9   tel. 066861002   www.larosetta.com.
Notes: Pantheon. Very small restaurant so better to make reservations. GF pasta and bread. English spoke.

La Scaletta Degli Artisti Srl   restaurant   €€-€€€
Via di Santa Maria dell'Anima   tel. 0668801872   www.lascaletta-roma.it
Notes: Navona.

La Soffitta Renovatio   restaurant, pizzeria   €€
Piazza del Risorgimento 46A   tel. 06 68892977   www.ristoranterenovatio.it
Notes: Prati.

La Veranda dell'Hotel Columbus restaurant   €€€-€€€€
Borgo Santo Spirito, 73   tel. 066872973   wwww.hotelcolumbus.net
Notes: Vatican. Reservations essential and mention GF. GF pasta.

La Pilotta da Mario   restaurant, pizzeria   €€-€€€
Via Porta Cavalleggeri, 35/37   tel. 06632643   www.lapilotta.com
Notes: Prati.

La Scaletta   restaurant   €€€
Via della Scala   tel. 0'065816317
Notes: Pantheon. Highly recommended. Many celiac clients.

Lanificio Cucina   restaurant   €€, AIC
Via di Pietralata, 159   tel. 6.4501384   www.lanificio.com
Notes: Montesacro/Talenti.

Larys Restaurant Rome restaurant €€-€€€, AIC
Via Basento, 54 tel. 6.8530513 www.larys.it
Notes: Pinciano.

Le Ben - Piacere sì, glutine no bakery €
Via di Ponziano, 19 tel. 0658332697 www.le-ben.it
Notes: Trastevere. Exclusively GF. Lots of treats.

Le Tre Lune a Roma Est restaurant, pizzeria €€-€€€, AIC
Via di Lunghezzina 75- Roma Est tel. 06.2203031/335.8185144 www.ristoranteletrelune.com
Notes: Zona Est.

Lievito72 hamburger, pizza €€
Via del Forte Braschi 82A tel. 06 6142829 www.lievito72.it
Notes: Balduina/Montemario.

Luana Inn Airport hotel, restaurant €€
Via Monte Forcelletta, 23 tel. 3396933742 www.bbluanainn.it
Notes: Airport. Restaurant caters to celiacs. GF breakfast too. Very close to airport.

Mama.Eat restaurant, pizzeria €€, AIC
Via di San Cosimato, 7 tel. 6.5806222 www.mamaeat.com
Notes: Trastevere.

Mamey_Roma Est bakery, pizzeria, bar €, AIC
Via G. Rosaccio, 8/22 tel. 6.41228009 www.mamey.it
Notes: Tiburtino.

Mamma Angela's Trattoria trattoria €€
Via Palestro, 53 tel. 0644341317 www.mammaangelas.com
Notes: Termini.

Mangiafuoco Pizza & Grill restaurant, pizzeria €€, AIC
Via Chiana, 37 tel. 0685357255 www.mangiafuoco.org
Notes: Trieste.

Margutta Vegetariano restaurant €€-€€€
Via Margutta, 118 tel. 0632650577 www.ilmarguttavegetariano.it
Notes: Spagna. Will prepare GF with advance notice.

Millennium restaurant, pizzeria pub €€€, AIC
Via Tor Tre Teste, 35 tel. 623269171 www.millenniumcenter.it
Notes: Beyond City Center (In Casilino). Closed at lunch.

Napoleoni bar, gelato €€
Via Appia Nuova 592 tel. 06 7804727 www.barnapoleoni.it
Notes: Tuscolano, Appia Antica.

New Food Gluten Free bakery €€, AIC
L.go A. Pepere, 25/26 tel. 6.58230394 www.newfoodglutenfree.it

Novotel Roma La Rustica hotel, restaurant AIC
Via A. Noale, 291 tel. 6.227661 www.novotel.com
Notes: Beyond City Center.

O' Masto pizzeria €€€, AIC
L.go Salinari, 8/16 tel. 065413448 www.omasto.com
Notes: Appia Antica. Closed Mondays. DS pizza point.

Ops! vegetarian restaurant €€
Via Bergamo 56 tel. 06 8411769 www.opsveg.com
Notes: Nomentano, Pinciano. GF items indicated on the menu.

Osteria del Gallo restaurant
Vicolo di Montevecchio, 27 tel. 066873781 www.osteriadelgalloroma.it
Notes: Navona.

Osteria del Pegno restaurant €€€
Vicolo di Montevecchio 8 tel. 06 68807025 www.osteriadelpegno.com
Notes: Centro storico (Navona).

Osteria dell'Ingegno restaurant €€-€€€
Piazza di Pietra, 45 tel. 066780662
Notes: Pantheon. GF pasta. Call ahead for reservations and GF requests.

Pantharei restaurant AIC
Via della Minerva, 18 tel. 6.89021922 www.pantharei.it
Notes: Historic District.

Papá Baccus restaurant €€€€
Via Toscana, 36 tel. 0642742808 www.papabaccus.com
Notes: Veneto. With advance notice, will prepare GF.

Pizza City 2 pizzeria €€, AIC
Via Sant'Arcangelo di Romagna, 55/57 - loc.Vitinia tel. 328.3140976
Notes: Vitinia.

Pomodori Verdi Fritti restaurant, pizzeria €€, AIC
Via dei Pescatori, 495 tel. 065212824 www.pomodoriverdifritti.it
Notes: Beyond City Center.

Potter Pizza pizzeria €, AIC
V.le dei Colli Portuensi, 346 tel. 0665740770
Notes: Ostiense.

Primi e Veloci fast food €
Via Sicilia 129 tel. 328 8755900 www.primieveloci.it
Notes: Termini.

Quattro Spicchi pizzeria, bakery €€, AIC
Via della Pisana, 51 tel. 6.64463644 www.quattrospicchi.it
Notes: Centro Storico.

Renovatio La Soffitta restaurant, pizzeria €€€, AIC
P.zza Risorgimento, 46/a (corner of Via Crescenzio) tel. 0668892977
www.ristoranterenovatio.it
Notes: Vatican. Very highly recommended by fellow celiacs. GF pizza, calzone, lasagne, beer.

Resta's Pizza Bar pizzeria, bar €, AIC
L.go La Loggia, 15 tel. 6.60669753

Ripa 12 Ristorante restaurant
Via San a Franceso Ripa, 12 tel. 065809093 www.ripa12.com
Notes: Trastevere.

Ristorante Bibliothè restaurant €
Via Celsa, 4 tel. 066781427 www.bibliothe.net
Notes: Navona.

Ristorante Tema restaurant €€€€
Via Panisperna, 96/98 tel. 06486484 www.ristorantetema.com
Notes: Monti. Very highly recommended by fellow celiacs.

Romolo restaurant €€€
Via di Porta Settimiana, 8 tel. 065818284
Notes: Trastevere. Will do GF with advance notice.

Sale e Argento restaurant AIC
Via Evandro, 8 tel. 6.78346526 www.saleeargento.com

San Carlo Suite hotel
Via del Corso, 112 tel. 0668392055 www.sancarlosuite.com
Notes: Centro storico (Spagna).

Sans de Ble' bakery €, AIC
Via G. Chiabrera, 58c tel. 389.9008807 www.sansdeble.it
Notes: Ostiense.

Sehgal Sanjiv Kumar Ristorante Indiano Maharaja restaurant €€€€
Via Dei Serpenti, 124 tel. 064747144
Notes: Monti.

Senza Pensieri Dolci bakery €€
Via dei Campani 53 tel. 340 9724215
Notes: San Giovanni. They specialize in GF.

Settimio all'Arancio restaurant €€€
Via Arancio 50 tel. 06 6876119 www.settimioallarancio.com
Notes: Centro storico.

Sheraton Golf Parco de' Medici hotel, restaurant €€€-€€€€
V.le Salvatore Rebecchini, 39 tel. 0665288 www.starwoodhotels.com
Notes: Beyond City Center (Autostrada Airport). Two restaurants. GF breakfast too.

Sora Lella restaurant €€€
Via di Ponte Quattro Capi, 16 tel. 066861601 www.soralella.com
Notes: Ghetto. Reserve 2 to 3 days ahead for GF.

Taberna Recina restaurant €€€, AIC
Via Elvia Recina, 22 tel. 6.7000413 www.tabernarecina.it
Notes: Esquilino, Aventino.

Taverna Angelica restaurant €€€
Piazza A. Capponi, 6 tel. 066874514 www.tavernaangelica.it
Notes: Prati. Call ahead for GF.

Taverna Barberini restaurant €€
Via Delle Quattro Fontane 160 tel. 06 4883619 www.tavernabarberini.it
Notes: Centro storico.

Toto restaurant €€€
Via delle Carrozze 10 tel. 06 6785558 www.toto1922.it
Notes: Centro Storico.

Trattoria Pizzeria Fiammetta restaurant, pizzeria €€
Piazza Fiammetta, 10 tel. 066875777 www.ristorantefiammetta.it
Notes: Navona. Highly recommended. GF pasta. English spoken. Owner is gluten intolerant.

Tullio restaurant €€€-€€€€
Via San Nicola da Tolentino tel. 064745560 www.tullioristorante.it.
Notes: Quirinale. Near Piazza Barberini. Closed Sundays.

Tutti i gusti gelato, bar €, AIC
Via Casilina, 381 tel. 6.24406269 www.fuoridiglutine.eu

V Hugo restaurant, pizzeria
Via Cristoforo Colombo, 90 tel. 065115709 www.hugorestaurant.it
Notes: Beyond City Center (Eur). Many celiac customers.

Villa Grant
Via Pratica di Mare, 181
Notes: Beyond City Center.
restaurant, reception hall
tel. 0650570832
€€€€, AIC
www.villagrant.it

Vintage Bistrot
Piazza Tarquinia 4A
Notes: San Giovanni.
restaurant
tel. 06 64764104
€€
www.vintagebistrot.com

Voglia di Pizza
Via dei Giubbonari, 33
restaurant, pizzeria
tel. 066875293
€€, AIC
www.vogliadipizzaglutenfree.com
Notes: Campo. Very highly recommended by fellow celiacs. Separate gluten-free menu.

Zen Fusion
V.le Eritrea, 69
restaurant
tel. 0686218365
€€-€€€, AIC
www.zenfusion.eu
Notes: Beyond City Center (African). Closed Sunday and Monday at lunch. Highly recommended; Japanese and Thai food.

Zia Rosetta
Via Urbana 54
Notes: Monti.
sandwich shop
www.ziarosetta.com
€€

Z'Imberto
Piazza San Giovanni della Malva
Notes: Trastevere. Closed Mondays.
restaurant
tel. 065816646
€€€

ROMA SUD-EST
Maison del Celiaco
Via Buscemi 37
bakery, sandwich shop
www.maisondelceliaco.it
€

ROMA-ACILIA
Cremeria Alpi
Via Sistina 5A
Notes: Centro Storico.
gelato
www.cremeriaalpi.it
€, AIC

Il Mulino Celiaco
Via U. Lilloni, 64/int.23
Notes: Veneto.
bakery
tel. 6.60661686
€, AIC
www.ilmulinoceliaco.it

ROMA-OSTIA LIDO
Al contadino non far sapere...
Via della Macchiarella 128
Notes: Ostia
restaurant, pizzeria
tel. 0656350219
€€€, AIC
www.alcontadinononfarsapere.com

Le Palme
L.re Amerigo Vespucci, 58
restaurant, bar
tel. 6.56470131
AIC

THE REST OF LAZIO
ACQUAPENDENTE
Agriturismo Belvedere
Loc. Belvedere snc - Torre Alfina
www.belvederetorrealfina.com/index_en.htm
Notes: The chef is a celiac himself.
agritourism, restaurant, pizzeria
tel. 763.716041
€€-€€€, AIC

ALATRI
La Rosetta
Via Duomo, 35
pizzeria
tel. 0775434642
€-€€, AIC

Papapidò
Via Circonvallazione, sn
pizzeria
tel. 0775442666
€, AIC

Ristorante Sisto
Via Circonvallazione Basciano, 55
restaurant/pizzeria
tel. 0775409158
€ - €€, AIC
www.ristorantesisto.it

Pantheon (D. Frost)

Villa Scerrato
Via Madonna della Sanità, 19

restaurant
tel. 0775440743

€€-€€€, AIC

ALBANO LAZIALE

Beccofino
Via Fleming, 5
Notes: DS pizza point. Closed Mondays.

restaurant, pizzeria
tel. 0693720309

€€, AIC

ANAGNI

Autogrill La Macchia Ovest
A1 Roma - Napoli

autogrill
tel. 775.768104

€, AIC

La Rena
Via La Rena, 10
Notes: Closed Tuesdays.

restaurant
tel. 07757681

€€-€€€, AIC
www.ristorantelarena.it

Villa Sorvillo
Via Carlo Alberto dalla Chiesa, 37

B&B
tel. 0775727080

AIC
www.villasorvillo.it

Zi Luciano
Via Fosso del Lupo, 4

pizzeria
tel. 0775725588

€, AIC

ANZIO

La Fornace
Via della Fornace, 47/a

restaurant, pizzeria
tel. 069870195

€, AIC
www.lafornacedianzio.it

Maison del Celiaco
Viale Antium, 6 C/O Centro Anteo

bakery, sandwich shop
tel. 6.986385

€, AIC
www.maisondelceliaco.it

APRILIA

Fresche Golosità
Via lombardia, 25/ 27

sandwich shop, bakery
tel. 6.64005936

€, AIC
www.freschegolosita.it

L'Oasi pizzeria €, AIC
Via Del Tronco, 14 tel. 069275334
Notes: Closed Mondays.

ARICCIA

Fori Porta restaurant €€, AIC
Via A. Chigi, 16 tel. 069333661 www.foriporta.it
Notes: Closed Tuesdays.

Taverna Antichi Sapori...e di più restaurant, pizzeria, bar €€, AIC
Via Indipendenza, 30 tel. 06.31055123 www.taverna.antichisapori/ilfroid

ARICCIA-FONTA NA DI PAPA

Zi' Ciana restaurant, pizzeria €€, AIC
Via Nettunense, Km 11 tel. 6.93496158
www.facebook.com/pages/Zi-Ciana/193452074169622

BASSANO IN TEVERINA

Osteria Belvedere restaurant €€€, AIC
Via Belvedere, 1/3 tel. 0761407546 www.osteriabelvedere.it

BELLEGRA

Sancamillo restaurant, hotel, bar AIC
Via San Francesco, 22 tel. 6.95617016 www.hotelsancamillo.it

BOLSENA

Verdeluna restaurant, pizzeria €, AIC
SS Cassia, Km 113,00 tel. 0761799023
Notes: DS pizza point. Closed Wednesdays.

BOMARZO

Il Quadrifoglio restaurant, pizzeria €€, AIC
Via Verga, 19 tel. 0761924281

BRACCIANO

Crazy Bull Cafe' Evolution restaurant, pizzeriaub €€, AIC
P.za Don Cesolini, 4 tel. 6.99802341 www.crazybullcafe.it

Il Grillo restaurant, pizzeria €-€€, AIC
Piazza Don Cesolini, 32 tel. 6.9987685 www.pizzeriailgrillo.com

Pizzando restaurant, pizzeria €€, AIC
Via Cavour, 36 tel. 6.99802932 www.pizzando.com

BROCCOSTELLA

New York Express restaurant €€-€€€, AIC
Via Stella, 96/b tel. 0776.1938150
www.osterianewyork.it/www.osterianewyork.it/Sito_in_allestimento.html

CANALE MONTERANO

Nonsolorose B&B AIC
Via Secchinetto tel. 0699838605 www.digilander.libero.it/bebnonsolorose

CAPODIMONTE

La Piroga pizzeria €, AIC
Via Verentana, km. 13,180 tel. 0761870780
Notes: DS pizza point. Self-service. Closed Tuesdays.

CAPRAROLA

La Bella Venere hotel/restaurant €€€€, AIC
Loc. Scardenato tel. 0761612342 www.labellavenere.it

Gluten-Free Italy by Region

CARPINETO ROMANO

La Rupe dei 7 Venti pizzeria €, AIC
Via Maenza, 26 tel. 069719507 www.pizzeriafeoli.it
Notes: DS pizza point. Closed Mondays.

CASSINO

Rocca Hotel Rist. hotel, restaurant €€-€€€, AIC
Via Sferracavalli, 105 tel. 0776311212 www.hotelrocca.it

CASTEL SANT'ELIA

La Vecchia Quercia restaurant, pizzeria €€-€€€, AIC
Loc. San Lorenzo tel. 0761599164
Notes: DS pizza point. Closed Wednesdays.

CASTRO DEI VOLSCI

Il Ruspante agritourism €€€, AIC
Località Pozzotello, 18 www.ilruspante.it
Notes: Closed Tuesday-Wednesday.

La Locanda del Ditirambo inn, restaurant €€€, AIC
Via dell'Orologio, 11/a tel. 0775662091
Notes: Closed Monday-Wednesday.

CECCANO

Caffè della Stazione bar, tavola calda €, AIC
Via Stazione tel. 775.604416

Il Giardino dell'Angelo restaurant, pizzeria €, AIC
Via Magenta, 51 tel. 0775604463

Il Ristorantino del Rio restaurant, pizzeria AIC
Colle Campanaro, 20 tel. 346.7771893

La Cantinella restaurant €, AIC
Via Cosa, 20 tel. 0775642019
Notes: Closed Mondays.

Whats App gelato (€, AIC) Via per Frosinone, 62

CEPRANO

Hotel Ida hotel, restaurant €€-€€€, AIC
Via Caragno, 27 tel. 0775950040 www.hotelida.it

CERVETERI

Il Casale di Montetosto restaurant, pizzeria €€-€€€, AIC
Via del Sasso, km.5 tel. 0699079327 www.ilcasaledimontetosto.it
Notes: DS pizza point. Closed Wednesdays.

La Brace da Guerrino restaurant, pizzeria €-€€, AIC
Via Fontana Morella, 221 tel. 6.99079202 www.ristorantelabrace.weebly.com

CIVITAVECCHIA

Il Pesce in Bottiglia restaurant AIC
Darsena Romana, 10 tel. 0766220699 www.ilpesceinbottiglia.it

L'Angoletto restaurant €€€, AIC
Via P. Guglielmotti, 2 tel. 076632825 www.langoletto.com
Notes: Closed Mondays and Sunday nights.

Le Delizie bar €, AIC
Via G. Baccelli, 128 tel. 766.672477

Lo Stuzzichino	restaurant	€€-€€€, AIC
Via P. Manzi, 30	tel. 766.32945	www.lostuzzichino.com
Ostaria La Babbiona	restaurant	€€€, AIC
Via Padri Domenicani, 11	tel. 0766560649	www.lababbiona.it
Pizzaland	restaurant, pizzeria bar	€, AIC
Via Enrico Berlinguer	tel. 3289596358	
Taverna dell'Olmo	restaurant	€-€€, AIC
Via Tevere,4	tel. 766.501331	www.ristorantetavernadellolmo.it

COLONNA

Pause	restaurant, pizzeria	€-€€, AIC
Via Frascati, 23	tel. 6.9438097	www.pausebirroteca.it

FERENTINO

Il Giardino	restaurant	€, AIC
Via Stazione 37	tel. 0775244128	www.pizzeriailgiardino.it
Primavera	restaurant	€€€-€€€€, AIC
Via Casilina Nord Km 70, 254	tel. 0775246521	www.ristorante-primavera.com
Notes: Closed Mondays and Sunday nights.		

FIUGGI

Forum et Ludus	restaurant, pizzeria	€-€€, AIC
Via delle Felci	tel. 0775506058	www.fiuggi.org/rforum.htm
Notes: Closed Tuesdays.		
Hotel Olimpic	hotel, restaurant	€€€, AIC
Via Prenestina sud, 63	tel. 0775515584	

FIUMICINO

Autogrill Fiumicino Satellite Ovest autogrill		€, AIC
Via Dell'Aeroporto, 1	tel. 6.65011112	
Luana	restaurant, pizzeria, B&B	AIC
Via Monte Nozzolo, 3	tel. 066520231	www.bbluanainn.it
Mychef Aeroporto Fiumicino Satellite C mychef		€, AIC
Fiumicino	tel. 6.65019911	www.mychef.it
Mychef Aeroporto Fiumicino Terminal A mychef		€, AIC
Fiumicino	tel. 6.65019911	www.mychef.it
Pizzeria Rosticceria del Porto pizzeria, tavola calda		€, AIC
V.le Traiano, 101	tel. 6.6521539	
www.facebook.com/PizzeriaRosticceriaDelPortoDarsena		

FONDI

Cantina di Galba	restaurant	€€€, AIC
Via Fabio Filzi, 29	tel. 0771523648	
Notes: Closed Mondays.		
Il Mulino	restaurant, pizzeria	€, AIC
Via Rene, 5	tel. 0771502891	
Martino Club Hotel	hotel, restaurant	€€€, AIC
Via Flacca, km 4.150	tel. 77.157464	www.hotelmartino.it

FORMIA

Chinappi	restaurant, pizzeria	€€€€, AIC
Via Anfiteatro, 8/10	tel. 0771790002	

I Dolci Pensieri   gelato (€, AIC)   Via dei Frassini

La Villetta   restaurant   €€€€, AIC
Via del Porticciolo Romano   tel. 0771723113
Notes: Closed Tuesdays.

Ristopub Cook   restaurant, pizzeria   €€, AIC
Via S. Maria Cerquito   tel. 0771720436

FRASCATI

Gamela Arte Pasticcera   cupcake shop   €, AIC
Via San Francesco D'Assisi, 10   tel. 6.9424148
www.facebook.com/GamelaArtePasticcera
Notes: 100% gluten-free.

Il Campo   restaurant, pizzeria   €€, AIC
Via Lunati, 3   tel. 6.942453   www.ilcampofrascati.it
Notes: 100% gluten-free.

FRASSO SABINO

La Taverna del Tiranno   restaurant, pizzeria   €€, AIC
Via Mirtense, Km 1   tel. 765.841708 www.latavernadeltiranno.com

FRAZ. GIULIANELLO

Al Ponte   restaurant, pizzeria   €, AIC
Via Velletri, 52   tel. 069665430   www.massimoalponte.it
Notes: DS pizza point. Closed Mondays, Tuesdays.

FROSINONE

La Ginestra   restaurant   €€-€€€, AIC
Via Adige, 1   tel. 0775824261

GAETA

B&B Elena   B&B   AIC
L.re Caboto,488   tel. 0771460466   www.elenabebgaeta.it

Il Follaro   restaurant   €€, AIC
L.mare Caboto, 624 A/D   tel. 771.18942   www.ristoranteilfollaro.it

Il Gazebo   restaurant, pizzeria   €€€, AIC
Via Flacca Km.20,600   tel. 3405838052

Tuttigusti   gelato (€, AIC)   P.zza Libertà, 22

GENZANO DI ROMA

Da Elio   restaurant, pizzeria   €, AIC
Via Emilia Romagna, 04   tel. 6.9391466

Papillon Club   restaurant, pizzeria   €€, AIC
Via Lucrezio, 9 - Colli di Cicerone tel. 069370555
www.sites.google.com/site/papillonclubsrl

Piazza Margherita   restaurant, pizzeria   €, AIC
Via Ettore Ronconi, 1   tel. 0693953062   www.piazza-margherita.it

Pizzeria MA.MI   pizzeria   €, AIC
Via S.Silvestri, 208   tel. 0694426685

Trattoria dei Cacciatori   restaurant   €€€, AIC
Via Italo Belardi, 76   tel. 069396060   www.trattoria-cacciatori.com

GROTTAFERRATA

Maison del Celiaco   bakery, sandwich shop   €
Via Delle Sorgenti 98 - Squarciarelli www.maisondelceliaco.it

GUIDONIA

La Taverna — restaurant, pizzeria — €€€, AIC
Via G. Motta, 36 — tel. 0774304179 — www.latrattoriaguidonia.it

GUIDONIA MONTECELIO

Pizza Pazza — restaurant/pizzeria — € - €€, AIC
Via Arsoli, 21 — tel. 3453327162

ITRI

Buenavistasurfmed — B&B — AIC
Contrada Campanaro, 21 — tel. 3473792183 — www.buenavistasurfmed.it

La Maison Galu' — B&B — AIC
Strada Prov. Itri/Sperlonga - Loc. Corano 9 — tel. 771.728325 — www.lamaisongalu.it

La Torre Rossa — agritourism, B&B — €€€, AIC
Contrada S. Stefano — tel. 0771729102 — www.latorrerossa.com

LABICO

Magic Garden — B&B — AIC
Via Colle Pirro, 1 — tel. 6.9510926 — www.bbmagicgarden.com

LADISPOLI

La Piana di Alsium — agritourism — €€€, AIC
Via Longarina dei Caselli, 7 — tel. 6.9946734 — www.pianadialsium.com

Ristorante Roma — restaurant, pizzeria — AIC
L.mare Regina Elena, 35 — tel. 6.83083267

LANUVIO

Al Tempio — restaurant, pizzeria — €€€€, AIC
Via G. Matteotti, 16 — tel. 069375614

LATINA

Fattoria Prato di Coppola — restaurant — €€-€€€, AIC
Via del Lido Km.4,200 — tel. 0773273411
I Milli — gelato (€, AIC) — Largo Cesti
Notes: Also GF crêpes. Closed Mondays.

I Milli 2 — gelato (€, AIC) — Strade Acque Alte, snc

Il Funghetto — restaurant — €€€€, AIC
Strada Litoranea, 11412 — tel. 0773208009
Notes: Closed Wednesdays and Sunday nights.

La Ginestra — restaurant — €€, AIC
Via dei Piceni, 63 — tel. 0773266021 — www.laginestravegetariano.it

La Pasticelia — bakery — €, AIC
Via Oslavia, 11 — tel. 340.3232905 — www.facebook.com/LaPasticelia

L'Euro — restaurant, pizzeria — €€, AIC
Via Isonzo, 269 — tel. 773.242415

Punto Snack — pizzeria — €, AIC
Viale P.L.Nervi, 166 — tel. 0773601512

LAVINIO DI ANZIO

Breezy — gelato (€, AIC) — Via Leonardo da Vinci, 21

Follia — restaurant, pizzeria — €€, AIC
Via Ardeatina, 632 — tel. 3318065876

MAGLIANO SABINA

Il Giglio
Vocabolo Colle Croce
restaurant, pizzeria, B&B
tel. 0744910078
€€, AIC
www.agriturismoilgiglio.it

MARINA DI S. NICOLA / LADISPOLI

Polipetto Goloso
gelato (€, AIC)
Via Orione, 1

MARINO

Forgione
Via Pal. Colonna, 32
restaurant, pizzeria
€€€, AIC

MENTANA

Il Sole e la Luna
P.zza Moscatelli, 36
sandwich shop, bakery
tel. 6.9001566
€, AIC
www.labilsoleelaluna.it

Sporting Life
Via Cannetacci, 50
restaurant, pizzeria
tel. 0690015826
€€€, AIC

MONTALTO DI CASTRO

Stella Polare
Viale Harmine, 58/a
Notes: Closed Wednesdays.
restaurant
tel. 0766801276
€€€, AIC
www.ristorantestellapolare.com

Il Rifugio dei Cacciatori
Via Tuscolana, km 26,700
restaurant, pizzeria
tel. 069406293
€€€, AIC

MONTE COMPATRI

Piccola Caffetteria del Corso
V.le Littoria, 1
bar
tel. 348.8556153
€, AIC

MONTE SAN BIAGIO

MONTEROTONDO

Maculato
Via Castelchiodato, 9
restaurant, pizzeria
tel. 069066065
€€-€€€€, AIC
www.maculato.it

MOROLO

La Mola
Via Recinto della Mola, 67
restaurant
tel. 0775229059
€€-€€€, AIC

NETTUNO

Al Centro
Piazza Colonna, 13
restaurant, pizzeria
tel. 6.9880946
€€-€€€, AIC
www.ristoranteosterialcentro.com

ORTE

Garibaldi 148
Corso Garibaldi, 148
bar
tel. 338.4280271
€, AIC

OSTIA LIDO

Don Pepe
L.re P. Toscanelli, 125
restaurant
tel. 065672408
€€-€€€, AIC

Il Corsaro
L.re Amerigo Vespucci, 164
Notes: Closed Mondays at lunch.
restaurant
tel. 055600317
€€€-€€€€, AIC
www.ilcorsaro beach.it

Il Mare del Gelato
gelato (€, AIC)
Via Pietro Rosa, 27

Mamey_Ro ma Ostia Lido
Via dei Pescherecci, 5
bar
tel. 6.64670436
€, AIC

Peccati di Gola
gelato (€, AIC)
Via Danilo Stiepovich, 245

Peppino a Mare
L.re Amerigo Vespucci, 102
restaurant
tel. 6.56320247
€€€€, AIC
www.peppinoamare.it

Pinzirò
Via Mar dei Sargassi, 68

restaurant
tel. 0656362203

€€-€€€, AIC
www.pinziro.it

PATRICA

Bar L'Incontro
Via Morolense, Km.5,500

tavola calda, bar
tel. 775.200734

€, AIC

POGGIO MIRTETO

Peter Pan 2
P.za della Vetreria 12

restaurant, pizzeria
tel. 765.24183

€-€€, AIC
www.ristorantepeterpan2.it

POMEZIA

Agriturismo Tonelli
Via Cesena, 15

agritourism
tel. 333.3300612

AIC
www.agriturismotonelli.it

Pizzeria Caroli
Via Catullo, 22

pizzeria
tel. 6.91620051

€€, AIC
www.pizzeriacaroli.com

PONTINIA

L'Arca
Via Migliara, 53 corner of Via Della Torre   tel. 0773853338

restaurant

€€€, AIC

POSTA FIBRENO

Ben Posta
Via Vicenne, 3

B&B
tel. 3391240889

AIC
www.benposta.it

RIETI

Al Bersagliere da Gualtiero
Via Castagneto, loc. S. Elia
Notes: Closed Tuesdays.

restaurant, pizzeria
tel. 0746210253

€€, AIC

Al Pincetto
Piazza Oberdan, 2

restaurant, pizzeria
tel. 746.272092

€-€€, AIC
www.ristorantealpincetto.com

Borgo Margherita
Via Sandro Pertini, 667

restaurant, pizzeria
tel. 0746218239

AIC

Cintia
Via Sandro Pertini, 667

restaurant, pizzeria
tel. 0746251527

€€, AIC

Da Valerio
Via Salaria per Roma

restaurant, pizzeria, hotel
tel. 746.606047

AIC
www.ristorantehoteldavalerio.it

Gelateria Crosby

gelato (€, AIC)

P.zza Marconi, 22

Il Picchio Allegro
Via Criano, 18

pizzeria
tel. 0746271826

AIC
www.picchioallegro.com

La Corte
Via Bevilacqua, 12

restaurant
tel. 746.218597

€€, AIC
www.lacortecatering.it

La Foresta
Via Foresta, 51

restaurant
tel. 0746220455

€€€-€€€€, AIC
www.ristorantelaforesta.it

La Lisca
Via Salaria per L'Aquila, 52

restaurant, hotel
tel. 746.271409

€€-€€€, AIC
www.laliscarieti.it

La Locanda del Carro
P.za S. Rufo, 7/8

restaurant
tel. 746.218507

€-€€, AIC

Lungovelino Cafè
Via Salaria, 26

wine bar, restaurant
tel. 0746.1970108

€€-€€€, AIC
www.lungovelino.it

Mondo Antico
Via Comunali, 23

restaurant, pizzeria
tel. 0746201665

€€, AIC

Notes: Closed Mondays.

Park Hotel Villa Potenziani   hotel, restaurant   AIC
Via San Mauro, 6   tel. 0746202765   www.villapotenziani.it
Notes: Closed Mondays and at lunch.

Quelli de Il Carro al Coccio   restaurant, pizzeria   €-€€, AIC
Via P. Borsellino, 11   tel. 746.760078
Notes: Great reviews.

Fontana (S. Wolozin)

RIETI - TERMINILLO ROSCE
Rosce Caffe'   restaurant, B&B   €€-€€€, AIC
Via degli Appennini,18   tel. 335.71026
RIGNANO FLAMINIO
Mediterranea   cupcake shop, deli   €, AIC
Via dei Montaroni, 26   tel. 320.3346866
www.facebook.com/pages/Laboratorio-Mediterranea-Senza-Glutine/156179137739726

RIVODUTRI
Agriturismo Tenuta Due Laghi   agritourism, restaurant   AIC
Via Campigliana, 29   tel. 746.685206   www.tenutaduelaghi.com

ROCCA PRIORA
Al Ritrovo da Uccia   restaurant, pizzeria   AIC
Via Mediana, 12   tel. 069406081   www.alritrovodauccia.it

S. MARTINO AL CIMINO-VITERBO
Balletti Park Hotel   hotel   AIC
Via Umbria, 2   tel. 07613771   www.balletti.com

Gelateria Balletti   gelato (€, AIC)   Via Umbria, 2

Tavernetta Il Cavaliere   restaurant, pizzeria   €€€, AIC
Via Umbria, 2/a   tel. 07613771   www.balletti.com

SABAUDIA

La Capricciosa   restaurant, pizzeria
€€, AIC   Via Tortini 33
tel. 0773515677
www.lacapricciosa.it

SAN MARTINO AL CIMINO
Ristorante Pizzeria da Saverio
restaurant, pizzeria   €€, AIC
Piazza Del Duomo, 2
tel. 761.379643
www.dasaverio.com

Cinquecento classico (J. Lubin)

SAN POLO DEI CAVALIERI

L'Agrifoglio   restaurant   €, AIC
Via Santa Liberata, 14 tel. 0774416384

SANTA MARINELLA
Girogustando   gelato (€, AIC)   Via Aurelia, 248

SERMONETA SCALO
La Valle dell'Usignolo agritourism   €€, AIC
Via Vigna Riccelli, 2   tel. 0773318629   www.lavalledellusignolo.it

SERRONE
Belsito   restaurant   €€€€, AIC
Via delle Rimembranze, 17/29 tel. 0775523106   www.belsitoserrone.com
Notes: Closed Wednesdays.

SPIGNO SATURNIA
Der Keller   pub   €, AIC
Via Grata, 8   tel. 077164187

TARQUINIA
L'Ambaradan   restaurant   €€€€, AIC
P.zza G. Matteotti, 14   tel. 0766857073
Notes: Closed Wednesdays.

Quadrifoglio   agritourism   €€€, AIC
Loc. Selciatella   tel. 3358080415   www.agriturismoquadrifoglio.it
Notes: Closed Tuesdays. Rooms for rent.

Valle del Marta   agritourism   AIC
Via St. Aurelia Vecchia Km.93 tel. 0766855475   www.valledelmarta.it

TERRACINA
La Perla   pizzeria   €, AIC
Via Grata, 8   tel. 0773730691

TOBIA
Poggio della Guardia   pizzeria, trattoria   €€€€, AIC
Str. Ciavaletta 15   tel. 0761263570   www.poggiodellaguardia.it

TOLFA

Tolfa Hotel
Via Lizzera, 44
hotel restaurant
tel. 076693286
€€€, AIC
www.tolfahotel.it
Notes: Restaurant is closed Mondays.

TORRICE

Drago Rosso
Via Piana, 50
restaurant, pizzeria
tel. 0775301675
€, AIC
www.trattoriadragorosso.com

VALENTANO

La Voltarella
Via Solferino, 25
restaurant
tel. 0761422197 www.facebook.com/locanda.lavoltarella
€€, AIC
Notes: 100% gluten-free. Closed Tuesdays.

VALMONTONE

Fashion Hotel
Via della Pace 1/2
hotel
tel. 6.9599631
AIC
www.fashion-hotel.it

Mone'
Via della Pace 1/2
restaurant, pizzeria, bar
tel. 6.95994751
€€€, AIC
www.fashionristorazione.com

VELLETRI

La Forbice
C.so della Repubblica, 466
restaurant, pizzeria
tel. 069638812
€, AIC
www.laforbice.it

VILLA S. GIOVANNI IN TUSCIA

Da Peppone
V.le Europa, 8
restaurant, pizzeria
tel. 761.476287
€€€, AIC
www.dapeppone.com

VITERBO

Da Oliviera
Str. Cassia Sud Km. 76 113/c
restaurant
tel. 761.263001
AIC
www.ristorantedaoliviera.it

Gustosi senza glutine
Piazza Santa Maria Nuova, 7
bakery
tel. 0761.1706154
€, AIC
www.gustosisenzaglutine.it

FLORENCE AND TOSCANA

PLACES IN FLORENCE TO BUY
GLUTEN-FREE FOOD PRODUCTS

Esselunga	Via Galliano, 136
Esselunga	Via Pisana, 130
Esselunga	Via Milanesi, 32/34
Esselunga	Via del Gignoro
Esselunga	Viale Gianotti, 75/77
Esselunga	Via Masaccio, 274
Esselunga	Via Di Novoli, 61
Esselunga	Via Canova, 164
Esselunga	Via del Argingrosso, 47
Farmacia all'insegna	Piazza S.Giovanni, 20 R
Farmacia Camilli	P.zza Degli OttaViani, 8/r
Farmacia Del Cinghiale	Piazza Mercato Nuovo, 4/R
Farmacia Paglici	Via Della Scala, 61R
Farmacia Zanobini	Via Pagnini, 17/R

GUARANTEED GLUTEN-FREE GELATO PLACES
(Sponsored by the Italian celiac society)

Antica Gelateria Fiorentina　　Via Faenza, 2/a
Notes: Santa Maria Novella.

Ciolli　　Via Ramazzini, 35/r
Notes: Campo di Marte.

Damiani　　Via Burchiello, 20/r
Notes: Monticelli.

Gelateria Conti　　Viale dei Mille 1A
Notes: Campo di Marte.

Gelateria Malotti　　Via di Novoli, 42/6

Gelateria Mascia　　Via Torcicoda, 60

Gelateria Senza Glutine　　Via 20 Settembre 126
Notes: Fortezza Basso.

Grom　　Via dell'Oche, 24/R
Notes: Duomo.

Il Gelato Gourmet　　Via M. Palmieri, 34/R
Notes: Santa Croce.

La Bottega del Gelato　　Via Por Santa Maria 33
Notes: Duomo.

La Sorbettiera　　P.zza Tasso, 11/r
Notes: Palazzo Pitti. Closed Wednesdays.

Mandorla e Limone 2　　Via Passavanti, 18/r

Roberto　　Via Mariti, 3/a
Notes: Novoli.

FLORENCE B&B'S AND HOTELS LISTED ALPHABETICALLY
(AIC = participates in the Associazione Italiana Celiachia program)

HOTELS

Albergo Londra
Via Jacopo di Diacceto, 16/20   hotel, restaurant
tel. 05527390   www.hotellondra.com
Notes: Santa Maria Novella.

B&B Cimatori
Via Dante Alighieri, 14   B&B
tel. 0552655000   www.cimatori.it
Notes: Duomo.

B&B Il Marzocco
V.le Fratelli Rosselli 78   tel. 055 274 1444   www.bbilmarzoccoflorence.net
Notes: Stazione Ferroviaria Santa Maria Novella.

B&B L'Argentiere
via G. Borelli 8   tel. 335 528 3741   www.largentiere.it
Notes: San Gaggio.

B&B La Mongolfiera
Via Guido Guinizzelli 1   tel. 055 553 5141   www.residenzelamongolfiera.it
Notes: Centro Storico Minore.

B&B Leopoldo Florence
Via Fabbroni 78   tel. 055 384 1202   www.leopoldohouse.it
Notes: Piazza Leopoldo.

B&B Monte Oliveto
Via Domenico Burchiello 67   tel. 055 231 3484   www.bebmonteoliveto.it
Notes: Monticelli.

B&B Villa La Sosta
Via Bolognese 83   tel. 055 495 073   www.villalasosta.com
Notes: Fortezza Basso.

Best Western Grand Hotel Adriatico
Via Maso Finiguerra 9   tel. 055 279 31   www.hoteladriatico.it
Notes: Santa Maria Novella.

Best Western Hotel Villa Gabriele D'Annunzio
Via G. D'Annunzio 141/a-b   tel. 055 602 960   www.dannunziohotel.it
Notes: Campo di Marte.

Casa di Barbano
Via Di Barbano 1   tel. 055 475 016   www.casadibarbano.it
Notes: Indipendenza.

Casa Toselli
Via Toselli 67   tel. 055 332 202   www.casatoselli.it
Notes: San Lorenzo.

Classic Hotel
Viale Machiavelli 25   tel. 055 22 93 51   www.classichotel.it
Notes: Michelangelo.

Dante e Beatrice relais
via Cavour 90   tel. 55 579232   www.danteandbeatrice.com
Notes: Indipendenza.

Eden Rock Resort
Via Clemente Biondetti 7   tel. 055 400 331   www.edenrockresort.it
Notes: Just outside city.

The Galileo Hotel
Via Nazionale 22/a   tel. 055 496 645   www.galileohotel.it
Notes: Santa Maria Novella.

Grand Hotel Baglioni
Piazza Unità Italiana 6   tel. 055 23 580   www.hotelbaglioni.it
Notes: Santa Maria Novella.

Grand Hotel Villa Medici
Via Il Prato 42   tel. 55 277 171   www.villamedicihotel.com
Notes: Stazione Ferroviaria Santa Maria Novella.

Hilton Florence Metropole
Via del Cavallaccio 36   tel. 055 787 11   www3.hilton.com
Notes: Just outside city.

Hotel Adler Cavalieri
Via Della Scala 40   tel. 055 277 810   www.hoteladlercavalieri.com
Notes: Stazione Ferroviaria Santa Maria Novella.

Hotel Alba
Via della Scala 22/38r   tel. 055 282 610   www.hotelalbafirenze.it/en
Notes: Stazione Ferroviaria Santa Maria Novella.

Hotel Albani Firenze
Via Fiume 12   tel. 055 26 030   www.albanihotels.com/firenze
Notes: Santa Maria Novella.

Hotel Alessandra
Borgo SS. Apostoli 17   tel. 055 283 438   www.hotelalessandra.com
Notes: Duomo.

Hotel Angelica
via Fiume 11   tel. 055210229   www.hotelangelicafirenze.com
Notes: Santa Maria Novella.

Hotel Annalena
Via Romana 34   tel. 055 222 402   www.annalenahotel.com
Notes: Palazzo Pitti.

Hotel Arizona
Via Luigi Carlo Farini 2   tel. 055 245 321   www.arizonahotel.it/en
Notes: Santa Croce.

Hotel Atlantic Palace
Via Nazionale 10   tel. 055 213 031   www.atlanticpalace.it
Notes: Santa Maria Novella.

Hotel Axial
Via dei Calzaiuoli 11   tel. 055 218 984   www.hotelaxial.it
Notes: Duomo.

Hotel Fiorino   inn   AIC
Via Osteria del Guanto, 6   tel. 055210579   www.hotelfiorino.it
Notes: Duomo. Only GF breakfast.

Il Guelfo Bianco   hotel   €€, AIC
Via Cavour, 29   tel. 0552883300   www.ilguelfobianco.it
Notes: Santa Maria Novella.

SUMMARY INFO: RESTAURANTS IN FLORENCE
LISTED ALPHABETICALLY WITH PRICES

Airport

Da Tito i Sette Peccati	Via Alderotti, 87/a	€-€€
Mychef Aeroporto Firenze A. Vespucci	Via del Termine	€

Campo di Marte

Aviazione Campo di Marte	Viale Malta, 8	€€
Ciolli	Via Ramazzini, 35/r	€€
Gelateria Conti	Viale dei Mille 1A	€€
Il Girasole	Via Aretina, 138/C r	€€
Il Povero Pesce	Via P.F. Calvi, 8	€€-€€€
Piazza del Vino	Via della Torretta, 18/r	€€-€€€
Pizza Man	Via Carlo del Prete, 10 R	€€
Pizza Man	Viale de Amicis 47R	€€
Trilli	Viale Marconi 19R	€

Duomo

La Bottega del Gelato	Via Por Santa Maria 33	€
B&B Cimatori	Via Dante Alighieri, 14	
Buca Lapi	Via del Trebbio, 1	€€€€
Cantinetta Antinori	Piazza Antinori 3	€€€
Cantinetta del Verrazzano	Via dei Tavolini, 18-20	€€€
Chiaroscuro	Via del Corso, 36r	€€
Da Pennello	Via Dante Alighieri, 4	€€
Giannino in S. Lorenzo	Borgo S. Lorenzo, 35/37 R	€€
Grom	Via dell'Oche, 24/R	€
Gustavino	Via della Condotta 37R	€€€
Hostaria Il Desco	Via delle Terme, 23/R	€€-€€€
Hotel Fiorino	Via Osteria del Guanto, 6	
La Giostra	Borgo Pinti, 12	€€€
Le Botteghe di Donatello	Piazza Duomo, 28/r	€€€
Oliviero	Via delle Terme, 51	€€€
Panino Vegano	Via M. Bufalini, 19/R	€€
Vecchia Firenze	Borgo degli Albizi, 18	€€

Fortezza Basso

Gelateria Senza Glutine	Via 20 Settembre 126	€-€€

Fucecchio

Osteria Numero Uno	Via del Moro, 18-20	€€€€

Indipendenza

Cafaggi	Via Guelfa 35	€€€-€€€€
Il Fresco Senza Glutine	Viale Spartaco Lavagnini 2	€-€€
La Cucina del Garga	Via S. Zanobi, 33 a/r	€€€€

Michelangelo

I Tarocchi	Via dei Renai, 14 R	€€

Monticelli

Damiani	Via Burchiello, 20/r	€
Pizza Man	Via Sansovino, 191	€€

Novoli

Baraka Cafè	Via di Novoli, 75/r	€
Pistocchi	Via del Ponte di Mezzo 20	€€
Roberto	Via Mariti, 3/a	€
Starbene Senza Glutine	Viale Alessandro Guidoni 83B	€

Oberdan

Grand Hotel Mediterraneo	Lungarno del Tempio, 44	
La Luna Nuova	Via Gioberti, 93/r	€€

Palazzo Pitti

Cammillo	B.go S. Jacopo, 57	€€€€
Fuor d'Acqua	Via Pisana, 37r	€€€€
La Sorbettiera	P.zza Tasso, 11/r	€€
Mamma Gina	Borgo San Jacopo, 37	€€€
Munaciello	Via Maffia 31	€€
Oronero	Piazza Pitti 1R	€€
Pasticceria Gualtieri	Via Senese, 18/R	€
Trattoria Cammillo	Borgo Sant Jacopo, 57R	€€€€
Vivanda	Via Santa Monaca 7R	€€

Piazza della Liberta/Savonarola

I Cinque Sensi	Via Pier Capponi, 3 a/r	€€€

Piazza San Martino

Ristorante Paoli	Via dei Tavolini, 12R	€€€€

Santa Croce

Bacca Rossa	Via Ghibellina, 46/r	€€€-€€€€
Cibreino	Via de' Macci, 118	€-€€
Don Chisciotte	Via Cosimo Ridolfi, 4	€€€€
Il Gelato Gourmet	Via M. Palmieri, 34/R	€
La Brasserie	Via dei Macci 77	€€€€
Nencioni	Via Pietrapiana 24R	€€
Trattoria Cibreo	Via de' Macci, 118	€€€

Santa Maria Novella

Albergo Londra	Via Jacopo di Diacceto, 16/20	
Antica Gelateria Fiorentina	Via Faenza, 2/a	€
Buca Mario	Piazza degli Ottaviani, 16/r	€€€€
Ciro & Son's	Via del Giglio, 26/28 R	€€€€
Coccole Cioccolato	Via dei Ginori 55	€
Etichetta Pinchiorri	Piazza Ognissanti 1	€€€
Harry's Bar	22R Lungarno Amerigo Vespucci	€€€€
I' Toscano	Via Guelfa, 70/r	€€€
Il Desco Bistrot	Via Cavour, 55/r	€€
Il Guelfo Bianco	Via Cavour, 29	€€
La Gratella	Via Guelfa, 81 R	€€
Quinoa	Vicolo Santa Maria Maggiore, 1	€€€
Ristorante Sabatini	Via Panzani, 9	€€€€
The Club House	Via De Ginori 10r	€€
Trattoria Antellesi	Via Faenza, 9R	€€€

Sascaro

L' Antica Badia	Via Faentina, 342	€€

Stazione Ferroviaria Santa Maria Novella

Bar Deanna	Piazza Stazione, 52/55 r	€€
Deanna - Terravision	Piazza della Stazione 52R	€€
Enotria Ristorante	Via delle Porte Nuove, 50	€€€
Il Portale	Via C. Alamanni, 29/r	€€€
La Carabaccia	Via Palazzuolo, 190/r	€€€

View of Florence (D. Frost)

FLORENCE RESTAURANTS AND BAKERIES
LISTED ALPHABETICALLY

Aviazione Campo di Marte   pizzeria, sandwich shop, pub   €€, AIC
Viale Malta, 8   tel. 55.5381058   www.aviazionecampodimarte.it
Notes: Campo di Marte.

Bacca Rossa   restaurant   €€€-€€€€, AIC
Via Ghibellina, 46/r   tel. 055240620   www.baccarossa.it
Notes: Santa Croce.

Bar Abbecedario   bar, tavola calda/fredda   €€, AIC
Viale Pieraccini, 22A   tel. 338.4483006

Bar Deanna   bar, tavola calda/fredda   €€, AIC
Piazza Stazione, 52/55 r   tel. 55.284092
Notes: Stazione Ferroviaria Santa Maria Novella.

Baraka Cafè   bar, tavola calda/fredda   €, AIC
Via di Novoli, 75/r   tel. 55.431495   www.barakacafe.it
Notes: Novoli.

Buca Lapi   restaurant   €€€€
Via del Trebbio, 1   tel. 055213768   www.bucalapi.com
Notes: Duomo. Reservations required for dinner.

Buca Mario   restaurant   €€€€
Piazza degli Ottaviani, 16/r   tel. 055214179   www.bucamario.it
Notes: Santa Maria Novella. GF pasta. English spoken. Closed in August.

Cafaggi   restaurant   €€€-€€€€
Via Guelfa 35   tel. 055294989   www.ristorantecafaggi.com
Notes: Indipendenza.

Caffetteria Raffaella - Tapinassi Bar bar, tavola calda   €, AIC
Via S. Caterina d'Alessandria, 26   tel. 055486268

Cammillo   trattoria   €€€€, AIC
B.go S. Jacopo, 57   tel. 055212427
Notes: Palazzo Pitti. Closed Tuesday-Wednesday.

Cantinetta Antinori   restaurant   €€€
Piazza Antinori 3   tel. 055292234   www.antinori.it
Notes: Duomo. Reservations recommended.

Cantinetta del Verrazzano   restaurant   €€€
Via dei Tavolini, 18-20   tel. 055268590   www.verrazzano.com
Notes: Duomo. Reservations recommended. Closed Tuesdays. English spoken.

Chiaroscuro   bar, tavola calda   €€, AIC
Via del Corso, 36r   tel. 055214247   www.chiaroscurofirenze.it
Notes: Duomo.

Cibreino   restaurant   €-€€
Via de' Macci, 118   tel. 0552341100 www.edizioniteatrodelsalecibreofirenze.it
Notes: Santa Croce. Small sister restaurant of Cibreo; same food, less pricey. No reservations nor credit cards accepted.

Ciro & Son's   restaurant, pizzeria   €€€€, AIC
Via del Giglio, 26/28 R   tel. 055289694   www.ciroandsons.com
Notes: Santa Maria Novella.

Coccole Cioccolato   tea salon, desserts   €
Via dei Ginori 55   tel. 05 5294750   www.coccolecioccolato.it
Notes: Santa Maria Novella.

Da Pennello   restaurant   €€
Via Dante Alighieri, 4   tel. 055294848   www.ristoranteilpennello.it
Notes: Duomo.

Da Tito i Peccati di Gola   restaurant, pizzeria   €€, AIC
Via Baracca, 149 rosso   tel. 055416726   www.datitoipeccatidigola.it

Da Tito i Sette Peccati   restaurant, pizzeria   €-€€, AIC
Via Alderotti, 87/a   tel. 0554360470

Da Tito il Sesto Girone   restaurant, pizzeria   €€-€€€, AIC
Via Villamagna, 77/a   tel. 0556530695

Deanna - Terravision   café, desserts   €€
Piazza della Stazione 52R   tel. 05 5284092
Notes: Stazione Ferroviaria Santa Maria Novella.

Don Chisciotte   restaurant   €€€€
Via Cosimo Ridolfi, 4   tel. 055475430   www.ristorantedonchisciotte.it
Notes: Santa Croce. Reservations recommended.

Enotria Ristorante   restaurant   €€€, AIC
Via delle Porte Nuove, 50   tel. 055354350   www.enotriawine.it
Notes: Stazione Ferroviaria Santa Maria Novella.

Etichetta Pinchiorri   restaurant   €€€
Piazza Ognissanti 1   tel. 05 527163770   www.stregisflorence.com
Notes: Santa Maria Novella.

Fuor d'Acqua restaurant €€€€
Via Pisana, 37r tel. 055222299 www.fuordacqua.it
Notes: Palazzo Pitti. Highly recommended seafood restaurant.

Giannino in S. Lorenzo restaurant €€, AIC
Borgo S. Lorenzo, 35/37 R tel. 0552333799 www.gianninoinflorence.com
Notes: Duomo.

Grand Hotel Mediterraneo hotel, restaurant, reception hall AIC
Lungarno del Tempio, 44 tel. 055660241 www.hotelmediterraneo.com
Notes: Oberdan.

Gustavino wine bar, restaurant €€€
Via della Condotta 37R tel. 05 52399806 www.gustavino.it
Notes: Duomo.

Harry's Bar restaurant €€€€
22R Lungarno Amerigo Vespucci (Grand Hotel) tel. 0552396700 www.harrysbarfirenze.it
Notes: Santa Maria Novella. Reservations required. English spoken.

Hostaria Il Desco restaurant €€-€€€, AIC
Via delle Terme, 23/R tel. 055294882 www.hostariaildesco.com
Notes: Duomo.

I Cinque Sensi restaurant €€€, AIC
Via Pier Capponi, 3 a/r tel. 55.5000315 www.ristoranteicinquesensi.com
Notes: Piazza della Liberta/Savonarola.

I Tarocchi restaurant, pizzeria €€, AIC
Via dei Renai, 14 R tel. 55.2343912
Notes: Michelangelo.

I' Toscano restaurant €€€, AIC
Via Guelfa, 70/r tel. 055215475 www.itoscano.it
Notes: Santa Maria Novella. Closed Tuesdays.

Il Desco Bistrot sandwich shop €€, AIC
Via Cavour, 55/r tel. 055288330 www.ildescofirenze.it
Notes: Santa Maria Novella. Closed at dinner.

Il Fresco Senza Glutine desserts, sandwich shop €-€€
Viale Spartaco Lavagnini 2 tel. 05 5491884
Notes: Indipendenza.

Il Girasole crepes, gelato €€, AIC
Via Aretina, 138/C r tel. 05 52477587 www.gelateriailgirasole.com
Notes: Campo di Marte.

Il Portale restaurant €€€, AIC
Via C. Alamanni, 29/r tel. 055212992
Notes: Stazione Ferroviaria Santa Maria Novella. Closed Sundays.

Il Povero Pesce restaurant €€-€€€, AIC
Via P.F. Calvi, 8 tel. 055671218 www.poveropesce.it
Notes: Campo di Marte.

L' Antica Badia pizzeria €€, AIC
Via Faentina, 342 tel. 0555002153 www.pizzerialalauna.it

La Brasserie French restaurant €€€€
Via dei Macci 77 tel. 05 52478326 www.labrasseriefirenze.it
Notes: Santa Croce.

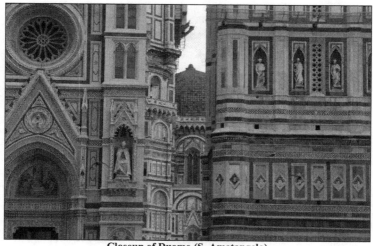

Closeup of Duomo (S. Amatangelo)

La Carabaccia   restaurant   €€€
Via Palazzuolo, 190/r   tel. 055214782   www.trattorialacarabaccia.com
Notes: Stazione Ferroviaria Santa Maria Novella. English spoken. Reservations recommended.

La Cucina del Garga   cooking school, restaurant   €€€€, AIC
Via S. Zanobi, 33 a/r   tel. 055475286   www.garga.it
Notes: Indipendenza.

La Giostra   restaurant   €€€
Borgo Pinti, 12   tel. 055241341   www.ristorantelagiostra.com
Notes: Duomo. English spoken. Reservations required.

La Gratella   trattoria   €€, AIC
Via Guelfa, 81 R   tel. 055211292
Notes: Santa Maria Novella.

La Luna Nuova   pizzeria, restaurant   €€, AIC
Via Gioberti, 93/r   tel. 055663810   www.pizzerialaluna.net
Notes: Oberdan.

Le Botteghe di Donatello   restaurant, pizzeria   €€€, AIC
Piazza Duomo, 28/r   tel. 055216678   www.botteghedidonatello.com
Notes: Duomo.

Lo Strettoio   restaurant   €€€€, AIC
Via di Serpiolle, 7   tel. 0554250044   www.lostrettoio.com
Notes: Closed Mondays and Sundays at dinner.

Mamey Firenze Ovest   bar   €, AIC
Via Pratese,211   tel. 055319223   www.mamey.it/firenze-ovest.html

Mamma Gina   restaurant   €€€
Borgo San Jacopo, 37   tel. 0552396009   www.mammagina.it
Notes: Palazzo Pitti. Reservations required for dinner.

Munaciello   restaurant, pizzeria   €€
Via Maffia 31   tel. 05 5287198   www.munaciello.it
Notes: Palazzo Pitti.

Mychef Aeroporto Firenze A. Vespucci mychef   €, AIC
Via del Termine   tel. 55.3427495   www.mychef.it

Nencioni   café   €€
Via Pietrapiana 24R   tel. 05 5241012
Notes: Santa Croce.

Oliviero   restaurant   €€€
Via delle Terme, 51   tel. 055287643   www.ristorante-oliviero.it
Notes: Duomo. GF pasta. Reservations required.

Oronero   café   €€
Piazza Pitti 1R   tel. 05 52302473   www.oronero-firenze.blogspot.com
Notes: Palazzo Pitti.

Osteria de' benci   osteria   €€€
Via de' Benci, 13   tel. 0552344923   www.debencisuite.com
Notes: English spoken. Reservations essential. Closed Sunday.

Osteria Numero Uno   osteria   €€€€
Via del Moro, 18-20   tel. 055284897   www.osteriadigiovanni.com
Notes: Fucecchio. English spoken. Reservations essential. Closed Sunday.

Panino Vegano   sandwich shop   €€, AIC
Via M. Bufalini, 19/R   tel. 333.8359787   www.paninovegano.it
Notes: Duomo.

Pasticceria Gualtieri   bakery   €, AIC
Via Senese, 18/R   tel. 55.221771   www.pasticceriagualtieri.com
Notes: Palazzo Pitti. Also vegan.

Piazza del Vino   restaurant, wine bar   €€-€€€, AIC
Via della Torretta, 18/r   tel. 055671404   www.piazzadelvino.eu
Notes: Campo di Marte.

Pistocchi   desserts   €€
Via del Ponte di Mezzo 20   tel. 05 50516939
Notes: Novoli.

Pizza Man   restaurant, pizzeria   €, AIC
Via Baracca, 148 A/B   tel. 0554379931   www.pizzaman.it

Pizza Man   restaurant, pizzeria   €€, AIC
Via Carlo del Prete, 10 R   tel. 55.433849   www.pizzaman.it
Notes: Campo di Marte.

Pizza Man   restaurant, pizzeria   €€, AIC
Via Sansovino, 191   tel. 055712738   www.pizzaman.it
Notes: Monticelli. DS pizza point.

Pizza Man   restaurant, pizzeria   €€, AIC
Viale de Amicis 47R   tel. 0550510049   www.pizzaman.it
Notes: Campo di Marte. DS pizza point.

Quinoa   restaurant, bar   €€€, AIC
Vicolo Santa Maria Maggiore, 1   tel. 55.290876   www.ristorantequinoa.it
Notes: Santa Maria Novella.

Ristorante Paoli   restaurant   €€€€
Via dei Tavolini, 12R   tel. 055216215   www.casatrattoria.com
Notes: Piazza San Martino. Reservations required.

Ristorante Sabatini restaurant €€€€
Via Panzani, 9 tel. 055282802 www.ristorantesabatini.it
Notes: Santa Maria Novella.

San Marcellino restaurant, pizzeria €, AIC
Via Chiantigiana,28 tel. 0553921039
www.facebook.com/sanmarcellinoristorantebarpizzeria

Star Bene Senza Glutine bar, desserts €
Viale S. Lavagnini tel. 055/491884 www.starbenesenzaglutine.it
Via Di Ripoli 4/6r tel. 055/6587549 www.starbenesenzaglutine.it

Starbene Senza Glutine bakery, sandwich shop €
Viale Alessandro Guidoni 83B tel. 05 59338350
www.starbenesenzaglutine.it/firenze-novoli.html
Notes: Novoli.

The Club House restaurant €€
Via De Ginori 10r tel. 055211427 www.theclubhouse.it
Notes: Santa Maria Novella. American food.

Trattoria Antellesi trattoria €€€
Via Faenza, 9R tel. 055216990
Notes: Santa Maria Novella.

Trattoria Cammillo trattoria €€€€
Borgo Sant Jacopo, 57R tel. 055212427
Notes: Palazzo Pitti. Reservations required.

Trattoria Cibreo restaurant €€€
Via de' Macci, 118 tel. 0552341100 www.edizioniteatrodelsalecibreofirenze.it
Notes: Santa Croce.

Trattoria da Garibaldi trattoria €€, AIC
Piazza del Mercato Centrale, 38 tel. 055212267 www.garibaldi.it

Trilli café €
Viale Marconi 19R
Notes: Campo di Marte.

Vecchia Firenze restaurant €€
Borgo degli Albizi, 18 tel. 0552340361 www.vecchiafirenze.eu
Notes: Duomo.

Vivanda restaurant €€
Via Santa Monaca 7R tel. 05 52381208 www.vivandafirenze.it
Notes: Palazzo Pitti.

THE REST OF TOSCANA
ALBERESE
Agriturismo Le Due Ruote agritourism €€€€, AIC
Strada Antica Dogana, 44 tel. 0564405361 www.agriturismoledueruote.it
Notes: Must make reservations.

ALTOPASCIO
Hotel Cavalieri del Tau hotel, restaurant AIC
Via Gavinana, 56 tel. 583.25131 www.cavalierideltau.it

ANTIGNANO
In Caciaia restaurant AIC
Via Dei Bagni, 38 tel. 0586580403

ARBIA-ASCIANO

Piccola Oasi — restaurant, pizzeria — €-€€, AIC
Piazza della Repubblica, 70 — tel. 0577365367

AREZZO

A Casa Tua — B&B — AIC
Via Montale, 85 — tel. 3291774790
Notes: S € 35 D € 50

Gelateria Cremì — gelato (€, AIC) — C.so Italia, 100

Gelateria Cremì — gelato (€, AIC) — Via Fiorentina,1 83 C

Gustolandia — pizzeria — €, AIC
Via Case Nuove di Ceciliano, 73/15 — tel. 0575320056

Il Sogno di Tutti — bar, tavola calda — €, AIC
Piazza Giotto, 17 — tel. 0575403590

La Bottega di Nonna Tina — sandwiches, bakery — €, AIC
Via Antonio Pizzuto, 46/a — tel. 575.27678 — www.labottegadinonnatina.it
Via Pietro Aretino, 11 — tel. 575.27678 — www.labottegadinonnatina.it

La Gola Non Ha Ora — restaurant — €-€€, AIC
Via Piave, 23 — tel. 0575905249 — www.lagolanonhaora.it

Minerva — hotel, restaurant — €€, AIC
Via Fiorentina, 4 — tel. 0575370390

Mivà — restaurant, pizzeria — €€, AIC
Via San Lorentino, 20 — tel. 0575. 300300 — www.mivaarezzo.com

Mivà di più — restaurant, pizzeria — €, AIC
Via Garibaldi, 36/38 — tel. 0575352182 — www.mivadipiu.com

Non Solo Caffè — bar, tavola calda — €, AIC
Via Giotto, 27 — tel. 3487956703

San Marco — gelato (€, AIC) — Via Romana, 66/a

Star Bene Senza Glutine — bar, desserts — €
Via Turati 57 — tel. 389.0357468 — www.starbenesenzaglutine.it

Vinosteria 4 Chiacchiere — restaurant — €€€ - €€€€, AIC
Via Guelfa, 14/16 — tel. 0575902524

AULLA

da Giovanna — restaurant — AIC
Località Bettola-Aulla — tel. 0187414117 — www.ristorantedagiovanna.com

AVENZA CARRARA

Il Giardino Antico — B&B — AIC
Via Toniolo, 8/bis — tel. 0585859667 — www.giardinoantico.it

Lavenza — pizzeria — €, AIC
Via Gino Menconi, 53 — tel. 058552451

BAGNI DI LUCCA

Antico Albergo Terme — hotel — €€-€€€, AIC
Via Paretaio, 1 — tel. 058386034

La Lira — restaurant, pizzeria — €-€€, AIC
P.zza Vitt. Veneto — tel. 0583867708 — www.lalirapub.it
Notes: Closed Wednesdays and lunch.

BAGNO A RIPOLI

Autogrill Chianti autogrill €, AIC
A1 Firenze - Roma tel. 55.6560063

BAGNO VIGNONI

Hotel Posta Marcucci B&B AIC
Via Ara Urcea, 43 tel. 0577887112 www.hotelpostamarcucci.it

Il Barrino bar, tavola calda €, AIC
Via del Gorello, 44 tel. 0577887112

BARBERINO DEL MUGELLO

Vanilla & Cioccolato gelato (€, AIC) Largo Nilde Iotti

BARBERINO DI MUGELLO

C.lo M.C.L. S. M.le Montecuccoli restaurant €€ - €€€€, AIC
Via Rocca Cerbaia, 3 tel. 055841035

Lo Scricciolo restaurant, pizzeria €-€€, AIC
Via delle Voltate, 2 tel. 558423116 www.ristoranteloscricciolo.it

Mychef Aglio Est mychef €, AIC
A1 Firenze - Milano tel. 55.841085 www.mychef.it

BARBERINO VAL D'ELSA

Il Paese dei Campanelli restaurant €€€€, AIC
Loc. Petrognano tel. 0558075318 www.ilpaesedeicampanelli.it

BARGA

Bar Pizzeria F.lli Rossi bar, restaurant, pizzeria €, AIC
Via P. Funai, 86/88 tel. '0583710193

Renaissance Tuscany Il Ciocco Hotels & Resort hotel, restaurant €€€-€€€€, AIC
Loc. Castelvecchio Pascoli tel. 0583719478 www.ciocco.it

BETTOLLE

Walter Redaelli restaurant €€€-€€€€, AIC
Via XXI Aprile, 10 tel. 0577623447 www.ristoranteredaelli.it

BIBBIENA

Bar Gelateria Edi gelato (€, AIC) Via Marcucci Poltri -p.zza Stazione
Notes: Closed Tuesdays.

Glutenfreedesi bakery, pizzeria €, AIC
Via Carlo Marx, 5 tel. 348.0905883 www.glutenfreedesi.it

BIENTINA

Succo d'Uva restaurant, pizzeria, bar €€-€€€€, AIC
Via XX Settembre, 2 tel. 0587757548

Villa delle Mimose restaurant, pizzeria €€€-€€€€, AIC
Via Corte Betti, 26/a tel. 0587714038 www.villadellemimose.it
.

BORGO A BUGGIANO

La Fiamma restaurant, pizzeria AIC
Via Cavour, 77/79 tel. 0572318116

BORGO SAN LORENZO

I' Corbezzolo restaurant/pizzeria € - €€, AIC
Via P. Caiani tel. 0558402197

Il Feriolo
Via Faentina, 32
restaurant
tel. 0558409928
€€-€€€, AIC
www.ristoranteilferiolo.it

La Griglia
V.le IV Novembe, 91
restaurant
tel. 0558458527
€-€€€, AIC

Star Bene Senza Glutine
Via Trieste n. 4/1
bar, desserts
tel. 055/0503822
€
www.starbenesenzaglutine.it

BUCINE

Le Mura
Loc. Le Mura, 31
agritourism
tel. 055992297
€€, AIC
www.agrilemura.it

Locanda Casariccio
Loc. Casariccio, San Leolino
agritourism
tel. 338.5679126
AIC
www.agricolasanleolino.it

CALENZANO

Happy Ice
gelato (€, AIC)
Via Giusti, 59

Il Borgo
Via del Molino, 87
restaurant, pizzeria
tel. 0558811377
AIC

CAMPAGNATICO

La Vecchia Oliviera
Via Piave
restaurant, pizzeria
tel. 0564996462
€€, AIC

CAMPI BISENZIO

Da Que' Grulli
Via Confini, 162
restaurant
tel. 3937461913
AIC
www.daquegrulli.it

Don Chisciotte
Via Barberinese, 157
restaurant, pizzeria
tel. 55.8954319
€€, AIC

La Gelateca
gelato (€, AIC)
Via S. Quirico, 165 (int I Gigli)

Sottozero
Via Barberinese 157
gelato
tel. 055 8970971
€, AIC
www.gelateriasottozero.com

CAMPIGLIA D'ORCIA

I Tre Rioni
Via Campotondo, 3
restaurant
tel. 0577872015
€€€, AIC
www.itrerioni.com

CAMPO NELL'ELBA

Select
Via per Portoferraio, 30
inn
tel. 0565976734
AIC

CAMPO NELL'ELBA-ISOLD D'ELBA

Gelateria Ghibli
P.zza Torino, 5
gelato
tel. 565.976156
€, AIC

Piccolo Hotel Versilia
Via dell'Acqued otto, 1580
inn, restaurant
tel. 0565976123
AIC
www.piccolohotelversilia.it

CAPALBIO

Villaggio Capalbio
Str. Pedemontana, 58
resort
tel. 0564899017
AIC
www.villaggiocapalbio.it

CAPOLIVERI- ISOLA D'ELBA

Angiò
Via del Pinone, 144 loc. Lacona
bar restaurant, pizzeria
tel. 0565964412
€-€€€, AIC

Capo di Stella
Loc. Capo di Stella-Lacona
inn
tel. 0565964052
AIC
www.capodistella.com

Pienza Val d'Orcia – "Falling into a painting" (J.Coyne)

Zero Gradi	gelato (€, AIC)	Via Roma, 38

CAPRAIAE LIMITE

Lowengrube
Via pr.le Limitese
pub   €, AIC
tel. 0571979253

CAPRESE

Il Rifugio
Lama di Caprese
restaurant, pizzeria   €€-€€€, AIC
tel. 0575793968

CARMIGNANO

Agrit. Casa Belvedere
Via S. Biagio, 10
agritourism restaurant   €€€, AIC
tel. 0558717301   www.agriturismobelvedere.it

CARRARA

Golosità Senza Glutine
Via Carriona, 265
pizzeria   €€, AIC
tel. 0585842409

CASCIANA TERME

Il Merlo
P.zza C. Minati, 5
restaurant, pizzeria   €-€€€€, AIC
tel. 0587644040

CASTAGNETO-CARDUCCI

Il Vecchio Frantoio
Via Gramsci, 8 /A
restaurant   €€, AIC
tel. 0565763731

CASTELFIORENTINO

Il Cigliere del Rustico
restaurant   €-€€€, AIC
Via O. Di Paolo, 24/e loc. Bellosguardo   tel. 0571582154
Notes: Closed Monday-Wednesday.

Peter Pan
gelato (€, AIC)   C.so Matteotti, 36

Special Pizza
Via Masini, 11
restaurant, pizzeria   AIC
tel. 571.633367

CASTELFRANCO DI SOPRA

Enjoy Toscano
P.zza V. Emanuele, 1-2
restaurant, bar   €€€, AIC
tel. 0559149763

CASTELLINA IN CHIANTI

Albergaccio di Castellina   restaurant   €€€€, AIC
Via Fiorentina, 63   tel. 0577741042
Notes: Closed Sundays.

L'Antica Delizia   gelato (€, AIC)   Via Fiorentina, 4
Notes: Closed Tuesdays.

CASTELMARTINI

Caffè Mirò   restaurant, pizzeria, bar   AIC
Via Martiri del Padule, 75   tel. 3392837117   www.caffemiro.com
Notes: Closed Mondays.

CASTELNUOVO BERARDENGA

Il Convito di Curina/Villa Curina restaurant   AIC
Loc. Curina   tel. 0577355647   www.ilconvitodicurina.it
Notes: Also B&B. Closed Wednesdays.

CASTELNUOVO DI GARFAGNANA

Il Baretto   restaurant, pizzeria   €€, AIC
Via Farini, 5   tel. 0583639136   www.ilbaretto.org

Il Ciulè   restaurant/pizzeria   €€, AIC
Via Giovanni Pascoli, 1   tel. 058362643

Osteria Vecchio Mulino   osteria   AIC
Via Vittorio Emanuele, 12   tel. 583.62192

Osteria Vecchio Mulino   osteria   €-€€, AIC
Via Vittorio Emanuele, 12   tel. 058362192   www.ilvecchiomulino.com

CASTIGLION FIORENTINO

Babette - Casale di Brolio restaurant, B&B   €€€, AIC
Via di Brolio, 74   tel. 0575652054   www.babetteristorante.it

Il Passaggio   restaurant   AIC
Via Adua, 68   tel. 575.659639

La Fenice   B&B   AIC
Via Santa Cristina - loc. Taragnano, 25 tel. 0575650176

CASTIGLIONCELLO

Bagno Bar Salvadori   restaurant, pizzeria   €-€€, AIC
L.re Colombo, 16   tel. 0586754194   www.bagnisalvadori.it

Il Coccodrillo   restaurant   €€-€€€, AIC
Lungomare Colombo, 18   tel. 0586752627

CASTIGLIONE DELLA PESCAIA

Bagno Bruna   bar, tavola calda   €, AIC
Via Isola Clodia   tel. 0564933613   www.bagnobruna.it

L'Approdo   hotel, restaurant   €€€, AIC
Via Ponte Giorgini, 29   tel. 0564933466   www.approdo.it

Roma Hotel   hotel   AIC
Via C. Colombo, 14   tel. 0564933542 www.hoteromacastiglione.it
Notes: Closed at lunch.

CAVRIGLIA

Locanda Cuccuini   B&B   AIC
V.le Caduti, 32   tel. 0559166419   www.locanda-cuccuini.com

Il Cedrino Via Aurelia Sud, 30	**CECINA** restaurant, pizzeria tel. 0586682233	€€€, AIC
L'Acquapazza Via Ginori, 89	restaurant tel. 0586621219	€€€, AIC www.ristorantelacquapazza.com
Mangia e Bevi Via 2 Giugno, 7	pizzeria tel. 586.62285	AIC
Marina (2 locations) V.le Galliano, 23 Via della Vittoria, 61	gelato (€, AIC)	

Slap	**CECINA MARE** gelato (€, AIC)	Viale Galliano, 10
PS Pianello Val Tidone, 41	**CERRETO GUIDI** restaurant tel. 0571559242	AIC www.ps-ristorante.it
Il Parco Via Agnoletti, 316	**CERTALDO** pizzeria, tavola calda tel. 571.65241	€, AIC
Il Rabarbaro Loc. La Maglianella, 30	**CHIANCIANO TERME** restaurant, pizzeria tel. 057864592	€, AIC
Villa Maria Via Macerina, 19 Notes: Closed October-April.	inn, restaurant tel. 057863003	€€, AIC www.villamariachianciano.it
Az. Bioagritur.Poggio ai Lupi Loc. I Renicci	**CHIANNI** agritourism tel. 0587648163	€€-€€€€, AIC

Rist.Nonna Rosa/H. Rosati Via dei Tulipani, 1 loc. Querce al Pino Notes: DS pizza point. Closed Mondays.	**CHIUSI** hotel, restaurant tel. 0578274408	€€€-€€€€, AIC www.hotelrosati.it

Terme della Versilia Via Gramsci, 2	**CINQUALE DI MONTIGNOSO** restaurant reception hall inn tel. 0585807792	€€€, AIC
Il Caggio di Sotto Loc. Il Gaggio, 26/Lano	**COLLE VAL D'ELSA** agritourism tel. 0577971255	AIC www.caggiodisotto.com
C.lo Arci Corniola Via di Corniola, 34/36	**CORNIOLA EMPOLI** pizzeria tel. 0571922202	€ - €€, AIC
Hotel Farneta Località Farneta, 3	**CORTONA** inn, restaurant tel. 0575610241	€€-€€€€, AIC
La Tufa Loc. Ossaia 67/a	restaurant, pizzeria tel. 0575677717	€-€€€, AIC www.hostarialatufa.it

DICOMANO

Il Geko	restaurant, pizzeria	€-€€€, AIC
V.le Vittorio Veneto, 10/12	tel. 0558387672	
Notes: Closed Tuesdays.		

Vigna la Corte	B&B	AIC
Loc. Rimaggio	tel. 0558397027	www.vignalacorte.com

DONORATICO

Ristorante Pizza In da Franco	restaurant, pizzeria	AIC
Via Aurelia, 1/ C	tel. 565.775343	

ELLERA - FIESOLE

B&B Eridu	B&B	AIC
Via Murri, 16/a	tel. 55.6592036	

EMPOLI

Cucina S. Andrea	restaurant	€€-€€€€, AIC
Via Salvagnoli,43/47	tel. 057173657	
Notes: Closed Mondays.		

La Fortuna	restaurant	AIC
P.zza G. Guerra, 40	tel. 571.700377	

Millevoglie senza glutine	sandwich shop	€, AIC
Via Carrucci, 78	tel. 571.74232	

Star Bene Senza Glutine	bar	€, AIC
P.zza Guido Guerra, 29	tel. 0571527259	www.starbenesenzaglutine.it

Un Monte di Bontà	gelato (€, AIC)	Via Ridolfi, 7/9

Zero	restaurant	€, AIC
Via Volontari della Libertà, 21/23	tel. 0571930099	

EMPOLI - PONTE A ELSA

Pizza e Godi	pizzeria	€-€€, AIC
Via Due Giugno, 63	tel. 571.932124	

FARNETA

Osteria da Mangiafoco	restaurant, pizzeria	€-€€, AIC
Via per Chiatri, 820/B	tel. 0583327288	
Notes: Closed Tuesdays.		

FIESOLE

Le Lance	restaurant, pizzeria	AIC
Via Mantellini, 2/b	tel. 055599595	www.lelance.it

Trattoria Le Cave di Maiano	restaurant	€€€
Via Cave di Maiano 16	tel. 05 559133	

FIGLINE VAL D'ARNO

Pasticceria Napoletana Delizie	bar	€-€€, AIC
Via Fiorentina, 19/A	tel. 55.9157053	

FOIANO DELLA CHIANA

C'era una volta	gelato (€, AIC)	Piazza Garibaldi, 4

La Lodola	B&B	AIC
Via Piana, 19	tel. 0575649660	wwwlalodola.com

FOLLONICA

Caribia	gelato (€, AIC)	Viale Italia, 212

La Lanternina 2 di Palmieri V.le Italia, 160	restaurant, pizzeria tel. 056642679	AIC www.ristorantepalmieri.com

FORNACI DI BARGA

La Bionda di Nonna Mary Via della Repubblica, 254 Notes: Closed Wednesdays.	restaurant, pizzeria tel. 058375624	€-€€€, AIC
Mara Meo Via Provinciale, 18	pizzeria tel. 0583758982	€, AIC

FORTE DEI MARMI

Imperiale	gelato (€, AIC)	Via Colombo, 97/a
Posidonia Via Mazzini, 202/d	restaurant, bar tel. 0584752843	€€-€€€, AIC

GABBRO ROSIGNANO M.MO

Villa Edera Via Ornellini, 90	restaurant tel. 0586742535	€€-€€€€, AIC

GALLICANO

Il Baretto Via Serchio, 17	restaurant, pizzeria tel. 058374066	€, AIC

GALLUZZO

Star Bene Senza Glutine Via Gherardo Silvani, 51	bar, desserts tel. 329.2616608	€ www.starbenesenzaglutine.it

GREVE IN CHIANTI

La Cantina Piazza Trento, 3	restaurant, pizzeria tel. 55.854097	AIC

GROSSETO

Bar Perugina Via Manin, 26	bar tel. 564.22263	€, AIC
Caffè del Teatro Via Goldoni, 12	restaurant, pizzeria tel. 3285633674	AIC
Caffè Nazionale P.zza Gioberti, 4	bar, tavola calda tel. 0564450601	€, AIC
Gelateria Papavera Piazza Gioberti, 6	gelato, crêperie tel. 348.2465214	€, AIC
Gli Attortellati S.P. 40 La Trappola, 39	restaurant tel. 564.400059	€€, AIC www.gliattortellati.com
Hungry Years Via Vinzaglio, 20	pub, restaurant tel. 564.413351	€€, AIC www.hungryyears.it
Il Carrettino Via Bengasi, 7	restaurant, pizzeria tel. 056428421	AIC www.ilcarrettinogr.it
In Florida	gelato (€, AIC)	Viale Giusti, 55
L'Uva e il Malto Via Mazzini, 165 Notes: Closed Sundays.	restaurant tel. 0564411211	€€-€€€, AIC www.luvaeilmalto.it
Mangiar Bene Via Tazzoli, 5	tavola calda tel. 3282913764	€, AIC

IMPRUNETA

Nyx pizzeria €, AIC
Via Imprunetana per Tavarnuzze, 8/c tel. 0552312262

Terzotempo restaurant, pizzeria €-€€€, AIC
Via Achille Grandi, 2 loc. Tavarnuzze tel. 0552373364 www.ristoranteterzotempo.it
Notes: Closed Saturday at lunch.

INCISA VAL D'ARNO

La Casa di Rita B&B AIC
Via S. Maria Maddalena, 27 tel. 0558330099 www.lacasadirita.it

IOLO

Bar Giotto gelato (€, AIC) Via Guazzalotri, 15

I Cavalieri restaurant, pizzeria AIC
Via Didaco Bessi, 3 tel. 574.622573

ISTIA D'OMBRON E

Ristorante Poggio Cavallo restaurant AIC
Loc. Poggio Cavallo - SP30 Sante Mariae tel. 564.409021

LAJATICO

Bellavista Toscana agritourism €€€, AIC
Via Aldo Moro, 11 tel. 0587643308 www.ristorantebellavistatoscana.it

LAMMARI CAPANNORI

Mara Meo pizzeria €, AIC
V.le Europa, 46 tel. 0583436400

LAMPORECCHIO

Il Poderino agritourism €€, AIC
Via Giugnano, 158 tel. 057388109

LASTRA A SIGNA

La...Strapizza grocery store €, AIC
Via Diaz, 132 tel. 0558723138 www.lastrapizza.com

LATERINA

Lo Strettoio restaurant, pizzeria €€, AIC
Via Agna -Loc. Pian di Chena tel. 057589161 www.ristorantelostrettoio.it
Notes: DS pizza point. Closed Wednesdays.

London Bar gelato (€, AIC) Via Vecchia Aretina, 60

LE CROCI - CALENZANO

Antica Sosta a Combiate restaurant €€€€, AIC
Via di barberino, 71 tel. 0558876980 www.anticasostacombiate.it

LE FONTANELLE

Le Fontanelle hotel, restaurant AIC
Via Trav. del Crocifisso, 7 tel. 0574730373 www.hotelfontanelle.com

LIDO DI CAMAIORE

Petit Hotel / Ristorante Piattofondo hotel, restaurant AIC
Via Don Minzoni, 22 tel. 584.619374 www.ptithotel.com

LIVORNO

All'Improvviso Pizzeria pizzeria AIC
Via Toscana, 69/69a tel. 586.903023

Aragosta	restaurant	€€€, AIC
Piazza dell'Arsenal e, 6	tel. 586.895395	www.aragostasrl.com
Bella Napoli	restaurant, pizzeria	€€, AIC
Via Sardi, 41	tel. 0586898731	www.pizzeriabellanapoli.it
Notes: Closed Wednesdays.		
Bistrot Manalù	restaurant	€€, AIC
Piazza della Vittoria, 9	tel. 586.958326	www.facebook.com/bistrotmanalu
Caciaia in Banditella	restaurant	€€€€, AIC
Via Puini, 97	tel. 0586 580403	
Chez Ugo	pizzeria	€, AIC
Scali del Monte Pio, 35	tel. 0586219230	
Notes: Closed Mondays.		
In Vernice	restaurant	€€, AIC
Via Sproni, 32/34	tel. 0586219546	
Notes: Closed Sundays.		
La Grotta delle Fate	restaurant	€€, AIC
Via Grotta delle Fate, 157	tel. 0586503162	www.grottadellefate.net
Notes: Closed at lunch.		
L'Origine	pizzeria	€, AIC
Via dell'Origine, 14	tel. 0586210157	
Notes: Closed Mondays.		
Orlandi Montallegro	restaurant inn	€€, AIC
P.zza di Montenero, 3	tel. 0586579030	
Notes: Closed Tuesdays.		
Star Bene Senza Glutine	bar, desserts	€
Mercato Centrale Livorno Box n° 47/48-49/50		www.starbenesenzaglutine.it
Trattoria L'Angelo d'Oro	trattoria	€€, AIC
Piazza Mazzini, 15	tel. 0'0586881295	

LOC. FRATTA DI CORTONA

Gina	pub, tavola calda	€, AIC
P.zza S. Margherita	tel. 3662747657	

LOC. OLMO FIESOLE

Il Trebbiolo Relais	hotel, restaurant	€€€, AIC
Via del Trebbiolo, 8	tel. 0558300583	www.iltrebbiolo.it

LOC. STABBIA - CERRETO GUIDI

Pizza Pazza a Pezzi	pizzeria	€, AIC
Via Provinciale Francesca, 139	tel. 0571956029	

LONDA

Da Fischio	restaurant, pizzeria	AIC
Loc. Il Lago	tel. 0558351608	
Notes: Closed Mondays.		

LORENZANA

Osteria Pian di Laura	osteria	€-€€, AIC
Via Papa Karol Wojtyla ,3	tel. 050662610	www.osteriapiandilaura.com

LUCCA

A Palazzo Busdraghi Residenza d'Epoca	hotel	€€€€, AIC
Via Fillungo, 170	tel. 0583950856	www.apalazzobusdraghi.it

Albergo Celide	hotel	AIC
Viale G.Giusti, 25	tel. 0583954106	
Notes: GF breakfast only.		

| **Ammodonostro** | restaurant | €€€-€€€€, AIC |
| Via della Fratta, 22 | tel. 0583953828 | www.ristoranteammodonostro.com |

Antica Tratt. Stefani da Benedetto	restaurant	€€-€€€, AIC
Via Borgo, 55- S.Lorenzo a Vaccoli	tel. 0583379031	
Notes: Closed Tuesday-Wednesday.		

| **Bar Caffetteria Moriani** | bar | €, AIC |
| Via Nuova per Pisa 5634/b | tel. 583.378324 | |

| **Bontà Yogurt** | gelato (€, AIC) | V.le Puccini, 183/187 |

Buca di S. Antonio	restaurant	€€€-€€€€, AIC
Via della Cervia, 3	tel. 058355881	www.bucadisantantonio.com
Notes: Closed Mondays and Sunday evenings.		

| **Cremeria Opera** | gelato (€, AIC) | Viale Luporini, 951 |

El Paso	restaurant, pizzeria	€, AIC
Via per Camaiore, 679	tel. 0583341273	
Notes: DS pizza point. Closed Mondays.		

| **Gelateria de' Coltelli** | gelato (€, AIC) | Via San Paolino, 10 |

| **Gli Orti di Via Elisa** | restaurant | €€€, AIC |
| Via Elisa, 17 | tel. 0583491241 | www.ristorantegliorti.it |

| **Grand Hotel Guinigi** | hotel, restaurant | AIC |
| Via Romana, 1247 | tel. 05834991 | www.grandhotelguinigi.it |

| **Grom** | gelato | €, AIC |
| Via Fillungo, 56 | tel. 583.436455 | www.grom.it |

| **Mara Meo** | pizzeria | €, AIC |
| P.zza S. Francesco, 17 | tel. 0583467084 | |

Pizzeria Felice	restaurant, pizzeria	AIC
Via Buonamici, 352	tel. 0583587412	www.pizzeriafelice.it
Notes: DS pizza point. Closed Mondays.		

| **Ristorante Giglio** | restaurant | €€€-€€€€, AIC |
| Piazza del Giglio, 2 | tel. 0583494058 | www.ristorantegiglio.com |

| **Star Bene Senza Glutine** | bar, desserts | € |
| Via Catalani 200 | tel. 338.8496184 | www.starbenesenzaglutine.it |

LUCCA-S. LORENZO A VACCOLI

Botton d'Oro	restaurant	€€€, AIC
Via del Ponte Guasperini, 873	tel. 0583370101	www.albergovillamarta.it
Notes: Closed Sundays.		

LUCIGNANO

La Maggiolata	restaurant	€€, AIC
Via G. Matteotti, 60	tel. 0575819008	www.ristorantelamaggiolata.it
Notes: Closed Wednesdays.		

| **La Rocca** | restaurant | AIC |
| Piazza Ser Vanni, 1 | tel. 0575836775 | www.larocca-ristorante.it |

| **Snoopy** | gelato (€, AIC) | Via Rosini, 20 |

LUCO DI MUGELLO

L'Orto sull'Uscio
Via Campagna, 48/1

B&B
tel. 0558401197

AIC
www.lortosulluscio.com

MARCIANA MARINA

Il Gastronomo
Via del Sette, 10
Notes: Closed Wednesdays.

restaurant, tavola calda
tel. 0565997021

€€, AIC

Isola Verde
Via San Giovanni

hotel, restaurant
tel. 0565904291

€€, AIC
www.hotelisolaverde.it

Publius
P.za del Castagneto-Loc. Poggio
Notes: Closed November-March and Mondays.

restaurant
tel. 056599208

AIC

Scaraboci
Via XX Settembre, 29
Notes: Closed January-April and at lunch.

restaurant
tel. 0565996868

€€€€, AIC

Zero Gradi

gelato (€, AIC)

P.zza For di Porta, 8

MARCIANO DELLA CHIANA

Albatros
Via Culle, 37
Notes: Closed Monday-Thursday and at lunch.

restaurant, pizzeria
tel. 0575845464

€€-€€€, AIC
www.albatrosristorante.it

MARINA DI ALBERESE

La Viola Ristoro
c/o Parco della Maremma

bar, tavola calda/fredda
tel. 335.7066047

€, AIC

MARINA DI BIBBONA

Gasperini & Zoppi

gelato (€, AIC)

Via dei Melograni lotto H 1

Il Ghiottone
Notes: Closed Tuesdays.

gelato (€, AIC)

Piazza dei Gerani, 1

Paradiso Verde
P.zza del Forte, 1

hotel, restaurant
tel. 0586600022

AIC
www.hotelparadisoverde.it

MARINA DI CAMPO-ISOLA D'ELBA

Bologna
Via delle Case Nuove, 71

restaurant, pizzeria
tel. 0565976105

€€, AIC
www.ristorantebologna.it

Zero Gradi

gelato (€, AIC)

Via per Portoferraio, 9

MARINA DI CARRARA

Bar Gelateria Bristol

gelato (€, AIC)

Via Rinchiosa, 40

Gelateria Paradiso
Gelateria Samba - Giorgia

gelato (€, AIC)
gelato (€, AIC)

Viale Colombo, 119/bis
Via Genova, 14 bis

MARINA DI GROSSETO

Bagno Le Poste Marina
Via Leopoldo di Lorena

bar, tavola calda
tel. 0564337811

€-€€, AIC

Bagno Moderno
L.re Leopoldo II di Lorena, 47

restaurant
tel. 056434255

€€€, AIC
www.bagnomoderno.it

Ristorante Pantagruel
Via Bellini, 5a

restaurant
tel. 340.0781754

AIC

MARINA DI MASSA

Bagno Arlecchino Via L.re di Levante, 14	restaurant tel. 3939387076	€, AIC
Bagno Hermitage L.re di Levante, 128	bar, tavola calda tel. 585.245341	€, AIC
Casa Faci Via Ernesto Lombardo, 16	inn tel. 0585869556	AIC www.casafaci.it
Excelsior/Rist. Il Sestante V. Cesari Battisti, 1	hotel, restaurant tel. 05858601	AIC www.hotelexcelsior.it
Gelateria Aruè	gelato (€, AIC)	P.zza Pellerano, 12
Hermitage L.re di Levante, 128	bar, tavola calda tel. 0585245341	€, AIC www.hotelhermitage.net
Hotel Italia V.le Amerigo Vespucci, 3 Notes: Closed October-March.	hotel tel. 0585240606	€€, AIC www.hotelitaliamarinadimassa.com
Roby Via Casamicciola, 3	hotel tel. 0585240686	AIC www.hotelroby.net
Tiffany Via Fosdinovo, 14	hotel, restaurant tel. 0585241196	AIC www.tiffany-hotel.it
Villa Tiziana Via delle Pinete, 266	hotel tel. 0585869724	AIC www.tizianahotel.com

MARINA DI PIETRASANTA

Da Totò e un Po' di Napoli Via L. da Vinci, 65 Notes: Closed Mondays and lunch.	pizzeria tel. 058423947	€, AIC
Hotel Esplanade Viale Roma, 235	hotel tel. 0584754883	€€€€, AIC www.hotelesplanadeversilia.it
Hotel Milton Via Puccini, 15	hotel tel. 058420258	€€€, AIC www.albergomilton.com
Hotel Villa Marzia Via Corridoni, 5	hotel, restaurant tel. 0584745818	€€€€, AIC www.hotelvillamarzia.it
Ivana e Daniela Via Dalmazia,38	restaurant tel. 584.20113	AIC
Nuova Sabrina Via Ugo Foscolo, 11	hotel tel. 058420253	AIC www.nuovasabrina.com
Villa Amelia Via Ugo Foscolo, 18	B&B tel. 3498526517	AIC www.villa-amelia.com

MARLIA

Granozero Tutto il Fresco Senza Glutine pizza, desserts Viale Europa, 271/A	tel. 583.929896	€-€€, AIC

MASSA

Caffè Gambrinus Via Democrazia, 15	bar, tavola calda tel. 585.41371	€, AIC
Haziel	gelato (€, AIC)	P.zza Aranci, 30

MASSA E COZZILE

Bar Si.Ba   bar, tavola calda   €, AIC
Via Biscolla, 48   tel. 572.70633

MERCATALE VAL DI PESA

Circolo M.C.L. - Il circolino   restaurant   AIC
Via Gramsci, 6   tel. 55.821586

MONSUMMANO TERME

Da Libe   pizzeria, bar   €-€€, AIC
Via Francesca Uggia 542   tel. 572.62583

MONTALCINO

Boccon Divino   restaurant   €€€€, AIC
Trav. Dei Monti, 201 loc. Colombaio   tel. 0577848233

MONTALE

Azzurra   gelato (€, AIC)   Via Martiri della Libertà, 119

MONTAVARCHI

Star Bene Senza Glutine   bar, desserts   €
Via Mincio 46   tel. 055/980216   www.starbenesenzaglutine.it

MONTE S. SAVINO

Bar Gelateria La Castiglia   gelato (€, AIC)   Via della Riconoscenza, 7
Notes: Closed Mondays.

Il Cioccolato di Carlo   gelato, bar   €, AIC
Corso Sangallo, 22   tel. 575.810586

La Torre di Gargonza   inn, restaurant   €€€-€€€€, AIC
Loc. Gargonza   tel. 0575847065   www.gargonza.it
Notes: Closed Tuesdays.

Podere Pendolino by Albatros   restaurant, pizzeria, B&B   €-€€€, AIC
Loc. Castellare, 44   tel. 0575849697

MONTECARLO

Antica Dimora Patrizia   B&B   AIC
Piazza Carmignani, 12   tel. 583.1797017

Circolo Acsi-La Torre   restaurant, wine bar   €€€€, AIC
Via Provinciale, 7   tel. 05832298298

MONTECATINI TERME

Hotel Adua Regina di Saba   hotel   €€€€, AIC
V.le Manzoni, 46   tel. 057278134   www.hoteladua.it

MONTELUPO

Lo Spigo   restaurant   €-€€, AIC
Via di Pulica, 139   tel. 0571929111
Notes: Closed Mondays.

MONTELUPO FIORENTINO

Antica Trattoria del Turbone   trattoria, pizzeria   €-€€, AIC
Via Turbone, 35-37-39   tel. 0571542035   www.anticatrattoriadelturbone.it

Il Coriandolo   restaurant, pizzeria   AIC
Piazza S. Rocco, 1   tel. 0571541021

Le Scuderie dell'Antinoro   restaurant, pizzeria   €-€€€€, AIC
Via Tosco Romagnola Nord, 6   tel. 0571913079   www.scuderieantinoro.it

MONTEMURLO

Sglutinando
Via Udine, 19/23

sandwich shop, bakery
tel. 328.8827111

€, AIC

MONTEPULCI ANO OVEST

Il Grifo
Via Milazzo, 19

B&B
tel. 578.738702

AIC

MONTERIGGIONI

Maison del Celiaco
Via Sandro Pertini 15/16

bakery, sandwich shop
www.maisondelceliaco.it

€

MONTERONI D'ARBIA

Gelateria Byblos
Notes: Closed Mondays.

gelato (€, AIC)

Via Roma, 199-203

MONTESCUDAIO

Bibere
Via della Libertà. 59 A

restaurant, wine bar
tel. 586.685888

AIC

MONTEVARCHI

Bar Pinco Pallino
Via Mincio, 46

bar
tel. 55.980215

€, AIC

Coffee Gallo
Via Leopardi, 27

restaurant, pizzeria
tel. 0559850530

€€, AIC
www.coffeegallo.com

MONTIANO

da Ghigo
P.zza Cappellini, 4

restaurant
tel. 0564589643

€€€, AIC
www.ristorantedaghigo.it

MONTICIANO

Castello di Tocchi
Loc. Tocchi Podere La Ripa

B&B
tel. 0577757102

AIC
www.castelloditocchi.it

Villa Ferraia
Loc. Tocchi

B&B
tel. 0577757102

AIC
www.villaferraio.com

MONTIERI

Al Pozzolone
Str. Delle Galleraie, 55

B&B
tel. 0566914314

AIC
www.pozzolone.it

MONTIGNOSO

Bar del Re
Via Romana Ovest, 19

sandwiches, crêpes
tel. 39329210009

€-€€, AIC

MULAZZO

Abramo
Via Provinciale, 23
Notes: Closed Mondays and at lunch.

restaurant
tel. 0187439388

€-€€, AIC

ORBETELLO

Gallery
Via Gioberti, 91

restaurant, B&B
tel. 0564860474

€€€-€€€€, AIC
www.orbetelloturismo.it/ristorante-gallery

Mixer
Notes: They also have crêpes. Closed Wednesdays.

gelato (€, AIC)

C.so Italia, 78

PELAGO

Boccon Divino
Via Cafaggiolo, 10 Loc. Palaie
Notes: Closed Tuesdays at lunch.

restaurant
tel. 0558311279

€€-€€€€, AIC
www.boccondivinofirenze.it

PESCAGLIA

La Fonte restaurant, pizzeria AIC
Loc. Trebbio, 34 tel. 0583359815 www.ristorantelafonte.com
Notes: Closed Tuesdays and at lunch.

PIAN DEGLI ONTANI

Pizzeria La Diga restaurant, pizzeria AIC
Viale Beatrice, 122 tel. 573.67307 pizzerialadiga@live.it

PIANOSINATICO

Silvio la Storia a Tavola restaurant €€, AIC
Via Brennero, 181/183 tel. 0573629204 www.ristorantesilvioabetone.com

PIAZZA AL SERCHIO

Il Tavolello pizzeria €, AIC
Via Comunale del Colli, 9 tel. 058360477
Notes: Closed Wednesdays.

PIENZA

La Terrazza del Chiostro restaurant €€€€, AIC
Corso del Rossellino, 26 tel. 0578748183 www.laterrazzadelchiostro.it
Notes: Closed Mondays and from November to March.

PIETRASANTA

La Rocchetta restaurant AIC
Via Montiscendi, 172 tel. 584.799728 ristoranterocchetta@yahoo.it

La Volpe e l'Uva osteria €€€-€€€€, AIC
P.zza Matteotti, 42 tel. 058472570 www.trovavetrine.it/la-volpe-e-luva

Star Bene Senza Glutine bar, desserts €
Via Barsanti 40 tel. 584.283279 www.starbenesenzaglutine.it

PIEVE A NEVOLE

Clarabella Caffè bar €, AIC
Via Marconi, 41/b tel. 572.954307

Gelateria 7 Nani gelato (€, AIC) Via Empolese, 90

PIEVE S. PAOLO-CAPANNORI

Paso pizzeria €, AIC
Via di Tiglio, 88 tel. 0583981750
Notes: DS pizza point. Closed Tuesdays.

PIOMBINO

Il Garibaldi Innamorato restaurant €€€, AIC
Via G.Garibaldi, 5 tel. 056549410 www.ilgaribaldiinnamorato.it

Il Tiramestoli restaurant €€€, AIC
Loc. Carbonifera tel. 565.20945 www.iltiramestoli.it

PISA

Biba Bar bar €, AIC
Via Turati, 57 tel. 389.0357468 www.bibabar-pisa.it

Caffè Letterario Voltapagina bar €, AIC
Via San Martino, 71 tel. 50.5202716 www.caffeletterariovoltapagina.it

Da Peppone osteria, pizzeria AIC
Via Fiorentina, 449 tel. 50.6203882 www.pizzeriadapeppone.com

Gelateria de' Coltelli gelato (€, AIC) Lungarno Pacinotti

La Pizza Magica	pizzeria	€, AIC
Via Vittorio Veneto, 3	tel. 3931824268	
Pizza Magica City	restaurant, pizzeria	AIC
Via Palestro, 29/33	tel. 50.580794	
Rist. Squisitia/H. San Ranieri	hotel, restaurant	€€-€€€€, AIC
Via Mazzei ang via S. Biagio	tel. 0509719555	www.sanranierihotel.com

PISTOIA

Gelateria Cipriani	gelato (€, AIC)	Via Curtatone e Montanara, 65
La Diligenza	restaurant, pizzeria	AIC
Viale Adua, 306	tel. 573.90417	

La Diligenza In... — bar, sandwich shop — €€, AIC
V.le Adua, 308 — tel. 0573904170
Notes: Closed Sundays and Monday mornings.

La Fenice — restaurant, pizzeria — €-€€€, AIC
Via Dalmazia, 73 — tel. 057321167 — www.lafeniceristorante.it
Notes: Closed Tuesdays.

Parè — gelato (€-€€, AIC) — Via Pacinotti, 83

Pizza Mania — pizzeria — €-€€, AIC
Via Udine, 4 — tel. 0573976063
Notes: Closed Sundays.

Verde Paradiso — B&B — AIC
P.zza della Resistenza, 15 — tel. 05731780352 — www.verdeparadiso.com

PODENZANA

La Gavarina d'Oro — restaurant — €€, AIC
Via Provinciale, 23 — tel. 0187410021 — www.lagavarinadoro.com

Mirador — inn, restaurant — €-€€, AIC
Via del Gaggio, 22 — tel. 0187410064

POGGIBONSI

Da Poldo Food&Love — sandwich shop — €, AIC
Largo Usilia, 24 — tel. 329.0806318

POGGIO A CAIANO
La Bottega del Gelato (ex Nonna Luisa) gelato (€, AIC) Via Soffici, 47

PONTASSIEVE
Al Trebbio — restaurant, pizzeria — €€, AIC
Via Montetrini, 10 Molino del Piano tel. 0558317292 — www.castellodeltrebbio.com

Le Fate Golose — gelato(€, AIC) — P.zza Libero Grassi, 22
Notes: Closed Mondays.

Locanda Toscani da Sempre — restaurant — €€€, AIC
Via F.lli Monzecchi, 13 — tel. 0558392952 — www.toscanidasempre.it
Notes: Also B&B.

Tenuta dei Cavalieri — agritourism, restaurant — €€, AIC
Via Santa Brigida, 3 — tel. 0558364332 — www.tenutadeicavalieri.com

PONTE A POPPI

Gelateria Edi — gelato (€, AIC) — Via Roma, 45

PONTEDERA

Il Marathoneta restaurant, pizzeria €€, AIC
Via R. Piaggio, 54/56 tel. 587.293152
www.facebook.com/pages/Il-Marathoneta-pizzeria-focacceria-e/514544348556462

La Losanga restaurant, pizzeria €-€€€€, AIC
Via Pisana, 157 tel. 0587562323
Notes: Closed Wednesdays.

La Polveriera restaurant €€€€, AIC
Via Marconcini, 54 tel. 058754765
Notes: Closed Sundays.

Pane per Noi sandwich shop, bakery €, AIC
Via della Repubblica 3 tel. 587.980426 www.facebook.com/pane.pernoi.1

Pizzeria Pasquale pizzeria, osteria €€, AIC
Via Roma, 110 ang R. Piaggio tel. 0587290633
Notes: Closed Sundays.

PONTREMOLI

Ca' del Moro restaurant €€€-€€€€, AIC
Loc. Casa Corvi, 9 tel. 0187830588 www.cadelmororesort.it

POPPI

Tutto Pizza pizzeria €€, AIC
Via Roma, 124 tel. 575.520482

PORCARI

Bar Caffetteria Moriani bar €, AIC
Viale Puccini, 1995 tel. 583.29587

Happy Time pizzeria, restaurant €€, AIC
Via Fratina, 23 tel. 0583297289 www.happytimeparcogiochi.it

Mara Meo pizzeria €, AIC
Via Roma, 120 tel. 058329113

Stefy 3 pizzeria €, AIC
Via Capannori, 59 tel. 0583210662
Notes: Closed Mondays and at lunch.

PORTO ERCOLE

Gelateria Creola gelato (€, AIC) Via Lungomare Strozzi, 8

PORTO S. STEFANO

Gelateria La Bontà gelato €, AIC
Via Corso Umberto tel. 328.7318428

PORTOFERRAIO-ISOLA D'ELBA

Viticcio hotel, restaurant AIC
Loc. Biodola, 1 tel. 0565939058 www.hotelviticcio.it

Zero Gradi gelato (€, AIC) Via Vittorio Emanuele, 18

PRATO

Antichi Sapori restaurant, pizzeria AIC
Via V. Da Filicaia tel. 0574461189
Notes: Closed Mondays.

Aroma di Vino osteria €€, AIC
Via Santo Stefano, 24 tel. 0574433800 www.pratoaromadivino.it

Circolo la Libertà   restaurant, pizzeria   €€, AIC
Via Pistoiese, 659   tel. 0574810618

Gelateria Sanmarco   gelato   €, AIC
Viale Vittorio Veneto, 16   tel. 340.9939636   www.gelateriasanmarcoprato.it

Il Pirana   restaurant   €€€€, AIC
Via G. Valentini, 110   tel. 057425746   www.ristorantepirana.it

Pepe Nero   restaurant   €€-€€€, AIC
Via Zarini, 289   tel. 0574550353

Ristorante Sabatini   restaurant   €€€, AIC
Via Ferrucci, 162-164   tel. 574.070038
www.facebook.com/RistorantePizzeriaSabatini

Rosso Pomodoro Prato   pizzeria   €€, AIC
Via delle Pleiadi, 16 c/o Omnia Center   tel. 574.056138   www.rossopomodoro.it

Sans Gluten   sandwich shop, bakery   €, AIC
Viale Montegrapp a, 298   tel. 574.830242   www.sansgluten.it

Sottozero (5 locations)   gelato (€, AIC)   www.gelateriasottozero.com
Via Montalese, 12   Via Garibaldi, 112   Piazza Mercatale, 4/5
Via Roma, 312/b   Viale Piave, 20

Star Bene Senza Glutine   bar, desserts   €
Via Frà Bartolomeo n. 203   tel. 0574/726422   www.starbenesenzaglutine.it

Starbene Senza Glutine   bakery   €, AIC
Via Frà Bartolomeo, 23   tel. 574.726422   www.gelateriasottozero.com

PRINCIPINA TERRA
Hotel Fattoria La Principina   hotel, restaurant   €€, AIC
Via San Rocco, 465   tel. 056444141   www.fattorialaprincipina.it

PROCCHIO-MARCIANA
Monna Lisa   hotel, restaurant   AIC
Via Fonte Leccio, 10   tel. 0565907904   www.hotelmonnalisa.it

QUARRATA
Il Calesse   agritourism, B&B   AIC
Via Carraia, 215   tel. 0573750344   www.agriturismoilcalesse.it

Il Mondo senza glutine   sandwich shop   €-€€, AIC
Via Montalbano, 154   tel. 573.774123
www.facebook.com/il.mondo.senza.glutine33

Pizza & Co   pizzeria   €-€€, AIC
Via Ceccarelli, 159/a   tel. 0573717686

QUATTRO STRADE LARI
Prima Gelateria   gelato (€, AIC)   Via Livornese ovest, 91
Notes: Closed Tuesdays.

RAPOLANO TERME
La Taverna Toscana   restaurant   €€€, AIC
Loc. Laticastelli   tel. 0577725513   www.latavernatoscana.it

REGGELLO
Il Muretto   gelato (€, AIC)   Via Gramsci, 50

Villa Pitiana
Via Pr.le per Tosi

hotel, restaurant
tel. 055860012

€€€€, AIC
www.villapitiana.com

ROCCATEDERIGHI

La Conchiglia
Via Roma, 24/c

restaurant, pizzeria
tel. 0564567430

€€€, AIC

RONCHI

Bagno Europa
Viale Lungomare di Levante, 106

bar, tavola calda
tel. 585.241474

€, AIC
www.bagnoeuropa.com

Cavalieri del Mare
Via Veterani dello Sport
Notes: Closed September-May.

hotel
tel. 0585868010

€€€, AIC
www.cavalieridelmare.net

Villa Elsa
Via Pistoia, 2

hotel
tel. 0585241097

AIC

ROSIGNANO MARITTIMO

Le simpatiche canaglie
Via Gramsci, 55

pizzeria
tel. 586.790139

€-€€, AIC

ROSIGNANO SOLVAY

Lo Scoglietto
L.re Monte alla Rena, 13
Notes: Closed October-April.

restaurant
tel. 0586767962

€€€-€€€€, AIC

RUFINA

Il Ritrovo
P.zza Umberto I,32

restaurant, pizzeria
tel. 0558396219

€-€€€, AIC

S. ALBINO MONTEPULCIANO

La Locanda del Vino Nobile
Via dei Lillà, 1/3

restaurant
tel. 0578798064

€€€ - €€€€, AIC
www.lalocandadelvinonobile.it

S. BRIGIDA-PONTASSIEVE

Nappino
Via S. Chiari, 1

restaurant/pizzeria
tel. 0558300439

€€€ - €€€€, AIC
www.nappino.it

S. CARLO TERME-MASSA

Alb. S. Carlo/Rist. Panoramique
Via Nicola Zonder, 3

inn, restaurant
tel. 058543193

€€-€€€, AIC

Buongustaio
Via Belvedere, 90

hotel, restaurant
tel. 058545741

€€-€€€, AIC

S. CASCIANO VAL DI PESA

B&B Art
Via della Volta, 6

B&B
tel. 0558290372

AIC
www.bbart.eu

Da I' Moro

gelato (€, AIC)

Via Empolese, 228

I Pini

gelato (€, AIC)

P.zza G. Matteotti, 7

Mamma Rosa
Via Cassia per Siena

restaurant, trattoria
tel. 0558249454

€€€€, AIC
www.trattoriamammarosa.it

S. FREDIANO A SETTIMO

Gelateria Sighieri
Notes: Closed Wednesdays.

gelato (€, AIC)

Via T. Romagnola,1078

S. GIMIGNANO

Taverna del Granducato
Piazza Martiri di Montemaggio

restaurant
tel. 0577940824

€€, AIC

S. GIOVANNI VALDARNO

Il Gelatone   gelato (€, AIC) ʼ   Corso Italia, 9

S. GIULIANO TERME

Io e Gelato   gelato (€, AIC)   Via Calcesana, 499 - loc. Mezzana

S. MARIA A MONTE

Black - White   restaurant, pizzeria   €€, AIC
Via San Donato, 106   tel. 0587473322
Notes: Closed Mondays and at lunch.

Il Germoglio-Bar Miro e Giusy-H.Da Neide restaurant, pizzeria, bar   €-€€, AIC
Via Francesca, 144   tel. 0587706286

Il Poeta/Il Verde Melograno   hotel, restaurant   €€, AIC
Via Francesca Nord, 248   tel. 0587709090   www.hotelilpoeta.it

Oasi al Lago   restaurant, pizzeria   €-€€€, AIC
Via Arnovecchio S. Donato, 1 tel. 0587709201
Notes: Closed Mondays.

S. MARIA DEL GIUDICE

Marta Guest House   B&B   AIC
Via del Querceto, 47   tel. 0583378555   www.martaguesthouse.it

S. QUIRICO D'ORCIA

La Taverna del Barbarossa/Casanova restaurant, pizzeria, inn   €€€€, AIC
SS.146 Loc. Casanova, 6 c   tel. 0577898299   www.tavernadelbarbarossa.com

S.FREDIANO A SETTIMO

Gelateria Sighieri   gelato (€, AIC)   Via T. Romagnola, 1078

SAN GIMIGNANO

Bar Combattenti Gelateria   gelato (€, AIC)   Via S. Giovanni, 124

Le Vecchie Mura   restaurant   €€€€, AIC
Via Piandornella, 15   tel. 577.94027   www.vecchiemura.it

SAN CASCIANO

I Pini   gelato (€, AIC)   Via Volterrana, 142

Osteria Cinque Divino   osteria   €€€-€€€€, AIC
V.le S. Francesco   tel. 0558228116   www.cinquedivino.it
Notes: Closed Mondays.

SAN MINIATO

Az. Agricola Marrucola   agritourism   €€-€€€, AIC
Via Calenzano, 40   tel. 0571418306   www.marrucola.it

SAN PIERO A SIEVE

I' Regolo   pizzeria   €€, AIC
Via Calimara, 4/a   tel. 55.849824   www.i-regolo.it

La Nuova Bisboccina   restaurant, pizzeria   €-€€€, AIC
Via Provinciale, 38   tel. 0558486950

SAN ROMANO

Dumbo   restaurant, pizzeria   €-€€, AIC
Via Cavour, 30/32   tel. 0571450999

SAN VINCENZO

Ristorante Lupo Càntero
Via Vittorio Emanuele, 10
restaurant   €€€, AIC
tel. 565.704651   www.facebook.com/ristorantelupocantero

SANSEPOLCRO

Al Coccio
Via N. Aggiunti, 83
restaurant   €€, AIC
tel. 0575741468   www.alcoccio.com

Don Chisciotte
Via G. Marcelli, 3
restaurant, pizzeria, pub   €€, AIC
tel. 575.741134

Ghignoni
Via Tiberina Sud, 850
gelato   €, AIC
tel. 575.7419   www.ghignoni.it

Hotel La Balestra
Via dei Montefeltro, 1
hotel, restaurant   €€, AIC
tel. 0575735151   www.labalestra.it

SANTA LUCIA - UZZANO

Pizza ... e altri rimedi
Via Provinciale Lucchese, 248
restaurant, pizzeria   €€, AIC
tel. 572.444085   www.pizzaealtririmedi.it

SANTA MARIA DEGLI ANGELI

Villa Cherubino
Via P. d'Italia, 39
restaurant   €€, AIC
tel. 0758040226

SCANDICCI

Gelatando
gelato (€, AIC)   Piazza Togliatti, 61

Gelateria Malotti
gelato (€, AIC)   P.zza Cavour, 14/15/16

La Taverna di Castruccio
Via Pisana, 129/A
restaurant   €€-€€€, AIC
tel. 55.751198   www.tavernadicastruccio.it

Maranatha
Via del Pantano, 1
B&B   AIC
tel. 55.751123   www.bedandbreakfast.it

Pizzeria Il Moro
Via G. Donizzetti, 29
pizzeria   €€, AIC
tel. 328.6621909   www.pizzeriailmoro.com

Star Bene Senza Glutine
ViaTurri, 29 A
bar, creperie   €, AIC
tel. 55.730927   www.starbenesenzaglutine.it

SEANO

I' Prugnolo
P.zza IV Novembre, 4
restaurant, pizzeria   €-€€, AIC
tel. 0558706933   www.ristoranteiprugnolo.it
Notes: Closed Mondays-Tuesdays.

SERRAVALLE PISTOIESE

Agriturismo Terra Mia
Via Lipe, 7
agritourism   €€, AIC
tel. 05731940064   www.terramiatoscana.it

SERRE DI RAPOLANO

Grand Hotel Serre
Racc. Autostr. Siena-Bettolle
hotel   AIC
tel. 0577704777   www.hotelserre.it

La Sosta
Via Serraia
restaurant   €€€€, AIC
tel. 0577704177   www.lasostaristorante.it
Notes: Closed Mondays.

SESTO DI MORIANO

Antica Locanda di Sesto
Via Lodovica, 1660
restaurant   €€€-€€€€, AIC
tel. 0583578181
Notes: Closed Saturdays.

SESTO FIORENTINO

Bar Baraonda Viale Ariosto,44	bar, tavola calda/fredda tel. 55.446352	€, AIC
Gelato Coop.Fi	gelato (€, AIC)	Via Petrosa, 19-23 (int. Centro Sesto)
Mandorla e Limone	gelato (€, AIC)	Via Verdi, 95
Matam Via Lucchese, 160	restaurant, pizzeria tel. 55.3454158	AIC
Novotel Firenze/Novotelcafé Via Tevere, 23	hotel, restaurant tel. 055308338	€€€-€€€€, AIC www.novotel.com
Star Bene Senza Glutine Via Di Calenzano 101	bar, desserts tel. 557950783	€ www.starbenesenzaglutine.it

SIENA

B&B Quattrocantoni Via San Pietro, 30	B&B tel. 338.1414094	AIC
Borgo Grondaie Via delle Grondaie, 15	B&B tel. 0577332539	AIC www.borgogrondaie.com
Garden Via Custoza, 2	hotel tel. 0577567111	€€€€, AIC
Grom	gelato (€, AIC)	Via Banchi di Sopra, 13
Grotta Gallo Nero Via del Porrione, 65	restaurant tel. 0577284356	AIC www.gallonero.it
Hotel Italia V.le Cavour, 67	B&B tel. 057744248	AIC www.hotelitalia.it
Il Camerlengo	gelato (€, AIC)	P.zza del Campo, 6
Il Campino Via Vittorio Veneto, 29 Notes: Closed Wednesdays.	osteria tel. 0577236545	€€-€€€, AIC www.ilcampino.com
Il Ghibellino Via dei Pellegrini, 26	restaurant tel. 0577288079	€€, AIC
Villa Liberty V.le Vittorio Veneto, 11	B&B www.villaliberty.it	AIC

SPAZZAVENTO - CARMIGNANO

Agriturismo Podere Midolla Via della Torre di Sant'Alluccio,10	agritourism, restaurant, B&B tel. 0558717086	€€€, AIC www.poderemidolla.com

SPICCHIO-VINCI

Osteria de'Nichi Via Limitese, 109	osteria tel. 3668093274 www.osteriadenichi.oneminutesite.it	€€€, AIC

TAVARNELLE VAL DI PESA

Osteria La Gramola Via delle Fonti, 1 Notes: Closed Tuesdays.	restaurant, catering tel. 0558050321	€-€€€€, AIC www.gramola.it

TERRANUOVA BRACCIOLINI

Acquolina Fraz. Cicogna, 96/E Notes: Request GF when you make a reservation.	osteria tel. 055977497	€€€, AIC

Il Canto del Maggio Via Penna,30/d	osteria tel. 0559705147	€€€, AIC www.cantodelmaggio.com
Il Casolare Fraz. Persignano, 111	osteria tel. 55.96939	AIC
Piansa Via Poggi Lupi, 580	tavola calda, bar tel. 0559737166	€, AIC
Podere San Lorenzo IV Str. Lungarno	agritourism tel. 0559199176	€€, AIC

TERRICCIOLA

Da Pasquino Via Volterrana, 308 - Loc. La Sterza Notes: Closed Fridays.	inn, restaurant tel. 0587674000	€€, AIC

TIRLI-CASTIGLIONE DELLA PESCAIA

Il Poggetto Loc. Fonte Poderana	restaurant tel. 3476761061	€€€, AIC www.ristoranteilpoggettotirli.com

TORRE DEL LAGO

L'Ocanda Viale Europa, 31 Notes: Not great reviews.	restaurant tel. 584.47446	€€€€, AIC www.locandamilu.it

VADA

Il Casale Mancini Strada Provinciale La Torre,41	B&B, restaurant, pizzeria tel. 586.789028	AIC www.casalemancini.it
La Ventola Via Dei Cavalleggeri, 171/b	inn, restaurant, pizzeria tel. 0586770170	€€€-€€€€, AIC www.laventola.it

VIAREGGIO

Barca Bertilla / Vela Mare Sportiva Dilettantistic a bar Darsena Italia Porto di Viareggio tel. 584.40727		€, AIC
Gran Varignano Via Paladini, 27 Notes: Closed Mondays.	pizzeria tel. 0584395734	€, AIC
Grom V.le Marconi, 77	gelato tel. 584.962263	AIC www.grom.it
La Posteria Via Fratti, 386	restaurant, pizzeria tel. 3477351890	€€€, AIC
Marechiaro V.le Europa, 14	restaurant tel. 0584391244	€-€€€, AIC www.bagnomarechiaro.it
Stabilimento Balneare De Pinedo Viale Europa, 3	bar, tavola calda tel. 584.39213	€-€€, AIC
Star Bene Senza Glutine Via Mazzini 151	bar, desserts tel. 584.631736	€ www.starbenesenzaglutine.it

VICCHIO

Agrit. Fattoria I Ricci Via Rostolena, 14	agritourism tel. 055844784	€€€€, AIC www.fattoriairicci.com
La Casa Matta Viale Beato Angelico, 79/81	restaurant, pizzeria tel. 55.8497104	AIC www.lacasamatta.eu
Locanda Antica Porta di Levante P.zza Vitt. Veneto, 5	hotel, restaurant tel. 055844050	AIC www.anticaportadilevante.it

VICOPISANO

D'Antonio
Via Prov.le Vicarese, 161
restaurant, pizzeria
tel. 50702001
€-€€, AIC

VOLTERRA

Don Beta
Via Matteotti, 39
restaurant
tel. 058886730
€€€-€€€€, AIC
www.donbeta.it

Il Pozzo degli Etruschi
Via delle Prigioni, 28/30
restaurant
tel. 058880608
€€, AIC
www.ilpozzodeglietruschi.com

Il Ritrovo
B.go S. Lazzero, 7
Notes: Pizza only at dinner.
restaurant, pizzeria
tel. 058880122
€-€€, AIC
www.ilritrovo-volterra.it

La Vecchia Lira
Via Matteotti, 19
restaurant
tel. 058886180
€-€€€€, AIC
www.vecchialira.com

Ombra della Sera
Via Gramsci, 70
Via Guarnacci, 16
pizzeria, tavola calda
tel. 058886663
tel. 058886663
€€€, AIC
www.ristoranteombradellasera.it
www.ristoranteombradellasera.it

Modern Couple (A. Smith)

VENICE AND VENETO

PLACES IN VENICE TO BUY GLUTEN-FREE FOOD PRODUCTS

Calle Dei Sapori
Sestiere Cannaregio, 2892, Venetian Ghetto

Erborista Cibele
Campielo dell Anconetta (near Calle del Pistor)

Farmacia Alla Vecchia
Sestiere San Marco, 4598

Farmacia Alle due Colonne
Via Cannareggio, 6045

Farmacia Dezuanni	Via San Salvador, 21
Farmacia Italo Inglese	Via San Marco, 3717
Farmacia S.S. Cosma e Damiano	Isola Giudeca, 446
Mea Libera Tutti Sas	Sestiere Cannaregio, 3803
Minimarket	Via Tiro, 14 Lido
Salumeria Bellenzier	San Polo1472

PLACES IN VENICE TO GET GUARANTEED GLUTEN-FREE GELATO (SPONSORED BY ITALIAN CELIAC SOCIETY)

Grom
Strada Nuova Cannaregio, 3844

Grom
Campo S.Barnaba - Dorsoduro 2852

Grom
Campo dei Frari

Gelateria Nico
Dorsoduro, 922 Zattere

B&B'S AND HOTELS IN VENICE LISTED ALPHABETICALLY

AD Place Venice
Fondamenta della Fenice, 2557/A, San Marco   tel. 041 241 32 34   www.adplacevenice.com

Aqua Palace
Calle de la Malvasia 5492 Castello   tel. 041 296 0442   www.aquapalace.it

Bella Venezia Hotel Venice
San Marco, 4710   tel. 0415288779   www.hotelbellavenezia.com

Best Western Hotel Ala
San Marco 2494   tel. 041 520 8333   www.hotelala.it

Best Western Hotel Biasutti
Via Enrico Dandolo,27/29   tel. 041 526 0120   www.hotelbiasutti.it

Best Western Premier Hotel Sant'Elena
Calle Buccari, 10   tel. 041 271 7811
www.book.bestwestern.it/EN/hotel_in_Venice_98238.aspx

Bonotto Hotel Belvedere
Via Generale Giardino, 14, 36065   tel. 0424529845   www.bonotto.it

Cà Pisani
Dorsoduro 979   tel. 041 240 1411   www.capisanihotel.it

Ca' Vendramin di Santa Fosca
Cannaregio 2400   tel. 041 275 0125   www.hotelcavendramin.it

Ca' del Campo
Campo della Guerra, San Marco 51   tel. 041 241 1660   www.cadelcampo.it

Ca' della Loggia
San Marco, Calle San Gallo 921/a   tel. 041 241 1267   www.cadellaloggia.it

Casa del Melograno
Cannaregio 2022   tel. 041 520 8807   www.locandadelmelograno.it

Ca' Nigra Lagoon Resort
Santa Croce 927   tel. 412750047   www.hotelcanigra.com

Domina Home Cà Zusto
Campo Rielo, Santa Croce 1358   tel. 041 524 2991   www.dominahomecazusto.com/en

Domina Home GiudeccaSt
Corte Ferrando 409C   tel. 041 296 0168   www.dominahome.it

Hotel A la Commedia
San Marco 4596/A, Corte del Teatro Goldoni   tel. 041 277 0235
www.commediahotel.com

Hotel Ai Due Principi
Castello 4971   tel. 041 241 3979   www.hotelaidueprincipi.com

Hotel Ai Mori d' Oriente
Fondamenta Della Sensa, Cannaregio 331   tel. 041 711 001   www.morihotel.com

Hotel Al Gazzettino
San Marco, 4971   tel. 041 528 6523   www.algazzettino.com

Hotel Al Piave
Ruga Giuffa Castello, 4838/40   tel. 41.5238512   www.hotelalpiave.com

Hotel Bonvecchiati
San Marco, Calle Goldoni 4488   tel. 041 528 5017   www.hotelbonvecchiati.it

Hotel Bucintoro
Castello 2135/a   tel. 041 528 9909   www.hotelbucintoro.com

Hotel Canal Grande
Santa Croce, 932, Campo San Simeon Grande   tel. 041 24 40 148
www.hotelcanalgrande.it

Hotel Da Bruno
Castello 5726/A   tel. 041 523 0452   www.hoteldabruno.com

Hotel Danieli
Riva degli Schiavoni 4196   tel. 041 522 6480
www.danielihotelvenice.com/?EM=GFHG_LC_72_ICM_EAME
Notes: GFM.

Hotel De L'Alboro Venice
Sestiere San Marco, 3894   tel. 0415206977   www.alborohotel.it
Notes: GF breakfast. Great location.

Hotel Dell'Opera
San Marco 2009   tel. 041 520 5243   www.hoteldelloperavenice.com

Hotel Donà Palace
San Marco 391   tel. 041 274 3511   www.donapalace.it

Hotel Excelsior Hotel
Via Zara, 3, Lido   tel. 0421370934   www.excelsior-jesolo.it

Hotel Rialto
Riva del Ferro, San Marco   tel. 0415209166   www.rialtohotel.com
Notes: GF breakfast on request.

Hotel Villa Beatrice
4 Via dei Villini, 30126 Lido di Venezia   tel. 041 731 072   www.hotelbeatrice.com

Il Glicine Fiorito Bed and Breakfast B&B
Via Orsmida Rosada, 32, Venice-Lido Venezia   tel. 041770537   www.ilglicinefiorito.com
Notes: GF breakfast.

Park Hotel Brasilia Hotel
Via Levantina, 2° acc. al mare, 3   tel. 0421380851   www.parkhotelbrasilia.com
Notes: GF breakfast on request.

Russott Hotel Venice
Via Orlanda, 4 I   tel. 0415310500   www.russotthotels.com

Reflections in the Grand Canal (A. Smith)

VENICE RESTAURANTS AND BAKERIES
LISTED ALPHABETICALLY
(AIC = participates in the Associazione Italiana Celiachia program)
(V=vaporetto stop)

RESTAURANTS

A la Vecia Cavana   restaurant
Cannaregio 4624   tel. 0415238644   www.veciacavana.it
Notes: Special celiac menu. Restaurant highly recommended.

Ai Gondolieri   restaurant   €€€€
Fondamenta dell'Ospedaletto, Dorsoduro 366   tel. 0415286396   www.aigondolieri.it
Notes: English spoken. Closed Tuesdays.

Al Giardinetto "da Severino "   restaurant   €€€€, AIC
Castello, 4928   tel. 0415285332   www.algiardinetto.it

Algiubagio'   restaurant   €€€€
Cannaregio 5039, Fondamenta Nuove   tel. 0415236084   www.algiubagio.net
Notes: English spoken. V: Fondamente Nuove.

Alla Vedova   restaurant   €-€€€€
Calle del Pistor 3912   tel. 0415285324
Notes: Highly recommended. No credit cards.V: Ca'D'Oro.

Antico Gatoleto   restaurant, pizzeria   €€€
Sestiere Cannaregio 6055   tel. 04 15221883   www.anticogatoleto.com

Aromi Restaurant and Aromi Bar restaurant   €€€
Giudecca 810   tel. 0412723311

Bancogiro   restaurant   €€-€€€

Avogaria   hotel, restaurant   €€€€
Calle Avogaria, Dorsoduro 1629   tel. 041296049   www.avogaria.com
Notes: GF with advance notice.

Campo San Giacometto, Santa Croce 122 (under porch)   tel. 0415232061
Notes: V:Rialto.

Cips Club   restaurant   €€€
at hotel Cipriani - Giudecca 10, 30133   tel. 0415207744
Notes: Reservations recommended. V: Zitelle.

Corte Sconta   restaurant   €€-€€€
Calle del Pestrin, Castello 3886   tel. 0415227024
Notes: GF pasta. English spoken. Reservations essential. Closed Sun., Mon. months of Jan., Feb., July and Aug. V: Arsenale.

Da Leoni   restaurant   €€€€
Riva degli Schiavoni, Castello 4171   tel. 0412700680   www.hotellondra.it
Notes: No GF pasta. English spoken. In Hotel Londra Palace. Reservations essential. V:San Zaccaria.

da Poggi   restaurant   €€, AIC
Rio terrà de La Madalena, 2103 Cannaregio   tel. 3926818463 www.ristorantedapoggi.it

Fortuny Restaurant   restaurant   €€€€
at the hotel Cipriani Giudecca 10, 30133   tel. 0415207744   www.hotelcipriani.it.
Notes: V: Zitelle. Reservations essential, jacket required, no children under 8 in evening.

Frary's   restaurant   €€, AIC
San Polo, 2558   tel. 41.72005
www.facebook.com/pages/Frarys/605774209449317

Gastronomia Le Quattro Stagioni restaurant, fast food   €€
Corso Mazzini 34   tel. 345 2695635

Il Molino   restaurant   €€€-€€€€
At the Hilton - Giudecca 810   tel. 0412723311

La Bitta   restaurant   €€
Calle lunga San Barbara, Dorsoduro 2753   tel. 0415230531
Notes: English spoken. Closed Sun. No lunch. V:Ca' Rezzonico.

La Favorita   restaurant, pizzeria   €€-€€€
Via Giovanni Rizzetti 18   tel. 04 23723474   www.lafavoritapizzeria.com

La Fontanella   restaurant   €€€-€€€€
Via Orlanda, 4 I   tel. 0415310500   www.russotthotels.com

La Zucca   restaurant   €
1762 Santa Croce, close to San Giacomo square   tel. 0415241570   www.lazucca.it
Notes: Reservations essential.

Oke Zattere   restaurant, pizzeria   €€-€€€, AIC
Dorsoduro, 1414   tel. 041.5206601/340.4529035

Ostaria al Garanghelo   restaurant   €
Via Garibaldi, 1621   tel. 0415204697   www.garanghelo.com

Ostaria Antico Dolo   restaurant   €€€€
Ruga Rialto, 778   tel. 0415226546   www.anticodolo.it
Notes: Many celiac customers. GF pasta. Highly recommended.

Osteria All Ombra   restaurant   €€-€€€
Canneregio 5603   tel. 041611905
Notes: In a small square bet. Campo die SS. Apostoli and Salizzada S. Giovanni Crisostomo.

Pane Vino e San Daniele   restaurant   €€-€€€
Calle dei Botteri, San Polo   tel. 0415237456   www.panevinoesandaniele.net

Restaurant da fiore   restaurant   €€€€
S. Polo, 2002 (Calle del Scaleter) tel. 041721308   www.dafiore.net

Parking (A. Smith)

Ristorante Gianni	restaurant	€€-€€€
Dorsoduro 918, Zattere	tel. 0415237210	

Ristorante Le Maschere   restaurant   €€€-€€€€
in San Clemente Palace hotel - Isola di San Clemente 1   tel. 0412445001
www.sanclemente.thi.it
Notes: GF with advance notice.

Trattoria AL Gazzettino   restaurant   €€€-€€€€
Sestiere San Marco 4972   tel. 04 15210497

Trattoria da Fiore   restaurant   €€€€
San Marco, Calle de le Botteghe, 3461   tel. 0415235310   www.dafiore.it
Notes: Very highly recommended but also very expensive. Near San Polo square.

Trattoria Da Nino   restaurant   €€€
Sestiere Castello 4668   tel. 04 15235886   www.trattoriadanino.com

Trattoria dai Peochi   restaurant   €€
Canneregio 2232   tel. 041721555

Vini da Gigio   restaurant   €€€
Sestiere Cannaregio, 3628   tel. 0415285140   www.vinidagigio.com
Notes: Great reviews.

VENEZIA - LIDO
Hotel Villa Beatrice   hotel   AIC
Via dei Villini, 4   tel. 41.731072   www.hotelbeatrice.com

THE REST OF VENETO
(AIC = participates in the Associazione Italiana Celiachia program)

ADRIA
Gastronomia Le Quattro Stagioni tavola calda   €€€, AIC
Corso Mazzini, 34   tel. 345.2695635   www.gastronomialequattrostagioni.it

ARBIZZANO
La Sfera   pizzeria   €, AIC
Via Valpolicella, 21   tel. 0456020018

ARCUGNANO

Enrico VIII
Via Spianzana, 20
restaurant
tel. 0444550440
€€-€€€, AIC
www.enricoottavo.it

ARIANO NEL POLESINE

Antico Delta
Via San Basilio 139
pizzeria
tel. 426.378403
€€, AIC
www.anticodelta.it

ARQUÀ POLESINE

Locanda Valmolin
Via Marzara, 694
restaurant, pizzeria
tel. 347.1334411
€€€€, AIC
www.locandavalmolin.com

Trattoria degli Amici
Via Quirina, 4
restaurant
tel. 042591045
€€, AIC
www.trattoriadegliamici.it

ARZIGNANO

Pizzeria Pasticceria Majn
Via Main, 7/B
pizzeria, bakery, gelato
tel. 444.674438
€, AIC
www.pizzeriamajn.it

ASIAGO

Albergo Rendola
Via Rendola, 41
inn, restaurant, pizzeria
tel. 0424464148
AIC
www.albergorendola.it

La Tana c/o Sporting Residence H. Asiago restaurant
Via 4 Novembre, 77
tel. 0424462521
Notes: Closed Mondays.
€€€, AIC

Magia
Viale Trento Trieste, 31
pizzeria
tel. 424.463338
€€, AIC

Pizzeria Ristorante Rendola
Via Rendola, 41
restaurant, pizzeria
tel. 0424600500
€€-€€€, AIC

Sporting Residence Hotel
Via 4 Novembre, 77
hotel
tel. 0424462177
AIC
www.sportingasiago.com

ASOLO

Villa Razzolin Loredana
Via Schiavonesca Marosticana, 15
restaurant
tel. 0423951088
Notes: Closed Mondays.
€€, AIC

BELLUNO

Al Borgo
Via Anconetta, 8
restaurant
tel. 0437926755
€€€, AIC
Notes: Closed Mondays at dinner, Tuesdays.

Alla Bella Napoli
Via Feltre, 240
restaurant, pizzeria
tel. 437.944054
€€-€€€, AIC

Excalibur
Via Tiziano Vecellio, 5/A
pizzeria
tel. 437.932078
€€, AIC
www.excaliburweb.it

La Delizia
gelato (€, AIC)
P.zza V.Emanuele, 9

Zodiaco
Via Travazzoi, 8
restaurant, pizzeria
tel. 0437941478
€, AIC
Notes: Closed Mondays.

BIBIONE

Al Villaggio c/o V.T.I.
Via Delle Colonie 2
restaurant/pizzeria
tel. 0431442630
€€, AIC
www.vti.it

BOLZANO VICENTINO

Nuvole di Latte gelato (€, AIC) Via Roma, 56

BOSCO CHIESANUOVA

Lenci Tre pizzeria €, AIC
Via M. Piccoli, 61 tel. 0457050057

BREDA DI PIAVE

Da Teddy trattoria, pizzeria €, AIC
Via Giuseppe Garibaldi, 44 loc. Pero tel. 0422904418

BREDA DI PIAVE - LOC PERO

Antica Bassa Da Teddy restaurant, pizzeria €€-€€€, AIC
Via Giuseppe Garibaldi, 44 loc. Pero tel. 422.904418 www.anticabassadateddy.it

BRENZONE

Hotel Eden hotel, restaurant AIC
Via Zanardelli, 6 tel. 45.7420102 www.consolinihotels.com

CADONEGHE

Da Silvio pizzeria €€, AIC
Via L. Bordin, 39 tel. 049702150
Notes: Closed Mondays.

CALDOGNO

Al Marinante restaurant €€€-€€€€, AIC
Via Cà Alta, 111 tel. 0444986039 www.almarinante.it
Notes: Closed Mondays, Tuesdays, and at lunch.

Molin Vecio trattoria €€€-€€€€, AIC
Via Giaroni, 116 tel. 0444585168 www.molinvecio.it
Notes: Closed Tuesdays.

CAMPODARSEGO

Ariston hotel AIC
Via Antoniana, 230 tel. 0499314401

Il Dolce Incontro gelato (€, AIC) Via Caltana, 48

CAORLE

Cleofe hotel, restaurant €€€-€€€€
Via Altinate, 2 tel. 042181082 www.hotelcleofe.it

Hotel Angelo hotel AIC
Via dei Calamari, 6 tel. 0421211728

Hotel Doriana hotel AIC
L.re Trieste, 48 tel. 042181104 www.hoteldoriana.it

CAPRINO VERONESE

Athena pizzeria €, AIC
Via Pertini, 10/h tel. 0456230813

CASELLE DI SOMMACAMPAGNA

da Brinchi trattoria €€-€€€, AIC
Via Tezze, 82 tel. 0458581106 www.trattoriadabrinchi.com

CASSOLA LOC. SAN GIUSEPPE

Alla Torre restaurant, pizzeria €€, AIC
Via Leonardo da Vinci, 23 tel. 424.33081 www.pizzeriallatorre.it

CASTEL D'AZZANO

Al Ventaglio
Via Pietro Mascagni, 92
restaurant, pizzeria
tel. 045512591
€€-€€€, AIC
www.pizzerialventaglio.it

CASTELCUCCO

Montegrappa
Viale Montegrappa, 8
hotel, restaurant, pizzeria
tel. 0423563123
€€, AIC
www.hotelmontegrappa.it

CASTELFRANCO VENETO

Da Gennaro
Via Castellana 17
restaurant, pizzeria
tel. 423.482188
AIC

CASTELGOMBERTO

Al Ponte
Via S. Cecilia, 73
pizzeria
tel. 445.491045
€€, AIC
www.pizzeriaalponte.it

CASTELNUOVO DEL GARDA

Agrit. Casa San Marco
Via Verona, 1
B&B
tel. 0456458906
AIC
www.agriturismocasasanmarco.com

CAVALLINO TREPORTI

Alla Fattoria c/o Union Lido
Via Fausta, 245
restaurant
tel. 041968376
€€-€€€€, AIC
www.lafattoria.it

Art & Park Union Lido Hotel
Via Fausta, 270
hotel
tel. 041968043
AIC
www.parkhotelunionlido.com

Carpaccio
Via Fausta, 266
restaurant
tel. 41.3098632
€€-€€€€, AIC
www.unionlido.com/en/things-to-do-en/gourmet-club/carpaccio-3

Cavallo Marino c/o Union Lido
Via Fausta, 258
restaurant
tel. 0415370840
€€, AIC

Riviera c/o Union Lido
Via Fausta, 258
restaurant
tel. 0415371344
€, AIC

CAZZANO DI TRAMIGNA

Corte del Sole
Via Costeggiola, 38
pizzeria
tel. 45.7675369
€€, AIC
cortedelsole@yahoo.it

CENCENIGHE

Da Makram
Via Roma, 62
restaurant, pizzeria
tel. 0437580328
€, AIC
Notes: DS pizza point. Closed Mondays.

CESSALTO

Airest Ristop Calstorta
Via Calstorta, 3
fast food
tel. 421.327179
€, AIC

CHIES D'ALPAGO

Locanda San Martino
Via Don Ermolao Barattin, 23
restaurant bar
tel. 043740111
€€€-€€€€, AIC
Notes: Closed Mondays, Tuesdays at dinner, Wednesdays.

CHIOGGIA

Grom
gelato (€, AIC)
P.zza del Quartiere Latino, 16

CHIRIGNAGO

Icebear
gelato (€, AIC)
Via Miranese, 286/M

CISMON DEL GRAPPA

Val Goccia — restaurant, pizzeria — €€, AIC
Via Giarre di Sicilia, 5 — tel. 0424432126 — www.valgoccia.com
Notes: Closed Tuesdays.

CITTADELLA

Antica Porta — gelato (€, AIC) — Via Garibaldi, 55

Torre di Malta — restaurant/pizzeria — €€, AIC
Via Ca' Nave, 2/d — tel. 0499401761 — www.ristorantepizzeriatorredimalta.it

CODOGNÈ

Giancarlo — restaurant — €€€-€€€€, AIC
Via Farmacia, 57 — tel. 3480177072 — www.resortmarcopolo.it

COGOLLO DEL CENGIO

Barricatella — trattoria, bar, gelato — €€, AIC
Via Strada del Costo, 1 — tel. 445.320158 — www.facebook.com/home.php

COLOGNA VENETA

Acquario — pizzeria — €, AIC
Via S.Andrea 27 — tel. 044285667

Rio (A. Smith)

COLOGNOLA AI COLLI

Chocolat — gelato (€, AIC) — Via Strà, 35

COSTA DI ROVIGO

La Rosa — pizzeria — €, AIC
P.zza San Rocco, 41 — tel. 0425497197

COSTABISSARA

Ca' Nostra — pizzeria — AIC
Via Mazzini, 8/10 — tel. 0444971181 — www.canostra .it

ERACLEA MARE

Dal Gelatiere	gelato (€, AIC)	Via Marinella, 12

FALCADE

Stella Alpina Piazza Municipio, 7	hotel, restaurant, bar tel. 437.599046	€€€€, AIC www.hotelstellalpina.com

FORNO DI ZOLDO

Bar Gelat. Centrale	gelato (€, AIC)	P.zza A. Santin, 4

FRATTA POLESINE

Villa Gardenia Via S. Giorgio, 188 Notes: Closed Tuesdays.	restaurant tel. 0425668497	€€, AIC www.villa-gardenia.it

GARDA

Pizzeria La Capannina Via Poiano 23	pizzeria tel. 45.6279159	€€-€€€, AIC www.lacapanninagarda.com

ISOLA DELLA SCALA

Pila Vecia Via Saccovener, 9 Notes: 100% gluten-free.	restaurant tel. 45.6630642	€€€, AIC www.risoferron.com

JESOLO

da Guido Via Roma Sinistra, 25	restaurant tel. 0421350380	€€€€ www.ristorantedaguido.com
Gelateria Lovat	gelato (€, AIC)	Piazza I Maggio, 15
Stefania Via Pordenone, 12 Notes: S € 23 D € 46	B&B tel. 3201776184	AIC

JESOLO LIDO

Hotel Domingo Via Gorizia, 31	hotel tel. 0421971922	€, AIC
Hotel Europa Via Bafile, 361	hotel tel. 0421371631	AIC www.hoteleuropajesolo.it
Hotel Galassia Via Treviso, 7	hotel tel. 0421370677	AIC www.hotelgalassia.it
Hotel Imperia Via Gorizia, 31	hotel tel. 0421370718	AIC www.hotelimperia.com
Hotel Nettuno Via Bafile XXIII A.M. 2	hotel tel. 0421370301	AIC www.hotel-nettuno.com
Hotel Stockholm Via dei Mille, 15	hotel tel. 0421371235	AIC www.hotelstockholm.it
Hotel Universo Via Treviso, 9/11	hotel tel. 0421972298	AIC
Ristorante Frontemare Via Bafile, 23° accesso al mare	restaurant tel. 0421370301	€€-€€€, AIC www.hotelnettuno.com

LAMOSANO DI CHIES

Teverone Piazza Roma, 9	pizzeria tel. 437.40189	€€, AIC

LIMANA

Az. Agric. I Boschi del Castagno B&B   AIC
Via I Boschi, 1   tel. 0437970114

L'Oasi   trattoria   €€€, AIC
Via Triches, 25   tel. 0437967298
Notes: Closed Sundays at dinner, Mondays.

LONIGO

Mondo nuovo   sandwich shop, bakery   €, AIC
Via Cesare Battisti, 168/F   tel. 3485422421
www.facebook.com/mondonuovoglutenfree

The Bridge   pizzeria   €, AIC
Via Madonna, 44   tel. 0444835460

MALO

Il Fornino   pizzeria, pub   €, AIC
Via Pace, 3   tel. 0445581427

MARGHERA

Grom   gelato   €, AIC
Via Pietro Arduino c/o Centro Comm.le Navedevero   tel. 041/920648   www.grom.it

MAROSTICA

Lunaelaltro   pizzeria   €-€€€, AIC
Corso della Ceramica, 33   tel. 424.478098   www.osterialunaelaltro.com

MARTELLAGO

Zeus Pizza   pizzeria   €€, AIC
Via Berna, 2   tel. 41.0994487

MASON VICENTINO

Icio & Paola   pizzeria   €, AIC
Via S. Pietro, 6   tel. 0424708232

MEL

Col di Neve   B&B   €€€, AIC
Via Tiago, 90   tel. 0437540342

MERLENGO PONZANO VENETO

Le Querce   restaurant   AIC
Via Talponera 130/A   tel. 422.99043

MESTRE

Al Corso   pizzeria   €, AIC
C.so del Popolo, 37   tel. 041981642

Gelateria Artigianale Al Parco   gelato (€, AIC)   Via Casona 23

Grom   gelato (€, AIC)   Via Palazzo, 37

Novotel Venezia/Novotelcafé   hotel, restaurant   €€€€, AIC
Via A. Ceccherini, 21   tel. 0415066511   www.novotel.com

RossoPomodoro   restaurant, pizzeria   €€, AIC
Via Don Federico Tosatto 26   tel. 41.2001288   www.rossopomodoro.it

MESTRE-ZELARINO

Antico Moro   hotel   AIC
Via Castellana, 149   tel. 41.5461834   www.anticomoro.com

MIRA

Isola di Caprera
Riviera S. Trentin, 13

hotel
tel. 0414265255

€€€€, AIC
www.isoladicaprera.com

MIRANO

Ostaria Nova
Via Cavin di Sala, 12

restaurant
tel. 41.5700761

€€€€, AIC
www.ostarianova.it

MOGLIANO VENETO

ICapriccio
Via Toti dal Monte, 29/31

restaurant, bar
tel. 415905304

€€€, AIC
www.icapriccio.com

MONTEBELLUNA

Al Grappolo d'Oro
Via Feltrina Sud, 181

pizzeria
tel. 0423303516

€, AIC
www.grappolodoro.com

MONTECCHIA DI CROSARA

Tregnago
Via Campitelli, 1

restaurant
tel. 0457460036

€€-€€€, AIC
www.ristorantetregnago.com

MONTEFORTE D'ALPONE

Abbazia
Via Giuseppe Garibaldi, 24

pizzeria
tel. 45.7613796

€€, AIC
www.monteolivetomaggiore.it

MONTEGROTTO TERME

Caffè del Corso
Corso delle Terme, 108/a

tavola calda
tel. 3402952513

€, AIC

Hotel Garden Terme
Corso Terme, 7

hotel, restaurant
tel. 49.8911699

AIC
www.gardenterme.it

MONTEMEZZO DI SOVIZZO

La Grippia
Via Fontanalunga, 13
Notes: Closed Mondays and at lunch.

pizzeria
tel. 0444551011

€, AIC

MONTICELLO CONTEOTTO

Ristorante Hotel Rizzi
Via Revoloni, 2
Notes: Closed Tuesdays.

hotel, restaurant, pizzeria
tel. 0444946099

€€€-€€€€, AIC

MUSILE DI PIAVE

Antica Trattoria alla Fossetta
Via Fossetta, 31

restaurant bar
tel. 0421330296

€€, AIC
www.fossetta.it

NERVESA DELLA BATTAGLIA

La Strana Coppia
Via Lungo Piave G. Da Bologna, 1
www.facebook.com/pages/Pizzeria-La-Strana-Coppia/323934487343

restaurant, pizzeria
tel. 422.77931

€€, AIC

NOALE

Zeus Pizza
Via Tempesta, 75

pizzeria
tel. 41.822257

€€, AIC

ORSAGO

La Dolce Flavia

gelato (€, AIC)

Via G. Mazzini, 22

PADOVA

Al Carmine
P.zza Petrarca, 8
Notes: Closed Mondays, Saturday and Sunday lunch.

restaurant, pizzeria
tel. 0498764952

€€, AIC

Gluten-Free Italy by Region

Autogrill Limena A4 Brescia - Padova	autogrill tel. 49.8648057	€, AIC
Bastioni del Moro Via P. Bronzetti, 18 Notes: Closed Sundays.	restaurant tel. 0498710006	€€€, AIC www.bastionidelmoro.it
Da Nadia Via A. da Bassano, 45-47	hotel, restaurant, pizzeria tel. 0498641661	€€, AIC
Forcellini 172 Via Forcellini, 172	pizzeria, restaurant tel. 0498033722	€€, AIC www.forcellini172.it
Grom **Grom** www.grom.it	gelato (€, AIC) gelato (€, AIC)	P.zza dei Signori, 33 Via Roma, 101
Per Bacco Piazzale Pontecorvo, 10 Notes: Closed Sundays.	restaurant tel. 0498752883	€€€€, AIC www.per-bacco.it
Perdinci Via C. Callegari, 43	pizzeria tel. 49.604578	€, AIC www.perdinci.it

PAESE

Zeus Pizza Via Marconi, 36	pizzeria tel. 422.1564431	€€, AIC www.misterimprese.it

PALAZZOLO DI SONA

Cà Fileno Via Prele, 48	restaurant tel. 0456080891	€€-€€€, AIC www.ristorantecafileno.com

PEDAVENA

La Birreria Pedavena Viale Vittorio Veneto, 76	restaurant tel. 439.304402	€-€€, AIC www.labirreriapedavena.com

PERAGA DI VIGONZA

Le Midì Ristoservice Via Germania, 9 Notes: Closed Saturdays, Sundays, and at dinner.	restaurant, tavola calda tel. 049629675	€, AIC www.lemidi.it

PERAROLO DI VIGONZA

Mai Sazio Via A. Diaz, 160	pizzeria tel. 0496226588	€, AIC www.maisazio.it

PESCHIERA DEL GARDA

Bellavista Lungolago Mazzini, 1	pizzeria tel. 0457553252	€€, AIC
Tortuga Cafè	gelato (€, AIC)	Via Lungolago Mazzini, 2/b

PESEGGIA

La Torre Via Vecchia Moglianese, 186	pizzeria tel. 0415830590	€, AIC www.pizzerialatorre.it

PIAZZOLA SUL BRENTA

Alle Logge Via delle Logge Palladiane, 6	restaurant tel. 0499601432	€€€€, AIC www.ristorantealletogge.it

PIEVE DI CADORE

Cavallino Via Nazionale, 4	inn, restaurant tel. 0435500467	€€-€€€, AIC www.hotelcavallinodolomiti.it

PIEVE DI SOLIGO

Agli Angeli
Via Tacchini, 45
Notes: Closed Wednesdays at dinner.
pizzeria
tel. 04381794966
€, AIC
www.angeli.it

PONTE DI NANTO

El Rosedal
Via Mercato, 48
pizzeria
tel. 444639044
€, AIC

PONTE NELLE ALPI

Mychef Ponte nelle Alpi Ovest
A27 Venezia - Belluno
mychef
tel. 437.990613
€, AIC
www.mychef.it

PONTE SAN NICOLÒ

Al Ponte
Via Roma, 37
pizzeria
tel. 49717437
€, AIC
www.pizzeriaristorantealponte.it

PORTO TOLLE

La Fraterna
Via Mentone, 13
B&B
tel. 0426384128
AIC
www.agriturismolafraterna.it

Nottedì
Via Alicata, 10 - loc. Cà Mello
B&B
tel. 3497237930
AIC

PREGANZIOL

Glutine Zero
Via Veneto 1
sandwich shop, bakery
tel. 422.1571101
€, AIC
www.glutinezero.it

L'Albera di Zeus
Via Terraglio, 249
pizzeria
tel. 04221721856
€, AIC

QUINTO DI TREVISO

Best Western Premier Bhr Treviso Hotel hotel, restaurant
Via Postumia Castellana, 2
tel. 04223730
€€€€, AIC
www.bhrtrevisohotel.com

QUINTO VICENTINO

Dolce Idea
Via Vittorio Veneto, 31
gelato
tel. 348.4000241 www.facebook.com/GelateriaDolceIdea
€, AIC

RECOARO TERME

La Linte
Via Roma, 19
restaurant
tel. 445.75566
€€, AIC
www.ristorantelalinte.it

ROMANO D'EZZELINO

Al Pioppeto
Via Barbarigo, 13
restaurant
tel. 0424570502
€€-€€€, AIC

Dalla Mena
Via Valle S. Felicita, 14
Notes: Closed Mondays.
inn, restaurant
tel. 042436481
€€, AIC

RONCADE

Pasqualino 90
Via Roma, 48
restaurant, pizzeria
tel. 0422708377
AIC

ROSOLINA MARE

Chiosco Bar Bagno Tamerici
Via Trieste, 140
bar
tel. 426.68424
€, AIC
www.bagniferro.it

Fiorella
Via Trieste, 17
restaurant, hotel
tel. 0426.68010
€€, AIC
www.albergofiorella.it

ROVIGO

Re Artù pizzeria €, AIC
Via Petrarca, 20 tel. 042533330
Notes: DS pizza point. Closed at lunch.

S. GIULIANO - VENEZIA

Russott Hotel Venezia hotel, restaurant €€€€, AIC
Via Orlanda, 4 tel. 0415310500 www.russotshotels.com

S. PIETRO IN CARIANO

Agriturismo Fioravante B&B AIC
Via Don C. Biasi, 7 tel. 0457701317 www.agriturismofioravante.it

S. ZENO DI COLOGNOLA AI COLLI

La Fenice pizzeria, osteria €-€€, AIC
Via Cesare Battisti tel. 0456152686
Notes: Closed Mondays.

S. ZENONE DEGLI EZZELINI

Ezzelino hotel, restaurant, pizzeria €€, AIC
Via Marconi, 55 tel. 0423964070
Notes: DS pizza point. Closed Mondays.

SACCOLONGO

Il Console restaurant AIC
Via Roma, 4 tel. 0498016648 www.ilconsole.com
Notes: Closed Tuesday-Saturday at lunch.

SALZANO

Belfiore pizzeria €, AIC
Via Roma, 234 tel. 041437010 www.belfiorehotel.it
Notes: DS pizza point. Closed Wednesdays.

SAN BONIFACIO

Mychef San Lorenzo Ovest mychef €, AIC
A4 Padova - Brescia tel. 340.1674815 www.mychef.it

SANDRIGO

La Colombara restaurant, pizzeria €€€-€€€€, AIC
Via Chiesa, 7/a fraz. Lupia tel. 0444750767
Notes: Closed Mondays, Tuesdays at lunch.

SCHIO

da Beppino restaurant €€€, AIC
Località Ceresara, 1 tel. 0445670139

Il Fornino pizzeria €, AIC
Via Pio X, 223/A tel. 445.672939 www.ilfornino.it

Il Piacere gelato (€, AIC) Via Batt. Val Leogra, 79/d

SEDICO

Ristorante Alla Stanga restaurant €€€, AIC
Via La Stanga, 24 tel. 043787611 www.ristoranteallastanga.it

SELVAZZANO DENTRO

Senza Spiga bar, tavola calda/fredda €, AIC
Via Brentella, 25 tel. 49.630915 www.senzaspiga.it

SETTIMO DI PESCANTINA

Settimo Cielo
Via Bernardi 1

restaurant, pizzeria
tel. 45.6703207

€€, AIC
www.pizzeriasettimocielo.net

SOAVE

Autogrill Scaligera
A4 Brescia - Padova

autogrill
tel. 45.7610398

€, AIC

SOTTOMARINA DI CHIOGGIA

Grom
Lungomare Adriatico ai Bagni Clodia   tel. 41.5542931

gelato

€, AIC
www.grom.it

Hotel Le Tegnùe
Via Lungomare Adriatico, 48

hotel
tel. 41.4917

AIC
www.hotelletegnue.it

SOVIZZO

Da Manfron
Via Alfieri, 44/46

restaurant
tel. 0444551960

€€€, AIC
www.ristorantemanfron.it

SPINEA

All'Antico Graspo d'Uva
Via Roma, 32
Notes: Closed Tuesdays.

pizzeria
tel. 041992759

€€, AIC

TAGLIO DI PO

Osteria La Pioppa
Via Milite Ignoto, 99
Notes: Closed Sundays.

restaurant
tel. 0426660440

€-€€€€, AIC

TESSERA VENEZIA

Airest Culto Caffè & Cioccolato "Cultino" fast food
Aeroporto Venezia "Marco Polo"- via L.Broglio, 8   tel. 041.2603871-2

€, AIC
www.airest.com

Airest Ristorante L'Orto
Aeroporto Venezia "Marco Polo"- via L. Broglio, 8   tel. 041.2603871-2 www.airest.com

fast food

€, AIC

THIENE

Gelat. Artig. Vale

gelato (€, AIC)

Via Divisione Julia, 45

TORREGLIA

La Griglia
Via S. Daniele, 39
Notes: Closed Tuesdays.

restaurant
tel. 0495211158

€€, AIC

TREVISO

Albergo Alla Scoa
Borgo Treviso, 196
Notes: GF dishes available on request.

hotel
tel. 0423723712

Conca d'Oro
Via T. Salsa, 351/G

bar, tavola calda, bakery
tel. 0422420623   www.pasticceria.com

€, AIC

Ezzelino Hotel
Via Marconi

hotel, restaurant
tel. 0423969448   www.hotelezzelino.com

Grigio Perla
Via S. Ambrogio da Fiera, 3/b

pizzeria
tel. 0422541456

€, AIC

Grom

gelato (€, AIC)

P.zza del Quartiere Latino, 16

TRICHIANA

Alla Lanterna
Via Casteldardo, 50/A

B&B
tel. 437.555469

AIC

La Pollùce	B&B	AIC
Via Confos, 79	tel. 437.757536	www.pollucebedandbreakfast.it

VERONA

Ai Glicini	restaurant, pizzeria	€€, AIC
Via Centro, 235	tel. 045584100	www.pizzeriaaiglicini.it

Fata Zucchina	restaurant	€€, AIC
Via Don Carlo Steeb, 25	tel. 045597897	www.sucabaruca.com

Gelat. Artig. Oasi	gelato (€, AIC)	Via L. Prina
Maracanà	gelato (€, AIC)	P.le Olimpia, 36/a

Quinto Miglio	pizzeria	€€, AIC
Via Valpantena, 62/a	tel. 45.550361	www.quintomiglio.it

VERONELLA

Prima o poi	pizzeria	€, AIC
Via O. Fontana	tel. 0442480130	

VICENZA

Antico Guelfo	restaurant	€€, AIC
c.da Pedemuro S. Biagio, 92	tel. 0444547897	www.anticoguelfo.it

Gelateria Brustolon	gelato (€, AIC)	Contrà Ponte Pusterla, 23

Giorgio e Chiara	pizzeria	€, AIC
Via Cà Balbi, 377	tel. 0444911004	www.giorgioechiara.it

Gocce di bio	gelato (€, AIC)	Strada di Saviabona, 97b

Ristorante Il Querini da Zemin	restaurant	€€€, AIC
V.le del Sole, 142	tel. 0444552054	

VIGOROVEA

Papillon	pizzeria	€, AIC
Via Trieste, 1	tel. 0499701891	

VILLAFRANCA DI VERONA

Il Gargano	restaurant	€€€€, AIC
Via della Pace, 137	tel. 0456301800	www.ristoranteilgargano.com

La Filanda	osteria	€€-€€€, AIC
Via Nino Bixio, 370	tel. 0456303583	www.osterialafilanda.com

VITTORIO VENETO

Europa	pizzeria	€, AIC
Via Dalmazia, 120	tel. 043859890	

Pizzeria Ristorantino Da Pietro	pizzeria	€, AIC
Via S. Antonio da Padova, 18	tel. 438.912419	

ZOVENCEDO

Ca' Martina	pizzeria	€, AIC
Via Croce, 18	tel. 444.893177	

MILAN AND LOMBARDIA

PLACES IN MILAN TO BUY
GLUTEN-FREE FOOD PRODUCTS

EsseMon.ga

Viale Regina Giovanna 34
Viale Zara 123
Viale Piave 38/B
Via Cagliero 14/a
Via Jenner ang.
Viale Cassala 22
Via Trilussa 24
Via Pezzotti
Via Morgantini 15   Via Monte Rosa
Via Losanna 20/22   Via Forze Armate
Via Feltre
Via Bergamo 10
Viale Papiniano 27   Via Mac Mahon 128
Via Solari, 29
Via Ripamonti 181

Viale Ungheria 12
Viale Vigliani 59
Via Amoretti 4/6
Viale Certosa 59
Via Legnone 3
Via Washington 55
Via Suzzani 221
V.Pellegrino Rossi 33

Via die Missaglia 61/A
piazza Ovidio

Via Morgantini 15

Ipercoop Bonola
Ipercoop La Torre
Ipercoop Piazza Lodi

c/o C.c. Bonola-Via Quarenghi 23
Via B. Gozzoli 130
Via Colletta 46b

Pam
Via Foppa 33
Viale Olona 1/3

Via Inganni 87
Via Archimede 8

PLACES IN MILAN TO GET GUARANTEED GLUTEN-FREE GELATO
(SPONSORED BY ITALIAN CELIAC SOCIETY)

Bar Gelateria Top del Gelato
Frozen Gelateria
Grom
Grom
Grom
Grom
Grom
Grom
Grom
Il Gelato Ecologico
L'Isola
Pinguino Blu

C.so di Porta Romana, 92
C.so Porta Ticinese, 96/98
Via Alberto da Giussano, 1
C.so di Porta Ticinese, 51
C.so Buenos Aires, 13
C.so XXII Marzo, 5
V. S.ta Margherita, 16
P.zza Argentina, 6
Piazza Gae Aulenti, 8
Via Ravizza, 5
Via Forze Armate, 50
Via Paolo Sarpi, 2

HOTELS IN MILAN LISTED ALPHABETICALLY

Best Western Hotel City
Corso Buenos Aires 42/5   tel. 02 2952 3382   www.hotelcitymilano.it
Notes: Stazione Centrale.

Best Western Hotel Galles
Piazza Lima 2   tel. 02 204 841   www.hotelcitymilano.it
Notes: Buenos Aires.

Boscolo Exedra Milano
Corso Matteotti 4 -6   tel. 02 7767 9611   www.milano.boscolohotels.com
Notes: Centro Storico.

Carlton Hotel Baglioni
Via Senato 5   tel. 02 77 077   www.baglionihotels.com
Notes: Centro Storico.

Carlyle Brera Hotel
C.so Garibaldi 84   tel. 02 2900 3888   www.hotelcarlyle.com
Notes: Moscova.

Crowne Plaza Hotel Milan City
Via Melchiorre Gioia 73   tel. 02 6671 7715   www.crowneplazamilan.com
Notes: Business district (Sondrio).

Doria Grand Hotel Milano
Viale Andrea Doria 2   tel. 02 6741 1411   www.doriagrandhotel.it
Notes: (Business district) Corso Buenos Aires.

Doubletree by Hilton Milan
Via Ludovico di Breme 77   tel. 02 928 831   www.dtmilan.com
Notes: Certosa.

Grand Hotel Puccini
Corso Buenos Aires 33   tel. 02 2952 1344   www.grandhotelpuccini.com
Notes: Stazione Centrale.

Grand Visconti Palace
Viale Isonzo 14   tel. 02 540 341   www.grandviscontipalace.com
Notes: Porta Romana.

Hotel Ambasciatori
Galleria del Corso 3   tel. 02 7602 0241   www.ambasciatorihotel.it
Notes: Centro Storico.

Hotel Ariston
Largo Carrobbio 2   tel. 02 7200 0556   www.aristonhotel.com
Notes: Centro Storico.

Hotel Berna Milan
Via Napo Torriani 18   tel. 02 677 311   www.hotelberna.com
Notes: Stazione Centrale.

Hotel Capitol Milano
Via Cimarosa Domenico 6   tel. 02 438 591   www.hotelcapitolmilano.com
Notes: Centro Storico.

Hotel Manzoni
Via Santo Spirito 20   tel. 02 7600 5700   www.hotelmanzoni.com
Notes: Centro Storico.

Hotel Mercure Milano Centro
Piazza Oberdan 12   tel. 02 2940 3907
www.accorhotels.com/gb/hotel-5705-mercure-milano-centro/index.shtml
Notes: Porto Venezia.

Hotel Pierre Milano
Via De Amicis 32   tel. 02 7200 0581   www.hotelpierremilano.it
Notes: Business district.

Hotel Principe di Savoia
Piazza della Repubblica 17   tel. 02 623 01
www.dorchestercollection.com/en/milan/hotel-principe-di-savoia
Notes: Moscova.

Meliá Milano
Via Masaccio 19   tel. 02 44 406
www.melia.com/en/hotels/italy/milan/melia-milano/index.html
Notes: Fiera.

NH Grand Hotel Verdi
Via Melchiorre Gioia 6   tel. 02 62 371
www.nh-hotels.com/hotel/nh-milano-grand-hotel-verdi
Notes: Moscova.

Novotel Linate/Novotelcafé
Via Mecenate, 121   tel. 02507261   www.novotel.com

Novotel Milano Nord/Novotelcafé
V.le Suzzani,13   tel. 02641151   www.novotel.com

Milano (A. Komorowski)

RESTAURANTS AND BAKERIES IN MILAN

(AIC = participates in the Associazione Italiana Celiachia program)

Autogrill Milano - Duomo Store Via U. Foscolo nr. 1	autogrill tel. 2.86331911	€, AIC
Bar Ted One Via Solferino, 32 Notes: Closed Sundays.	bar, tavola calda tel. 0206575260	€, AIC
Be Bop Viale Col di Lana, 4	restaurant, pizzeria tel. 028376972	€-€€, AIC
Cantina Piemontese Via Laghetto, 2	restaurant tel. 02784618	€€€€, AIC www.cantinapiemontese.it
Capoverde Via Leoncavallo, 16	restaurant, pizzeria tel. 0226820430	€, AIC
Cook Window via Amatore Sciesa, 18	restaurant, pizzeria tel. 0255186997	€, AIC www.cookwindow.it
Da Hakim Via Vallazze, 74	pizzeria tel. 0270630315	€, AIC
Doris Diner Viale Sarca, 336/F	restaurant tel. 0287250184	AIC
Eco Hotel La Residenza Via Scialoia, 3	hotel, restaurant tel. 2.6461646	AIC www.ecohotelresidenzamilano.it
Guyot Via Arnaldo da Brescia, 3 Notes: Garibaldi.	restaurant, wine bar tel. 0287237103	AIC www.tavernaguyot.com
Il Giorno Bistrot c/o Hotel Hermitage hotel, restaurant Via Messina, 10 tel. 2.31817 www.fedegroup.it/ristorante/ristorante-il-giorno-bistrot		€€€, AIC
Il Grissino Via Legioni Romane 37 Notes: Bande Nere.	restaurant, pizzeria tel. 024046141	€€, AIC www.algrissino.it
Il Papiro Via F.lli Bressan, 9 Notes: Villa San Giovanni.	pizzeria/restaurant tel. 022579589	€, AIC www.pizzeriaristoranteilpapiro.it
Il Piccolo Padre Via Cenisio, 54 (da Via Princ.Eugenio) tel. 023494906 Notes: Monumentale.	restaurant, pizzeria	€, AIC www.ilpiccolopadremilano.com
Il Piccolo Principe Via Pelizza da Volpedo, 16 Notes: Fiera.	restaurant, pizzeria tel. 2.498275	€€, AIC www.ilpiccolopadremilano.com
Isa e Vane Via Perugino, 1 Notes: Porta Vittoria.	restaurant, bar tel. 2.36515288	€€€, AIC www.isaevane.com
Kitchen Ristorante Via Neera, 40 Notes: Navigli.	restaurant tel. 0284895749	€€€, AIC www.kitchenristorante.com

La Basilicata   restaurant, pizzeria   €, AIC
Via E. De Marchi, 44   tel. 0266987892
Notes: Turro Gorla Greco. DS pizza point. Closed Mondays.

La Rosa dei Venti   restaurant   €€€, AIC
Via Piero della Francesca,34   tel. 02347338   www.ristorantelarosadeiventi.it
Notes: Monumentale.

La Tellina   restaurant, pizzeria   €, AIC
Via Palanzone, 26   tel. 0266108063
Notes: Bicocca.

Le Specialità   restaurant, pizzeria   €€€-€€€€, AIC
Via P. Calvi, 29   tel. 027388235   www.ristorantelespecialita.com
Notes: Porta Vittoria. Many GF choices. Very accommodating staff.

Lepontina   restaurant, pizzeria   €€€, AIC
Via Lepontina, 8   tel. 2.39820772   www.residencelepontina.it
Notes: Garibaldi.

Mychef Aeroporto Linate   mychef   €, AIC
Viale Forlanini   tel. 2.7383742   www.mychef.it

Mychef Centro Direzionale San Siro   mychef   €, AIC
Via Caldera, 21   tel. 2.40910101   www.mychef.it

Mychef Politecnico di Milano-Facol tà Ingegneria   mychef   €, AIC
P.zza L. da Vinci, 32   tel. 2.2666681   www.mychef.it

Mychef Self Service Corso Italia   mychef   €, AIC
Corso Italia   tel. 2.8812831   www.mychef.it

Osteria dei 5 Sensi   restaurant   €€€-€€€€, AIC
Via Cicco Simonetta, 17   tel. 0258102650   www.osteriadei5sensi.com
Notes: Centro Storico. Closed Saturdays at lunch and Mondays.

Out of Gluten   bakery, pasta shop, sandwich shop   €€, AIC
Via San Michele del Carso, 13   tel. 2.433004   www.facebook.com/outofgluten/info
Notes: Washington.

Panta Rei Club   restaurant, pizzeria   €€€-€€€€, AIC
Viale Pasubio, 14   tel. 026597370   www.pantareiclub.com
Notes: Moscova.

Pasticceria Navotti Senza Glutine   cupcake shop   €€, AIC
Via Paisiello, 7   tel. 2.29401244
www.facebook.com/pasticceria.navotti.senzaglutine

Peperino Pizza & Grill   pizzeria   €€€, AIC
Viale F. Crispi, 1   tel. 0263793078   www.peperinopizza.it
Notes: Moscova.

Petit Paradis   pizzeria   €€, AIC
Via Fezzan, 3   tel. 2.471378   www.ristorantepetitparadis.com
Notes: Washington.

Rigolo   restaurant   €€€€, AIC
Via Solferino, 11 ang. L.go Treves   tel. 02804589   www.rigolo.it
Notes: Moscova.

Splendini & Co.   bakery   €, AIC
Via Pietro Custodi, 1   tel. 2.87066449   www.splendini.it
Notes: 100% gluten-free.

Trattoria Casa Fontana 23 Risotti restaurant   €€, AIC
P.zza Carbonari, 5   tel. 026704710   www.23risotti.it
Notes: Garibaldi. Closed Saturdays at lunch and Mondays.

THE REST OF LOMBARDIA
ABBIATEGRASSO
Riti e Conviti   restaurant, pizzeria   €€-€€€, AIC
Galleria Mirabello, 10   tel. 2.945247   www.ritieconviti.com

AGNOSINE
Da Nicola   restaurant, pizzeria   €, AIC
Via G. Marconi, 94   tel. 03065896145

ALBESE CON CASSANO
Al Pesce Vela   pizzeria   €, AIC
Via Nazionale, 132   tel. 031426129   www.pescevela.it
Notes: DS pizza point. Closed Mondays.

ALBINO
Az. Agrituristica Monte Cura agritourism   €€-€€€, AIC
Via Monte Cura, 6   tel. 035754745   www.montecura.it
Notes: Closed Monday-Thursday.

APRICA
Magie di zucchero   bakery   €-€€, AIC
Via Valtellina, 24   tel. 392.8383207

Stambèch   pizzeria   €, AIC
C.so Roma, 77   tel. 340.1642782

ASSAGO
Autogrill Carrefour Assago2   autogrill   €, AIC
Viale Milanofiori   tel. 2.57701953

Autogrill Forum Palazzetto dello Sport autogrill   €, AIC
Via G. Di Vittorio   tel. 2.45709966

AZZANO S. PAOLO
Artigel   gelato (€, AIC)   Via Cremasca, 34

BAGNATICA
Pizzeria al 18   pizzeria   €, AIC
Via Papa Giovanni XXIII   tel. 035680406   www.pizzeriaal18.com

BARZIO
Rifugio Campelli   restaurant, B&B   €, AIC
Loc. Piani di Bobbio s.n.   tel. 0314910576   www.baiadipare.it

BELLAGIO
Salice Blu   restaurant   €€€€, AIC
Via per Lecco, 33   tel. 031950535   www.ristorante-saliceblu-bellagio.it

BELLANO
Villa Anita   B&B   AIC
Strada Nuova per Oro, 11   tel. 0341820225   www.villanita.lc.it

BERGAMO
Albergo 900   pizzeria   €, AIC
Via Statuto, 23   tel. 035255210

Bombyx Inn   B&B   AIC
Via Lunga, 42   tel. 35.322786   www.bombyxbed.com

| Byron | pizzeria | €, AIC |
| Via Palma il Vecchio, 33 | tel. 035233477 | |

| Casa Chiara | B&B | AIC |
| Via A. Balestra, 8 | tel. 035257733 | www.casachiarabeb.it/bed-breakfast |

| Charlot | restaurant, pizzeria | €€€€, AIC |
| Via A. Fantoni, 4 | tel. 35.213544 | www.ristorantebernabo.it/it/index.asp |

| Grom | gelato | €, AIC |
| V.le Papa Giovanni XXIII, 60 | www.grom.it | |

| Le 5 Vie | B&B | AIC |
| P.zza Pontida, 14 | tel. 035240141 | www.le5viebb.com |

| Osteria Risico | restaurant | €€, AIC |
| Via Nullo, 7/a | tel. 340.8923518 | www.osteriarisico.it |

BIASSONO

| L'Officina dei Sapori | restaurant | €€€€, AIC |
| P.zza S. Francesco, 242 | tel. 0392754029 | www.lofficinadeisapori.com |

BINASCO

Hosteria della Pignatta	restaurant	€€€, AIC
Largo Loriga, 5	tel. 029054046	
Notes: Closed Sundays.		

BOCCASERIO DI MONTODINE

| La Palazzina | trattoria | €€, AIC |
| S.P. Crema- Codogno, 591 | tel. 373.667301 | www.trattorialapalazzina.it |

BORGHETTO LODIGIANO

La Locanda dei Sapori	restaurant, pizzeria	€€€-€€€€, AIC
Via XXV Aprile, 3	tel. 037180588	
Notes: Closed Mondays.		

BORMIO

Rifugio Garibaldi	restaurant, hotel	€€€, AIC
Località Passo dello Stelvio	tel. 342.904312	
www.facebook.com/rifugio.garibaldialladamello		

BOVEZZO

| Al Pescatore | restaurant/pizzeria | €€, AIC |
| Via dei Prati, 19 | tel. 0302711390 | www.hotelimpero.it |

BRESCIA

| Al Serbatoio | restaurant, pizzeria | €€-€€€, AIC |
| Via G. Galilei, 4 | tel. 30.38151 | www.ristorantealserbatoio.com |

| Alergo | bakery | €, AIC |
| Via Diaz, 30 | tel. 30.5236299 | www.alergo.it |

| Bierhaus | pizzeria | €, AIC |
| Via Triumplina, 103 | tel. 0302005500 | |

| Castello Malvezzi | restaurant | €€€€, AIC |
| Via Colle S.Giuseppe,1 | tel. 0302004224 | www.castellomalvezzi.it |

| Cormorano | pizzeria | €, AIC |
| Via Salodini, 2 | tel. 30.394504 | www.misterimprese.it |

| Da Nicola | restaurant, pizzeria | €€-€€€, AIC |
| via Duca degli Abruzzi, 27 | tel. 0302425015 | |

Gluten-Free Italy by Region

Gentileria	gelato, bar	€, AIC
Via Levi Sandri, 3	tel. 339.5442535	www.facebook.com/la.gentileria

I Silvani	restaurant, pizzeria	€, AIC
Via Triumplina, 86	tel. 0302040008	

Il Piacere restaurant, pizzeria €€, AIC
Viale Piave, 53 tel. 030362082
www.pizzaleggera.it/brescia/pizzeria.html

Il Vicolo Corto restaurant, pizzeria €€-€€€, AIC
Vicolo S. Agostino, 3 tel. 30.2808264 www.facebook.com/IlVicoloCorto

Impero hotel, restaurant, pizzeria €-€€€, AIC
Via Triumplina, 8 tel. 030381483

La Duchessa restaurant, pizzeria €-€€, AIC
Via Montello, 28/c tel. 0303384814

Mamey Cafè bar, tavola calda €, AIC
Via Casazza, 5 tel. 30.2092315 www.mamey.it

Mangiarè pizzeria €, AIC
Via Valle Camonica, 16 tel. 0303735869 www.mangiare.brescia.it

Mille Gusti bakery, bar €, AIC
Via Lamarmora, 256 tel. 331.4384968

Novotel Brescia/Novotelcafé hotel, restaurant €€€-€€€€, AIC
Via Montello, 28/c tel. 0302286811 www.novotel.com

Osteria Molin del Brolo osteria €€€, AIC
Via Cadorna, 14 tel. 0303757507 www.molindelbrolo.it

Possi Gelatieri gelato (€-€€, AIC) Via Triumplina, 245

BUCCINASCO
Baia Blu pizzeria €, AIC
Via della Resistenza, 15/a tel. 2.48843729 www.ristorantebuccinasco.it

Mamey Cafè tavola calda, bar €, AIC
Via Resistenza, 121 tel. 2.45716212 www.mamey.it

BURAGO DI MOLGORA
Brianteo Hotel and Restaurant hotel, restaurant €€€, AIC
Via Martin Luther King, 3/5 tel. 0396080436 www.brianteo.it

BUSTO ARSIZIO
Limin Chinese restaurant €-€€, AIC
Viale Borri, 32 tel. 331.63919 www.limin.it

CADREZZATE
Miralago restaurant, pizzeria bar €€, AIC
Via Mogno, 441 tel. 0331953284 www.miralagoweb.com

CALUSCO D'ADDA
Pizza Leggera Calusco pizzeria €, AIC
Via Marconi, 1459 tel. 35.791852 www.calusco.pizzaleggera.it

CALVAGESE DELLA RIVIERA
L'Oasi del Chiese pizzeria €, AIC
Via Basse Sopra, 1 tel. 0306000060

9 Muse
Via G. Bruno, 42/a

Le Vigne
Via Vergani, 21
Notes: Closed Wednesdays.

Pizzeria Vecchia Napoli
via Fossano, 18

Rossopeper oncino
via Como, 23

Gelatando

LeoBar
via Vittorio Veneto, 52

Agriturismo Villa Serica
Via Ombria, 2/a

Ristorante Il Ritrovo
Via U. Bassi, 1 bis

Giardino
C.ne Papa G.ni Paolo II, 24

Tourlè Pizza Club
p/le Miglio sn

Novotel Malpensa/Novotelcafè
Via al Campo

Il Giaguaro
Via Bergamo, 444

La Vecchia Ruota
via R. Paladini, 18

Orlandi Pasticceria
Piazza Mira, 3

Da Grillo
Via Galvani,15

Il Dolce Sogno

Il Marchese del Grillo
Via Galvani,15

CANNETO SULL'OGLIO
B&B   AIC
tel. 03358007601   www.9muse.it
CANTÙ
restaurant, pizzeria   €, AIC
tel. 031711088

pizzeria   €, AIC
tel. 31.701256

pizzeria   €, AIC
tel. 31.7073925   www.rossopeperoncino.org

CAPRIANO DEL COLLE
gelato (€, AIC)   Via Martiri Piazza Loggia, 2/4

CAPRIATE SAN GERVASIO
tavola calda, bar   €, AIC
tel. 2.9090169

CAPRINO BERGAMASCO
agritourism   AIC
tel. 339.3818967   www.villaserica.it

CARATE BRIANZA
restaurant   €€€€, AIC
tel. 0362902287   www.osteriadelritrovo.it

CARAVAGGIO
restaurant   €-€€€, AIC
tel. 036350581   www.giardinoristorante.it
CARBONATE
pizzeria   €-€€, AIC
tel. 345.1394803   www.tourle.it

CARDANO AL CAMPO
hotel, restaurant   €€-€€€, AIC
tel. 0331266611   www.novotel.com

CARONNO PERTUSELLA
pizzeria, restaurant   €€, AIC
tel. 029650380   www.ilgiaguaro.com

CASIRATE D'ADDA
pizzeria   €, AIC
tel. 036387200

CASORATE PRIMO
bakery   €, AIC
tel. 2.9056384   www.orlandipasticceria.com

CASSANO MAGNAGO
restaurant   €€-€€€, AIC
tel. 0331206830   www.ristgrillo.it

gelato (€, AIC)   Via Nenni, 7

restaurant   AIC
tel. 331.20683   www.marchesedelgrillo.com/Ristorante

CASTANO PRIMO

A Modo Mio c/o C.C.le Castano
Via Adua ang. S.P. 34
restaurant
tel. 0331882797
AIC
www.amodomio.it

CASTEL D'ARIO

Trattoria Castello
Via di là dell'acqua, 8
restaurant
tel. 376.661565
AIC

CASTEL GOFFREDO

La Rotonda
Via Principe Amedeo, 2
pizzeria
tel. 0376770738
€, AIC

CASTELLANZA

Il Dolce Sogno
gelato (€, AIC)
Via Don Minzoni, 45

CASTIGLIONE OLONA

Elisir
Via C. Battisti, 3
pizzeria
tel. 0331824954
€, AIC

CASTIONE ANDEVENNO

Sisti
Via Margella, 41
restaurant, pizzeria
tel. 0342358310
€€, AIC
www.sisti1891.it

CAVA MANARA

Il Büus del Rat
Via Garibaldi, 88
pizzeria
tel. 0382554997
€, AIC
www.ilbuusdelrat.it

CAVARIA

The King
via IV Novembre, 402
pizzeria
tel. 331.735949
€€€, AIC
www.pizzeriatheking.it

CAZZAGO SAN MARTINO

Il Braciere
Via Rizzini, 38
restaurant
tel. 30.7254778   www.ristoranteilbraciere.net/home.html
€€, AIC

CERMENATE

L'Alambicco
Via Cavour, 13
pizzeria
tel. 31.774217   www.facebook.com/lalambicco.cermenate
€€, AIC

CERNUSCO LOMBARDONE

I Gelsi
Via S. Dionigi, 11
agritourism
tel. 39.990279
AIC
www.igelsi.com

CESANO BOSCONE

Le Betulle
Via delle Betulle, 11
pizzeria
tel. 2.4580282
€€, AIC
www.ristorantelebetulle.com

CESANO MADERNO

No Stop Il Giropizza
Via San Carlo Borromeo, 121
pizzeria
tel. 362.54199
€€, AIC
www.nostopilgiropizza.it

CHIESA IN VALMALENCO

Tremoggia
Via Bernina, 4
hotel
tel. 0342451106
€€€€, AIC

CINISELLO BALSAMO

A Modo Mio
Via De Amicis
restaurant
tel. 2.6125776
€€€, AIC
www.amodomio.it

Liberi dal glutine
Via XXV Aprile, 142
sandwich shop, bakery
tel. 2.61298704
€, AIC
www.liberidalglutine.com

Artigiana Gelati

CLUSONE
gelato (€, AIC)   P.za Uccelli, 22

CODOGNO
Park Club
P.zza Cairoli, 26
restaurant, pizzeria   €, AIC
tel. 037735153   www.parkclub.com

COLOGNO AL SERIO
Corona
Via Antonio Locatelli, 74
pizzeria   €-€€€€, AIC
tel. 035896104

COMERIO
Ristorante Movida
Via Garibaldi, 3
restaurant   €€€-€€€€, AIC
tel. 0332743240   www.ristorantemovida.it

COMO
Cremeria Bolla
gelato (€, AIC)   Via Boldoni, 6

In Centro
Via Cesare Cantù, 53
pizzeria   €€, AIC
tel. 31.272692   www.pizzeriaincentro.com

L'Antica Trattoria
Via Cadorna, 26
restaurant   €€€€, AIC
tel. 031242777

Locanda dell'Oca Bianca
Via Cadorna, 26
inn, restaurant   €€€€, AIC
tel. 031025605   www.hotelocabianca.it

Osteria L'Angolo del Silenzio
V.le Lecco, 25
restaurant   €€-€€€€, AIC
tel. 0313372157

CONCESIO
Al Grillo
Via Bevilacqua, 13
restaurant, pizzeria   €-€€€, AIC
tel. 0302751408

CONCOREZZO
La Camilla
Via Dante, 267
agritourism   €€€€, AIC
tel. 039647289   www.lacamilla.it

CORSICO
Pomodoro & Basilico
Viale Italia, 31
pizzeria   €€€, AIC
tel. 2.4511948   www.pomodoroebasilico.com

CREMA
Cascina Loghetto
Via Milano, 4
agritourism   €€-€€€, AIC
tel. 0373230209   www.cascinaloghetto.it

Ice Cream
gelato (€, AIC)   P.zza Giovanni XXIII, 26

CREMONA
Dordoni
Via Del Sale, 58
restaurant, pizzeria   €€€€, AIC
tel. 037222703

Grom
gelato (€, AIC)   C.so Campi, 1 corner of via Cavour

CUASSO AL MONTE
Al Vecchio Faggio
Via Garibaldi, 8
trattoria   €€€€, AIC
tel. 0332938040

CURTATONE
A Modo Mio
Via Gen. Lauger
restaurant   €, AIC
tel. 0376348065   www.amodomio.it

DALMINE
Bobadilla Feeling Club
Via Pascolo, 34
restaurant   €€€€, AIC
tel. 035561575

A Modo Mio
Via Dell'Industria, 1

DAVERIO
restaurant
tel. 0332947159

€, AIC
www.amodomio.it

Rose e Sapori
Lungo Lago C.Battisti, 89

DESENZANO DEL GARDA
restaurant
tel. 0309144585

€€€€, AIC
www.roseesapori.eu

Bar Gelateria I Delfini

DESIO
gelato (€, AIC)

Largo Primo Levi, 4

Charleston
Via Milano, 189

restaurant, pizzeria
tel. 362.62708

€€, AIC
www.ristorante-charleston.it

La Taverna
Via Tripoli, 28

restaurant, pizzeria
tel. 0362303329

AIC

Autogrill Dorno

DORNO
autogrill (€, AIC)

A7 Milano - Serravalle

Acqua, Farina e Brace
V.le Lecco, 25

ERBA
pizzeria
tel. 031610878

€, AIC

Tourlè Erba
via Cascina California, 2

pizzeria
tel. 348.9622384

€, AIC
www.tourle.it

La Corte dei Sapori
Via Cesare Battisti, 55

FAGNANO OLONA
restaurant
tel. 331.619076

€€€, AIC
www.lacortedeisapori.it

Borgonuovo
Via Volta, 3

FALOPPIO
restaurant, pizzeria
tel. 31.986163

€€-€€€€, AIC
www.ristoranteborgonuovo.com

FERNO
Mychef Aeroporto Malpensa Terminal 1 mychef

€, AIC

I Fontanili
Via Assisi, 103

GALLARATE
pizzeria
tel. 0331772516

€, AIC

La Locanda Nord Est
Via Varese, 34

restaurant/pizzeria
tel. 0331248355

€€, AIC

GAMBOLÒ
Regina Margherita
C.so Vittorio Emanuele II, 52/b

pizzeria
tel. 0381939554

€, AIC
www.pizzeriareginamargheritagambolo.it

El Mamacita
Via A. Gosa, 164/f

GAVARDO
restaurant, pizzeria
tel. 036534275

€-€€, AIC

Giocabosco Parco Didattico
Via del Colle, 21
Notes: Funpark for kids.

tavola calda
tel. 339.5631539

€, AIC
www.giocabosco.it

Trattoria alle Trote
Via Bariaga, 24

restaurant/trattoria
tel. 036531294

€€€€, AIC

Vecchio Ottocento
Viale Ticino, 33

GAVIRATE
restaurant, pizzeria
tel. 0332735693

AIC

L'Angelato

GERENZANO
gelato (€, AIC)

Via C. Berra, 8

Albergo Pineta
Piana di Fenile, 5

GEROLA ALTA
inn, restaurant
tel. 03426901809

€€€, AIC

All'Angolo
Via Fornacette, 27

GRASSOBBIO
restaurant, pizzeria
tel. 0354522111

€-€€€€, AIC

Paradiso
Via Rovaschiera, 48/c

GROSIO
B&B
tel. 03409655279

AIC
www.bbparadiso.it

Garni Le Corti
Via Patrioti, 73

GROSOTTO
B&B
tel. 342.848624

AIC
www.garnilecorti.it

GRUMELLO CREMONESE
Locanda San Martino
Str. Prov.le 47 - Cascina S. Martino, 1
Notes: Closed Monday-Thursday.

agritourism
tel. 03472878756

€€-€€€, AIC

Osteria dell'Angelo
Via Fontana, 25

GUSSAGO
restaurant
tel. 0302770139

€€€€, AIC
www.osteriadellangelo.it

Da Arrigo
Via Trento, 39

IDRO
inn, restaurant, pizzeria
tel. 0365823371

€, AIC
www.daarrigoristorante.it

Mama's Pizza
Via Roma II

ISEO
pizzeria
tel. 0309822247

€, AIC

Il Mare Mosso
Via Vittorio Veneto, 15
Notes: Italian-Chinese restaurant with GF pizza too.

LACCHIARELLA
restaurant, pizzeria
tel. 2.90076673

€€, AIC
www.pizzeriamaremosso.it

Latenasca
Via Mengato, 11

LAINATE
osteria
tel. 0293780995

€-€€, AIC
www.latenasca.it

Al Rustico da Luisa e Marco
Via S. Carlo, 3

LAMBRUGO
restaurant
tel. 031608125

€€€€, AIC
www.ristorantealrustico.it

Grom

LECCO
gelato (€, AIC)

P.zza XX Settembre

Ricky e Alex

gelato (€, AIC)

Via Bovara, 15

Gambero Rosso
Via per Busto Arsizio, 37

LEGNANO
restaurant
tel. 0331450519

€, AIC

Oasi
Via Viganovo, 47

LENO
restaurant, pizzeria
tel. 0309067105

AIC
www.oasileno.it

Trattoria al Murun
Piazza S. Vito, 22

LENTATE SUL SEVESO
trattoria
tel. 0362566034

€, AIC
www.almurun.it

Gasoline Road Bar
Via Grandi, 5

LISCATE
restaurant, pizzeria
tel. 029587740

AIC
www.gasolinemilano.it

Hotel Nevada
Via Saroch, 35

LIVIGNO
hotel, restaurant, pizzeria
tel. 0342996551

€€, AIC
www.hnevada.it

La Corte del Moro
Via Vigentina, 8

LOCATE TRIULZI
restaurant, pizzeria
tel. 2.90428177

AIC
www.ristorantelacortedelmoro.com

Agripizza
Via Ada Negri, 20

LODI
pizzeria
tel. 0371417017

€, AIC
www.agripizzaitalia.eu

Calicantus Food
Viale Agnelli, 27

pizzeria
tel. 0371772043

€, AIC
www.calicantuscafe.com

Isola Caprera
Via Isola Caprera,14

restaurant
tel. 0371421316

€€€-€€€€, AIC

Artigiana Gelati

LOVERE
gelato (€, AIC)

Via Gregorini, 15

Barboglio
Via Marconi, 95

bar-cafe
tel. 035964571

€, AIC

Le Terrazze
P.le Marconi, 4

restaurant, pizzeria, bar
tel. 035983533

€€€, AIC
www.ilristoranteleterrazze.it

Sampei
Via Madre Lucia Seneci, 26

LUMEZZANE
pizzeria
tel. 0308925772

€, AIC

Il Pane di Anna
C.na Ciocchino Strada per Trenzano

MACLODIO
sandwich shop, bakery
tel. 30.9780014

€, AIC
www.ilpanedianna.it

Grotta Azzurra
Via Roma, 23

MAGHERNO
restaurant, pizzeria
tel. 0382966959

€, AIC

Osteria degli Angeli
Via Brusa, 5

MALNATE
restaurant
tel. 0332427614

€€€-€€€€, AIC
www.osteriadegliangeli.net

King's Pizza
Via Vallesabbia, 145

MALONNO
pizzeria
tel. 0364635048

€, AIC

Regina Major
Via Vallesabbia, 145
Notes: Closed Tuesdays.

Alla Nuova Marasca
P.zza L.B. Alberti, 19/20

Grom

Dolci Tentazioni
Via Matteotti, 9/e

Mastro Marco
Lungolago Marconi, 1

Top 2000
Via Bardellina, 63

I Girasoli Cafè
Galleria Gandhi, 6

Fattoria Laghetto
Via Laghetto, 2

Dal Dosso Sala Mensa
Via Romero Mons. Oscar, 69

La Margherita
Via Santa Margherita, 6

Burger Club
Via Mentana, 24

L'Oasi del Celiaco
via Pavoni, 9/C

Bella Europa
Via Europa, 33/a

Marabù
Via Brescia, 179

Al Mulino
Via Al Molino, 18

Lo Sfizio
Via Milano, 11

MANERBIO
restaurant, pizzeria
tel. 0309380709 — €-€€, AIC — www.reginamajor.it

MANTOVA
trattoria
tel. 0376322620 — €€€€, AIC — www.nuovamarasca.it

gelato (€, AIC) — Via Paolo Sarpi, 2

MARIANO COMENSE
gelato, bakery — €, AIC
tel. 339.7346505 — www.dolcitentazionisenzaglutine.it

MARONE
restaurant, pizzeria
tel. 30.9877885 — €€€€, AIC — www.mastromarco.eu

MARTIGNANAPO
pizzeria — AIC
tel. 375.260121

MAZZO DI RHO
bar — €, AIC
tel. 2.93900552 — www.girasolicafe.altervista.org

MERATE
agritourism
tel. 399902283 — €€€-€€€€, AIC — www.fattorialaghetto.com

MONTICHIARI
restaurant
tel. 030961025 — €€€-€€€€, AIC — www.daldossosalamensa.com

restaurant, pizzeria
tel. 348.9115151 — €-€€€€, AIC — www.misterimprese.it

MONZA
bakery
tel. 39.2020129 — €€, AIC — www.burgerclub.it

tavola calda, grocery store — €, AIC
tel. 39.9634374 — www.oasidelceliaco.it

MUGGIÒ
pizzeria — €, AIC
tel. 39.792892 — www.ristorantebellaeuropa.com

NAVE
pizzeria — €, AIC
tel. 30.2531563

NUVOLENTO
B&B — AIC
tel. 338.9736532 — www.bebalmulino.it

OGGIONO
pizzeria, bar — €€, AIC
tel. 341.579557

Near Bellagio (D.Kraushaar)

OLGIATE OLONA

Giuseppe Verdi   restaurant, pizzeria   €-€€, AIC
Via Piave, 1   tel. 0331642129

OLGINATE

La Locanda   restaurant, pizzeria   €-€€€€, AIC
Via S. Maria La Vite, 16   tel. 0341650506   www.ristorantelalocanda.com

OSIO SOPRA

Autogrill Brembo   autogrill (€, AIC)   A4 Milano - Brescia

OSTIGLIA

Maison del Celiaco   bakery, sandwich shop   €
Via Abetone Brennero 56   www.maisondelceliaco.it

PALESTRO

Vecchio Mulino   restaurant   €€€, AIC
Via Umberto I, 99   tel. 384677105

PAVIA

Locanda del Carmine   restaurant   €€€-€€€€, AIC
P.zza del Carmine, 7/A   tel. 038229647

Pizza Leggera Pavia   pizzeria   €, AIC
Via Brambilla, 70/f   tel. 0382527429   www.pavia.pizzaleggera.it

Vecchia Pavia   trattoria, pizzeria   €, AIC
Via Mantovani, 3   tel. 038227178   www.vecchiapavia.it

PEGOGNAGA

Ca' Rossa   B&B   AIC
Str.Prov.le Est, 6   tel. 0376559072

La Pastizzeria
Via Vittorio Veneto, 93

PEREGO
bakery   €, AIC
tel. 39.570325

Dadaumpa
Via S. Francesco, 33

PIOLTELLO
restaurant, pizzeria   AIC
tel. 0292590342

Baobab Lounge Cafè Pizzeria
Piazza Mercato, 7

PISOGNE
pizzeria   €, AIC
tel. 364880117   www.ristorantecucupizzeriabaobab.it

Il Cucu Osteria
P.zza Corna Pellegrini, 12/b

restaurant   €€€€, AIC
tel. 036486288

Il Poggio
Via Panoramica, 4

POGGI RIDENTI
restaurant   €€€€, AIC
tel. 0342380800

Pasticceria Alessandro
Via Pontesecco, 26

PONTERANICA
bakery   €, AIC
tel. 35.572167   www.pasticceriaalessandro.com

B&B La Marinella
Via Osteno, 29

PORLEZZA
B&B   AIC
tel. 344.72298   www.bblamarinella.com

Darna
via Osteno, 50

pizzeria   €, AIC
tel. 3334064833   www.darna.it

Brother and Sister
Via Milano, 55

POZZO D'ADDA
pizzeria   €, AIC
tel. 0290960850   www.barpizzeria.net

L'Altra Oasi
Via Garibaldi, 36

PRALBOINO
pizzeria   €, AIC
tel. 030954259

Due Lune
Via Al Palazzo, 6

PRATA CAMPORTACCIO
restaurant, pizzeria   €, AIC
tel. 034320633

Black Horse
Via Vittorio Veneto, 279

PRESEZZO
restaurant, pizzeria   €€, AIC
tel. 35.610247   www.blackhorsebg.it

Trattoria Al Fondaco
Via Padovani, 6

QUINZANO D'OGLIO
trattoria   AIC
tel. 30.992423   www.alfondaco.com

San Gottardo
via S. Gottardo, 23

RASA DI VARESE
pizzeria   €, AIC
tel. 0332224189 www.ristorantepizzeriasangottardo.it

Trattoria Da Vira
Via Bossi, 33

RESCALDINA
trattoria   AIC
tel. 331.465794

RHO

Autogrill Ristorante Bistrot Milano SS. del Sempione, 28   Fieramilano   €, AIC

Dal Fluminese	restaurant	€€€€, AIC
Via Lura, 24	tel. 0293504592	www.dalfluminese.com

Notes: Closed Tuesdays.

Pomerol	restaurant/wine bar	€€€€, AIC
Via Pomè, 3	tel. 029311019	www.pomerol.it

Trattoria Dodici Volte	restaurant	€€€-€€€€, AIC
Via Larga, 24	tel. 0293900460	

Trattoria La Barca	restaurant	€€€€, AIC
Via Achille Ratti, 54	tel. 029303976	www.trattorialabarca.it

RIVOLTELLA DEL GARDA

Le Caravelle	restaurant, pizzeria	€, AIC
Via Papa Giovanni XXIII, 69	tel. 0309110198	

RODIGO

Agriturismo Corte Canova	B&B	AIC
Strada Camignana, 5	tel. 03383932112	www.cortecanova.it

Corte Catenaccio	restaurant, pizzeria	€, AIC
Strada Francesca Est, 109/B 1	tel. 0376681003	

RONCARO

Il Sorriso	restaurant, pizzeria	€€, AIC
Via Dell'Aia, 11	tel. 038294257	www.ristoranteilsorriso.it

SALA COMACINA

La Comacina	restaurant	€€€, AIC
Via Statale, 14	tel. 344.55035	www.ristorantelacomacina.it

SALICE TERME

Pizza Leggera Salice Terme	pizzeria	€, AIC
Via delle Terme, 129	tel. 038392753	www.salice.pizzaleggera.it

SALÒ

Antica Cascina San Zago	restaurant	€€€, AIC
Via dei Colli, 13	tel. 036542754	www.anticacascinasanzago.it

Il Lucaniere	restaurant, pizzeria	€€€, AIC
Via Bortollo Pollini	tel. 365.521185	www.illucaniere.com

Pijei Osteria& Vineria	restaurant, wine bar	€€, AIC
Via Europa, 9	tel. 365.42111	

www.facebook.com/pages/Osteria-PJ/210402645713014

PJ	osteria	€€€, AIC
Via Valle, 1	tel. 03654211	

SAN DAMIANO AL COLLE

Trattoria Fugazza	trattoria	€€€€, AIC
Frazione Boffalora, 11	tel. 385.75183	www.latrattoriafugazza.it

SAN MARTINO IN STRADA

Witch Pub	restaurant, pizzeria	AIC
Via Vittorio Emanuele II 53	tel. 0371476078	

SAN PELLEGRINO TERME

Orizzonte
Via Vittorio Veneto, 8
restaurant, pizzeria
tel. 345.23116
€€-€€€€, AIC

SAN ZENO NAVIGLIO

La Rocchetta
Via Volta, 23/c
pizzeria
tel. 30.3546623
€€, AIC

SAREZZO

Ciar de Luna
Via Cimabue, 1
restaurant, pizzeria
tel. 0308901491
€-€€, AIC

SCHIGNANO

La Zoca di Strii
Via S. Maria, 13
agritourism
tel. 031819721
€€€, AIC
www.lazocadistrii.it

SEDRINA

B&B da Isa
Via Roma, 87/a
B&B
tel. 345.6112
AIC
www.bed-and-breakfast.it

La Lanterna
Via Roma, 85
restaurant, pizzeria
tel. 345.6112
AIC
www.lalanternasedrina.it

SEGRATE

Biolunch
Via C. Battisti, 51
pizzeria
tel. 0226928155
€ - €€, AIC

Velò
gelato, bar (€ - €€, AIC)
Via Pacini, 20

SIRMIONE

Hotel du Lac
Via XXV Aprile, 60
hotel
tel. 030916026
€€, AIC

Hotel Riel Ristorante Pizzeria Al Braciere hotel, restaurant
Via San Martino, 2
tel. 0309905561
€€-€€€, AIC
www.hotelriel.it

La Paul
Via XXV Aprile, 26
hotel, restaurant, pizzeria
tel. 030916077
€-€€, AIC
www.hotelapaul.it

Lisca
Via Brescia, 41
pizzeria
tel. 30.9904191
€€, AIC
www.ristorantisirmione.com/lisca

Mauro
Via Lazzarini, 25
hotel
tel. 030919031
€€, AIC

SOAVE DI PORTO MANTOVANO

Corte Casone
Strada Soana 17/a
B&B
tel. 0376300545
AIC

SOLFERINO

La Speranza
Via S. Martino, 6
trattoria
tel. 0376854191
€€€, AIC
www.la-speranza.it

SOMMA LOMBARDO

Desiree
via Bellini, 14/C
pizzeria
tel. 331251400
€€€, AIC
www.desiree.va.it

Mychef Aeroporto Malpensa Terminal 2 mychef
€, AIC

SOMMALO MBARDO

Autogrill Milano Malpensa 2000 autogrill (€, AIC)   Aeroporto Malpensa Terminal 1

SORICO

Il Beccaccino
Via Boschetto, 49
restaurant
tel. 034484241
€€€€, AIC
www.beccaccino.it

SOTTO IL MONTE GIOVANNI XXIII

La Taverna
Via Roncalli, 18
restaurant, pizzeria
tel. 035799599
€€€, AIC

STOCCHETTA

Risorgimento
Via Triumplina, 238
restaurant, pizzeria
tel. 0302008304
AIC

SULBIATE SUPERIORE

Agrit. Fondo Brugarolo
Via Manzoni, 15
agritourism
tel. 039623735
€€€, AIC
www.fondobrugarolo.it

TELGATE

Il Leone D'Oro
Via Roncalli, 18
hotel, restaurant, pizzeria
tel. 0354420803
€-€€€€, AIC
www.hotelleonedoro.it

TIGNALE

Al Torchio
Via Triumplina, 238
restaurant, pizzeria
tel. 0365760296
AIC
www.altorchiotignale.it

Apollo XI
Via Badiale, 4
restaurant, pizzeria
tel. 0365760293
€-€€, AIC

TIRANO

Vineria
Via XX Settembre, 25
restaurant
tel. 0342702116
€€, AIC
www.vineriatirano.com

TORRICELLA VERZATE

Più e Più
Piazzale Oltrepo, 1
restaurant, pizzeria
tel. 0383876327
€, AIC

TOSCOLANO MADERNO

Villa dei Roccoli
Via Sanico, 11
restaurant
tel. 0365541592
€€€-€€€€, AIC
www.ristorantevilladeiroccoli.com

TREZZO SULL'ADDA

Le Cave del Ceppo
Via Val Porto, 28
agritourism
tel. 2.90962295
AIC
www.lecavedelceppo.it

TROMELLO

Il Boss delle Balze
S.S. per Mortara, 21
pizzeria
tel. 038286401
€, AIC

URGNANO

La Rocca
Via Battisti, 132
pizzeria
tel. 35.892838
€, AIC
www.facebook.com/pages/Pizzeria-la-Rocca/177027599023362

VALMADRERA

Bar Baia
Via Parè, 29/a
pizzeria
tel. 341.207156
€, AIC
www.baiadipare.it

VANZAGO

Bigatt
Via S. Giovanni Bosco, 7
B&B
tel. 0240709422
AIC
www.bigatt.com

Al Vecchio Convento Via Montello, 8	**VARESE** restaurant tel. 0332261005	€€€€, AIC
Dolci Brividi	gelato (€, AIC)	C.so Matteotti, 2
Grom	gelato (€, AIC)	Piazza Montegrapp a, 13
La Vecchia Varese Via Ravasi, 37	restaurant tel. 332.287104	€, AIC www.lavecchiavarese.it
Montello Via Montello, 8	restaurant tel. 0332286181	€€€-€€€€, AIC
Osteria Caffè di Villa Giavazzi Via Don Giavazzi, 6	**VERDELLO** restaurant, bar tel. 35.4191159	€€-€€€, AIC www.villagiavazzi.it
A Modo Mio S.S. dei Giovi	**VERTEMATE** restaurant tel. 31.887349	€€, AIC www.amodomio.it
Al Salice Via Giovanni XXIII, 16	pizzeria tel. 31.90035	€€-€€€, AIC www.alsalice.com
Trattoria San Sebastiano Via per Rogorbello, 19	**VERVIO** restaurant, trattoria tel. 348.7147595	AIC
Casa del Parco dell'Adamello Via Nazionale, 132	**VEZZA D'OGLIO** hotel, restaurant tel. 036476165	€, AIC
Agorà Via Sacchetti, 1	**VIGEVANO** restaurant, pizzeria tel. 038184384	€, AIC
Fantasy V.le Commercio, 318	restaurant, pizzeria tel. 0381346650	€, AIC www.pizzeriafantasy.com
Geko Cafè C.so Torino, 299	restaurant, pizzeria tel. 381.329903	€€, AIC www.gekocafe.com
Primavera C.so Torino, 48	restaurant, pizzeria tel. 0381326415	€, AIC
Primavera Express Via Buozzi, 31	pizzeria tel. 038178464	€, AIC www.primaveraexpress.it
Le Coccinelle Via M. D'Azeglio, 5	**VILLA CORTESE** pizzeria tel. 0331430043	€, AIC
Agriturismo Belotti Via C. Battisti, 11	**VILLA DALEGNO DI TEMÙ** agritourism tel. 364.9185	€€, AIC www.agriturismobelotti.it
Al Ponte Via Nazionale, 63	**VILLA DI TIRANO** restaurant, pizzeria tel. 0342795703	€€, AIC
Stazzona Via Giambonelli, 10 fraz. Stazzona	B&B tel. 0342795538	AIC www.agristazzona.com

Il Veliero
Via Roma Nord, 290

VILLA POMA
restaurant/pizzeria   € - €€, AIC
www.ristoranteveliero.net

La Sosta
V.le Brescia, 32

VILLANUOVA SUL CLISI
restaurant/pizzeria   €, AIC
tel. 0365374412

A Modo Mio
Via Tiziano Vecellio

VILLASANTA
restaurant   €, AIC
tel. 0392051369   www.amodomio.it

Le Tatin
Via Garibaldi, 40

bakery, sandwich shop   €, AIC
tel. 366.3198387   www.letatin.com

A Modo Mio Steak House
Via Torri Bianche, 16

VIMERCATE
restaurant   €€, AIC
tel. 39.6084662   www.amodomio.it

Pomodoro & Basilico
Via Burago, 28

restaurant, pizzeria   €€-€€€€, AIC
tel. 39.6614109   www.pomodoroebasilico.com

La Voglia Matta
P.zza della Repubblica, 14

ZANICA
pizzeria   €€, AIC
tel. 35.672058   www.pizzerialavogliamatta.it

Da Tonino
Via Pollini, 135

ZINASCO NUOVO
pizzeria   €, AIC
tel. 0382915110

GENOA, LIGURIA
AND THE ITALIAN RIVIERA

PLACES IN GENOA TO BUY GLUTEN-FREE FOOD PRODUCTS

Conad
Via Gaspare Murtola, 12
Via Giovanni Trossarelli, 1

Coop Liguria   Corso Aldo Gastaldi

Ipercoop   Via Romairone 10

Pam
Via Manuzio 11
Via Don Giovanni Verità 6/R
Via Lagaccio 48/R

PLACES IN GENOA TO GET GUARANTEED GLUTEN-FREE GELATO
(SPONSORED BY ITALIAN CELIAC SOCIETY)

Caffè Balilla   Via Cesarea, 121/R

Gelateria Artigianale Alfredo Via Giovannetti, 83/R

Gelateria Rota   Via A. Manuzio, 20/R

Grom   Via S. Lorenzo, 81/83

Grom   Via S. Vincenzo, 53/r

Genoa (S.Amatangelo)
RESTAURANTS AND HOTELS IN GENOA
(AIC = participates in the Associazione Italiana Celiachia program)

GENOA

HOTELS

Boccascena	hotel	€€€€, AIC
Via C. Barabino, 62/r	tel. 0105740006	www.hotelboccascena.it
Helvetia	hotel	AIC
Piazza della Nunziata, 1	tel. 0102465468	www.hotelhelvetiagenova.it
Notes: Only GF breakfast.		
Il Vico	B&B	AIC
Vico del Dragone 4/6	tel. 339.5753845	www.ilvicogenova.it
Iris	hotel	AIC
Via G. Rossetti, 3	tel. 0103760703	www.hoteliris.it
Notes: Only GF breakfast.		
Novotel Genova City	hotel, restaurant	€€€, AIC
Via Cantore, 8 C	tel. 01064841	www.novotel.com
Quitocchilcieloconundito	B&B	AIC
Via Cesare Cabella, 11/12	tel. 0104071304	www.quitocchilcieloconundito.it
Veronese	hotel	AIC
Vico Cicala, 3	tel. 0102510771	www.hotelveronese.com

RESTAURANTS

Alla Tavola di Malqù	restaurant	AIC
Via Carloforte,8 R	tel. 010.6965049	
Antica Cantina i Tre Merli	restaurant	€€€, AIC
V. Dietro il Coro d. Maddalena, 26/R	tel. 0102474095	www.itremerli.it
Notes: Closed Sundays.		
Antica Osteria del Bai	osteria	€€€€, AIC
Via Quarto, 12	tel. 010387478	www.osteriadelbai.it
Notes: Closed Mondays.		

Bar Cose Buone bar, tavola calda €, AIC
Via Fereggiano, 43/r tel. 010810834
Notes: Closed Sundays.

Bar Pizzeria I Due Fratelli restaurant, pizzeria €€, AIC
Via alla Chiesa di Prà, 71/73 n tel. 010.6399944
www.facebook.com/pages/Bar-Pizzeria-I-Due-Fratelli/490571951014189

Cafè Rest.and More La Porcigna tavola calda €, AIC
Via Ronchi, 12 tel. 393.3363349 www.laporcigna.it

Caffetteria San Giorgio bar €, AIC
Via Colombo, 24/r tel. 347.3994421

Castello Raggio pizzeria €, AIC
Via S. Giovanni D'Acri, 29/r tel. 0108690494
Notes: Closed Saturdays and at lunch.

Gran Gotto restaurant €€€€, AIC
Viale Brigate Bisagno, 69 R tel. 010564344 www.grangotto.com
Notes: Closed Saturdays at lunch and Sundays.

I Tre Merli Restaurant & Wine Bar restaurant €€€-€€€€, AIC
Via Calata Cattaneo, 17 (ex Porto Antico Edif. Millo) tel. 0102464416 www.itremerli.it

Il Focone pizzeria €, AIC
Via 5 Maggio N tel. 0103773313

Il Focone/Centro Divert."La Fiumara" pizzeria €, AIC
Via Operai, 1 tel. 010413999

iPizza pizzeria €, AIC
Via Bologna, 21r tel. 010.4031409 www.facebook.com/ipizzapizzeria

J'Aime Les Crêpes creperie €, AIC
Stradone S. Agostino tel. 0102465345 www.jaimelescrepes.eu
Notes: Closed Sundays.

Kapperi Cucina Medit. e Sushi restaurant €€€, AIC
V.co dei Lavatoi, 6/r tel. 010869 6901 www.ristorantekapperi.it
Notes: Closed Mondays.

Kilt Express pizzeria €, AIC
Viale Brigata Bisagno, 8-10R tel. 010580211 www.kilt-express.it

La Ola pizzeria €, AIC
Via Quinto, 14/r canc tel. 0103202817 www.pizzerialaola.it
Notes: DS pizza point. Closed Mondays.

La Rose en Table Vino e Desinare restaurant €€-€€€, AIC
L.re di Pegli, 79/R tel. 010.4074156 www.laroseentable.it

Le Bistrot bar €, AIC
Via Porta degli Archi, 21/r tel. 010590649
Notes: Closed Sundays.

Mychef San Ilario Nord mychef €, AIC
A12 Genova - Roma tel. 010.3726387 www.mychef.it

Officine Senza Glutine bakery, gastropub €, AIC
Piazza De Caroli, 34R tel. 348.4503260 www.officinesenzaglutine.it

Osteria dei Cacciatori osteria, pizzeria €€, AIC
Via Serra di Bavari, 15 tel. 0103450323 www.osteriadeicacciatori.it

Gluten-Free Italy by Region

Pacetti Antica Ostaria Via Borgo Incrociati, 22R	restaurant tel. 0108392848	€€€ - €€€€, AIC www.ostariapacetti.com
Pizza Rò Via Felice Cavallotti, 1a/R	pizzeria	€, AIC
Pizzeria Franco Via G. B. Piovera, 22R	pizzeria tel. 0106452255	€, AIC
Pockeat Via Colombo, 3-5RR	gastropub tel. 010.0985341	€, AIC www.pockeat.it
Rossopomodor o c/o Centro Divertimenti Fiumara Via Paolo Mantovani 62/4	pizzeria tel. 10.460757	€€, AIC www.portoantico.rossopomodoro.it
Rossopomodoro (Porto Antico) Calata Molo Vecchio, 16-17-18 N	pizzeria tel. 010.2466376	€€, AIC www.portoantico.rossopomodoro.it
Scabeccio Via D. Oliva, 42 R	restaurant tel. 0106591511	€€€, AIC
Teresa P.zza Lido, 5/6 R	restaurant tel. 010.6973774	€€€€, AIC www.ristoranteteresa.com
Trattoria Alle Due Torri Salita del Prione, 53 R Notes: Closed Sundays.	trattoria tel. 0102513637	€€, AIC www.alleduetorri.com
Trattoria da Patan Via Oberdan, 157/R	restaurant tel. 010323897	€€€, AIC www.patan.biz
Zeffirino Via XX Settembre, 20/7	restaurant tel. 0105705939	€€€€, AIC www.zeffirino.com

THE REST OF LIGURIA
ALASSIO

Golfo Blu Via XX Settembre, 142 Notes: Closed Tuesdays.	pizzeria tel. 0182640492	€-€€, AIC
Hotel Ristorante Toscana Via Flavio Gioia, 4	restaurant, hotel, bar tel. 0182.640657	AIC www.hoteltoscanaalassio.it

ALBENGA

Osteria e B&B del Tempo Stretto Regione Rollo, 40	osteria, B&B tel. 0182.571387	AIC www.osteriadeltempostretto.it
Planet Pizza Via Del Roggetto, 2 Notes: Closed Mondays.	restaurant, pizzeria tel. 018252024	€-€€, AIC

ALBISOLA SUP.

Isla Morada C.so Ferrari, 221 Notes: Closed Wednesdays.	restaurant, pizzeria tel. 0194004372	€-€€€, AIC

ALBISSOLA MARINA

Au Caruggiu Via Isola, 12	restaurant, pizzeria tel. 019485252	€€, AIC www.pizzaworld.it

ARENZANO

Aranciamara Via Manni, 25	restaurant, pizzeria tel. 0109135095	€, AIC

138 The Gluten-Free Guide to Italy

Cremeria del Sasso
C.so Matteotti, 158 R

gelato
www.cremeriadelsasso.it

€, AIC

BADALUCCO

Il Ponte
Via Ortai, 3/5
Notes: Closed Wednesdays.

restaurant
tel. 0184408000

€€, AIC
www.ristoranteilponte.it

BONASSOLA

Hotel delle Rose
Via Garibaldi, 8

hotel
tel. 0187813713

€€, AIC
www.hoteldellerosebonassola.it

BUSALLA

Verdebasilico
Via Milite Ignoto, 13/a, 13/b

restaurant, pizzeria
tel. 0109642557

€, AIC

CAMOGLI

Locanda I Tre Merli
Via Scalo, 5
Notes: GF breakfast only.

hotel, bar
tel. 0185776752

AIC
www.locandaitremerli.com

Ristorante Rosa
Via Ruffini, 13
Notes: Beautiful view.

restaurant
tel. 0185.773411

€€€€, AIC
www.rosaristorante.it

Antico Borgo

CARCARE
gelato (€, AIC)

Via Roma, 44

San Giovanni
Via Monsignore Podestà, 1

CASARZA LIGURE
restaurant
tel. 0185467244

€€€€, AIC

Nervi (S. Amatangelo)

Al Bacio
Via Aurelia, 235

CASTELNUOVO MAGRA
pizzeria
tel. 0187676255

€, AIC
www.pizzeriaalbacio.it

Focacceria Cinquecento restaurant, pizzeria €€-€€€, AIC
Via Aurelia, 71 tel. 0187693511 www.focacceriacinquecento.it

CASTIGLIONE CHIAVARESE LOCALITÀ CAMPEGLI

Azienda Agricola Arca di Nenè agritourism, pizzeria €-€€, AIC
Via Arturo Rossi, 21 tel. 3333128653 www.agripizza.com

CAVI DI LAVAGNA

Pizzeria Ugo pizzeria €, AIC
Via Aurelia, 1935 tel. 0185395762

Ziki Paki pizzeria €, AIC
Via Aurelia - Loc. Lo Scoglio tel. 0185390285 www.zikipaki.com

CELLE LIGURE

Albergo Gioiello inn €€, AIC
Via Lagorio, 24 tel. 019990201 www.albergogioiello.it

Torre hotel, restaurant €€-€€€, AIC
Via Aurelia, 20 tel. 019993465 www.hoteristorantetorre.it

CEPARANA

Vecchia Napoli pizzeria €, AIC
Via Genova, 69 tel. 0187933669

CERIALE

Bar Noemi bar-cafe €, AIC
Lung.re A. Diaz, 55 tel. 03455943306

CERIANA

Vecchia Fattoria restaurant, pizzeria, inn, B&B €-€€€, AIC
Via Armea Sud, 2006 tel. 0184551742 www.ristorantevecchiafattoria.com

CHIAVARI

Boccon Divino restaurant €€€€, AIC
Via Entella, 18 tel. 0185362964
www.facebook.com/pages/Boccon-Divino/260945860669774

La Bitta restaurant, pizzeria €-€€€, AIC
C.so Garibaldi, 99 tel. 0185.312963 www.labitta.it

Pizzeria Verdi pizzeria €, AIC
C.so Dante, 70 tel. 0185.303178 www.pizzeriaverdi.com

CHIUSAVECCHIA

Le Giare agritourism, restaurant, inn €€-€€€, AIC
Via XX Settembre, 14 - Sarola tel. 03493788253
Notes: Open only by reservation.

CISANO SUL NEVA

Peperoncino Rosso pizzeria € - €€, AIC
Via Pineta, 1 tel. 018220853

COSSERIA

Le 4 Ruote bar restaurant, pizzeria €, AIC
Fraz. Lidora, 83M tel. 019517328

DIANO MARINA

G.H. Diana Majestic hotel, restaurant €€€€, AIC
Via degli Oleandri, 15 tel. 0183402727 www.dianamajestic.com

Olympic hotel €€€€, AIC
P.zza Mazzini, 10 tel. 0183498844 www.hotelolympic.it

Hotel del Bambino-Villa Ada Via Genova, 4	**FINALE LIGURE** hotel tel. 019601611	€€€, AIC www.hoteldelbambino.it
Villa Italia Via Torino, 111	inn tel. 019690617	AIC www.hotelvillaitalia.it
Amelia Via Carli, 6 Loc. Piani	**IMPERIA** pizzeria tel. 0183780235	€, AIC
Dalla Padella alla Brace Via Ospedale, 31	trattoria tel. 0183294159	€€-€€€, AIC www.dallapadellallabrace.com
Hotel Rossini al Teatro P.zza Rossini, 14	hotel tel. 018374000	AIC www.hotel-rossini.it
Il Vascello Via C. Colombo, 200	pizzeria tel. 0183667269	€, AIC
U Fogu Acesu Via Nino Siccardi,43	pizzeria tel. 0183.667056	€, AIC www.foguacesu.it
Hosteria al Leon d'Oro Via Baracchini, 16	**LA SPEZIA** restaurant tel. 0187702295	€€, AIC www.hosterialeondoro.it
Hotel Firenze E Continentale Via Paleocapa, 7	hotel tel. 0187.713200	AIC www.hotelfirenzecontinentale.it
Il Lagora P.zza Cesare Battisti, 38	pizzeria tel. 018722242	€, AIC www.pizzeriasopraillagora.it
La Bella Napoli Via Gramsci, 175	pizzeria tel. 0187714750	€, AIC www.bellanapolionline.it
Parco del Colombaio Via dei Pioppi, 1	restaurant tel. 0187712336	€€, AIC www.parcodelcolombaiolaspezia.it
Vesuvio Via S. Bartolomeo,833	restaurant, pizzeria tel. 0187520646	€, AIC
Il Gabbiano Via S. Benedetto, 26	**LAVAGNA** restaurant tel. 0185390228	€€€, AIC www.ristoranteilgabbiano.com
Il Gambero Via della Libertà, 143	**LE GRAZIE** restaurant tel. 0187798023	€€-€€€, AIC
B&B Al Lizzo Località Tre Strade, 5	**LERICI** B&B tel. 0187.970308	AIC www.allizzo.it
La Rosa Canina Loc. Monti Branzi, 16	agritourism tel. 0187966719	€€-€€€, AIC www.larosacanina.net
Ristorante da Paolino Via Gerini, 50	restaurant tel. 0187.967801	€€-€€€, AIC www.ristorantepaolinolerici.it
La Loggia P.zza del Popolo, 7	**LEVANTO** restaurant tel. 0187808107	€€€€, AIC

Gluten-Free Italy by Region

LOANO

Aurora
V.le Tito Minniti, 5
hotel, restaurant
tel. 019669992
€€, AIC

Da Rino Mare
Corso Roma, 64
pizzeria
tel. 019671278
€, AIC

La Buona Luna
Via Stella, 2
restaurant
tel. 019673239
€€€, AIC

Ristorante Piatti Spaiati - Le Marionette restaurant
Via Stella, 34
tel. 019670948
€€€-€€€€, AIC

Trattoria Matamà
Via Ghilini, 26
restaurant
tel. 019677459
€€€, AIC

MALLARE

All'Eremo
Via Santuario Eremita, 2 R
restaurant
tel. 019586402
€€, AIC

MELE

Mychef Turchino Ovest
A26 Genova - Gravellona
mychef
tel. 010.6319205
€, AIC
www.mychef.it

MONEGLIA

Moneglia/Pizz. La Pagoda
Via Figarolo Monte, 1
pizzeria
tel. 018549778
€-€€, AIC

Villa Edera
Via Venino,12
hotel, restaurant
tel. 018549291
€€-€€€€, AIC
www.villaedera.com

MONTEROSSO AL MARE

La Barcaccia
Via Molinelli, 6/8
restaurant
tel. 0187829009
€€-€€€, AIC

NEIRONE

Da Beppe
Via Banchella, 29
B&B
tel. 0185936011
AIC
www.dabeppe.it

NOLI

Pappus
gelato (€, AIC)
Via Colombo, 12

ORCO FEGLINO

Il Portico
Via S. Rocco, 34
restaurant
tel. 019699207
€€€, AIC

ORTONOVO

da Fiorella
Via per Nicola, 46
restaurant
tel. 018766857
€€-€€€, AIC
www.ristorantedafiorella.com

PIETRA LIGURE

Ca' di Trincia
Via Maglio, 2
agritourism
tel. 019615591
€€, AIC
www.caditrincia.it

Gelateria Papero
gelato (€, AIC)
Via Garibaldi, 32

Il Capanno
Via Cappelletta, 63 fraz. Ranzi
restaurant
tel. 019625198
AIC
www.ristoranteilcapanno.com

Villa Marina
C.so Italia, 221
hotel, restaurant
tel. 019615823
€-€€, AIC
www.hotelvillamarina.eu

Best Western Tigullio Royal
P.zza IV Novembre, 3

Ciro
Via Mameli, 322

Hotel Canali
Via Pietrafraccia, 15

L'Arca tra gli Ulivi
Salita al Pianello, 17/b

da O Vittorio
Via Roma, 160
Notes: Closed Tuesdays.

La Giara
Via Cavour,79

Lino
Via Roma, 70
Notes: Closed Mondays and Tuesdays at lunch.

Vitturin 1860
Via dei Giustiniani, 50

La Ca' dell'Alpe
Via Alpe, 6

Groppo Rosso
Via Badinelli, 1

C'era una Volta
P.zza Cavallotti, 3
Notes: Closed Mondays and Tuesdays at dinner.

da Paladini
Via Aurelia,95

Regina Elena
L.re Milite Ignoto, 44

Gluten Free
Piazza S. Siro, 15

Grom

Hotel Eveline Portosole
C.so Cavallotti, 111

Salsadrena
C.so Imperatrice, 45
Notes: Closed Wednesdays.

Victory Morgana Bay
C.so Trento Trieste, 16

RAPALLO

hotel
tel. 0185273805
AIC
www.hoteltigullioroyal.it

pizzeria
tel. 018551000
AIC

hotel
tel. 018550369
AIC
www.hotelcanali.com

agritourism
tel. 018550890
€€-€€€, AIC
www.arcaulivi.it

RECCO

inn, restaurant
tel. 018574029
€€€-€€€€, AIC
www.daovittorio.it

hotel, reception hall
tel. 018574224
€€, AIC
www.hotel-lagiara.com

restaurant
tel. 018574336
€€€-€€€€, AIC
www.ristorantedalinorecco.com

restaurant
tel. 0185720225
€€€-€€€€, AIC
www.vitturin.it

RIALTO

agritourism
tel. 019688030
€, AIC
www.agriturismofinaleligure.it

S. STEFANO D'AVETO

inn
tel. 018588054
€€, AIC

S. TERENZIO-LERICI

restaurant
tel. 0187971382
€€€, AIC

S.MARGHERITA LIGURE

trattoria
tel. 0185.261405
€€€, AIC
www.trattoriapaladini.it

hotel
tel. 0185287003
€€€€, AIC
www.reginaelena.it

SANREMO

sandwich shop, bakery, gastropub
tel. 329.4026810
€-€€, AIC

gelato (€, AIC)
C.so Garibaldi 3/4

hotel
tel. 0184503430
AIC
www.evelineportosole.com

pizzeria
tel. 0184663754
€-€€€€, AIC
www.salsadrena.it

restaurant
tel. 0184591620
€€€-€€€€, AIC
www.victorymorganabay.it

SANREMO FRAZ. VEREZZO

Tratt. del Ponte — trattoria — AIC
Str. S. Antonio, 5 — tel. 0184559028

SARZANA

Arribabà — pizzeria — €, AIC
Via San Bartolomeo, 1 — tel. 0187620533

Il Giardinetto del Mauri — pizzeria — €, AIC
Via dei Molini, 112 — tel. 0187620333

SAVONA

Caffè Ligure — bar, tavola calda — €, AIC
Via Astengo, 10-12 R — tel. 349.3417893 — www.caffeligure.mysupersite.it

Gelateria Cora — gelato (€, AIC) — C.so Vittorio Veneto, 33/R

Giardino del Sole — hotel, restaurant, pizzeria — €-€€€, AIC
Via G. Bove, 61 r — tel. 019.8621773
www.hotelgiardinodelsolesavona.com

Ristorante Barbarossa — pizzeria — €-€€, AIC
Via Niella, 36R — tel. 019.8148042 — www.barbarossasavona.com

Sleek Burger Cafe — bar, tavola calda — €€, AIC
Via Montenotte, 58R — tel. 19.808658 — www.sleekcafe.com

SESTRI LEVANTE

I Due Gabbiani — restaurant, pizzeria — €-€€€, AIC
Via Nazionale, 500 — tel. 018543807

L'Albero del Pane — pizzeria — €, AIC
Via Sara, 47 — tel. 0185480803

Pizzeria Dodo — restaurant, pizzeria — €, AIC
Via Antica Romana Occidentale, 71 tel. 0185459838

Ristorante Tigullio — restaurant, pizzeria — AIC
Via Sara, 111 — tel. 0185.458291 — www.ristorantitigullio.com

SPOTORNO

Gelateria Sagapò — gelato (€, AIC) — Viale Europa, 19

TERZORIO

Antichi Sapori — restaurant, pizzeria — €€€-€€€€, AIC
Strada per Pompeiana — tel. 3357847010 — www.antichisapori-terzorio.com

VARAZZE

I Giardini di Marzo — gelato (€, AIC) — P.zza Dante, 28

VENTIMIGLIA

La Grotta — restaurant/pizzeria — €, AIC
Passeggiata Oberdan, 23 — tel. 018433440

Le Due Lanterne — pizzeria — €-€€, AIC
Pass. Oberdan, 37 — tel. 0184.841749

Angelo (J. Kelly)

PERUGIA, ASSISI AND UMBRIA
(AIC = participates in the Associazione Italiana Celiachia program)

PERUGIA

LODGING

B&B Nubes Alba	B&B	AIC
Via G. Calderini 17	tel. 393.6549889	www.nubesalba.com
C'era una Volta B&B	B&B	AIC
Str. San Marino, 6/i	tel. 393.9871968	www.ceraunavoltabeb.it
Mille Soli	B&B	AIC
Str. Mugnano Poggio Montorio	tel. 0753744885	www.casalemillesoli.it

RESTAURANTS

Caffè di Roma	bar	€, AIC
P.zza Matteotti 31	tel. 75.5731752	
Celimangiamo	sandwich shop, bakery, rotisserie	AIC
P.zza Umbria Jazz 1	tel. 75.5001573	
E'nonè	restaurant, wine bar	AIC
Corso Cavour, 61	tel. 75.572195	
Etruscan Chocohotel	hotel	AIC
Via Campo di Marte, 134	tel. 75.5837314	www.chocohotel.it
Hotel Giò Wine e Jazz Area	hotel, restaurant	AIC
via R. D'Andreotto	tel. 75.57311	www.hotelgio.it
Ilgo Hotel-I Girasoli	inn, restaurant	€€€, AIC
Via Agostino di Duccio, 1	tel. 0755736641	www.hotelilgo.com
La Botte	restaurant	AIC
Via Volte della Pace, 31	tel. 75.5722679	www.ristorantelabotte.com

La Casina Rossa Via Pievaiola, 246	restaurant tel. 75.5149524	AIC www.lacasinarossa.it
La Luna Nel Pozzo Via Settevalli, 838 - Loc. Pila	restaurant, pizzeria tel. 0755287839	AIC www.lalunanelpozzo.biz
Lago Verde Str. Cappuccinelli 20/D	restaurant tel. 75.46291	AIC
Les Crè Fantastique P.zza Danti (Pozzo Etrusco)	creperie, pizzeria tel. 3925742917	€-€€, AIC
L'Officina Borgo XX Giugno, 65	restaurant tel. 75.5721699	AIC www.l-officina.net
Lupi Cafè Via Brunamonti 4 b/c/d	bar tel. 75.96613	€-€€, AIC www.facebook.com/cafelupi
Mediterraneo Via Piccolpasso 149	restaurant, pizzeria tel. 75.5002451	€€, AIC www.mediterraneopastaepizza.it
Osteria di Pinocchio Via Tazio Nuvolari, 19	restaurant, pizzeria tel. 75.5052591	€€, AIC www.osteriapinocchio.it
Osteria il Gufo Via della Viola 18	restaurant tel. 75.5734126	€€, AIC www.osteriailgufo.wordpress.com
Pian di Marte - Ospitalità rurale Località Pian di Marte 9	hotel, restaurant tel. 75.845342	AIC
RossoPomodoro Via della Valtiera 181 (C. Com Collestrada) tel. 75.397201	pizzeria	€-€€, AIC www.rossopomodoroperugia.it
S. Martino RO.ME. Via Pontani, 15	restaurant tel. 0755053366	€, AIC
Sotto Sopra Settevalli strada 834	pub tel. 75.5270675	€, AIC www.sottosopraperugia.it
Trattoria del Borgo Via della Sposa 23/A	restaurant tel. 75.572039	AIC www.trattoriadelborgoperugia.it
Tuttotesto C.so Garibaldi, 15	restaurant, creperie tel. 0755736666	€, AIC
Villa Taticchi-Agrit. Il Covone Str. Fratticciola, 2	restaurant agritourism tel. 075694503	€€-€€€, AIC www.villataticchi.it
Zero7Cinque Strada Bellocchio S. Faustino, 54	restaurant, pizzeria tel. 0755058294	€€€€, AIC www.zero7cinque.it

Cioccolato Augusta Perusia	gelato (€, AIC)	Via Pinturicchio, 2
Gelateria Veneta	gelato €, AIC	P.zza Italia
Grom	gelato €, AIC	Via Mazzini, 31
Gel Art. La Terrazza	gelato (€, AIC)	Via Mastrodicasa 107
Menchetti	gelato (€, AIC)	Strada Trasimeno Ovest

PERUGIA- LOC. PONTE VALLECEPPI

Pegaso-Hotel Vega hotel, restaurant, pizzeria €€, AIC
Strada Bellocchio S. Faustino, 54 tel. 0756929534 www.hotelvegaperugia.com
Notes: Closed Mondays.

THE REST OF UMBRIA

AMELIA

Scoglio dell'Aquilone Via Orvieto 23	restaurant, hotel tel. 744.982445	€€-€€€€, AIC www.scogliodellaquilone.it

ASSISI

LODGING

Alla Madonna del Piatto Via Petrata 37	B&B tel. 075.8199050	AIC www.incampagna.com
B&B I Nidi Fraz. San Gregorio 42	B&B tel. 075.8038123	AIC www.assisionline.com/inidi
B&B Le Tortorelle Via della Conciliazione, 18	B&B tel. 338.3504883	AIC www.assisi-letortorelle.com
Chiara Via Pietro Uber, 10	B&B tel. 3384387238	AIC

RESTAURANTS

Agrit. Tordoni Daniela Via del Paduletto, 24 Notes: Closed Mondays.	agritourism tel. 0758065810	€€, AIC www.valledelsubasio.it
Le Silve di Armenzano/ Romantik Hotel restaurant, hotel Loc. Armenzano 89 tel. 75.8019		AIC www.lesilve.it
Millematti Via Assisiana 43	pizzeria tel. 75.8064175	€-€€, AIC
Valle del Subasio Via del Paduletto, 24	agritourism tel. 75.806581	AIC www.valledelsubasio.it

ASSISI - SANTA MARIA DEGLI ANGELI

Starbene senza glutine Via della Repubblica 8 A	restaurant, pizzeria, Pan tel. 75.8043627	AIC
Villa Cherubino Via P. d'Italia, 39	restaurant tel. 75.8040226	AIC

AVIGLIANO UMBRO

La Tenuta dei Ciclamini Loc. Casa Pancallo, 3	agritourism tel. 074493431	€€€-€€€€, AIC
Le Bandite Country & Relax Voc. Suffragio, 5	B&B www.lebanditecountryrelax.com	AIC

BASTIA UMBRA

Pane e Ciliegie Via S. Lucia, 34	restaurant catering tel. 0758004959	€€-€€€€, AIC www.paneeciliegie.it
Villa Rabasco Strada Assisiana, 147 - Bastiola	hotel, restaurant tel. 0758010011	€€€, AIC

CASALINA

Country House L'Antico Forziere Via della Rocca, 2	restaurant tel. 0759724314	€€€, AIC www.anticoforziere.it

CASCIA

Agriturismo Baldassari Loc. Avendita	agritourism, restaurant, pizzeria tel. 743.755086	AIC www.agriturismocascianorcia.it

CASTIGLIONE DEL LAGO

H. Aganoor/R. La Cantina
Via Vitt. Emanuele, 91
hotel, restaurant
tel. 0759652463
AIC
www.hotelaganoor.it

Isola Polvese
Loc. Isola Polvese
restaurant
tel. 0759659545
AIC

La Pigra Tinca
Via Divis. Partigiani Garibaldi
restaurant
tel. 0759652480
€-€€, AIC

CENERENTE

Poggio del Sole
Str. Forcella, 49/a
restaurant, pizzeria
tel. 075690752
AIC

Relais Poggio del Sole
Str. Forcella, 49/a
restaurant, pizzeria, hotel
tel. 75.690752
AIC

CITTÀ DI CASTELLO

Artcafè Gel. Cremì
gelato (€, AIC)
C.so Vittorio Emanuele 31/b

BomBarolo
Piazza Pertini 1
restaurant, pizzeria
tel. 75.8511097
AIC

Caffe' Magi
Piazza Gabriotti 9/B
restaurant
tel. 333.8610403
AIC

Con e Senza
Via P. della Francesca
tavola calda, bar
tel. 075 8520903
€-€€, AIC

Il Sesto Canto
Piazza Giovanni XXIII
restaurant, pizzeria
tel. 75.8553251
AIC

Molenda
Loc. S. Paterniano Voc. Monini, 10
B&B
tel. 0758521416
AIC
www.molenda-bedandbreakfast.com

Tankard
Via Luca della Robbia, 21 - C. Comm.le Le Fonti
pizzeria
AIC
tel. 75.8554495

Trattoria Pappa e Ciccia
Via del Popolo 16
restaurant
tel. 075.8521386/380.7817333
AIC

Uomini di Mare
Via R. De Cesare 8
restaurant, pizzeria
tel. 075.85569909
€-€€, AIC
www.ristoranteuominidimare.it

Villa San Donino
Località San Donino
hotel, restaurant
tel. 75.8578108
AIC
www.hotelvillasandonino.it

CORCIANO

Al Borgo
Via Collesi, 1
B&B
tel. 393.7659437
AIC
www.laportadicorciano.it

L'arte del Gelato
P.zza dei Caduti, 6
bar
tel. 75.6978867
€-€€, AIC

DERUTA

Country House L'Antico Forziere
Casalina
restaurant
tel. 75.9724314
AIC
www.anticoforziere.it

ELLERA DI CORCIANO

Best Wester Golf Hotel Quattrotorri
Via Corcianese,26 0
hotel, restaurant
tel. 75.5171722
, AIC

Revolution
Via Juri Gagarin 1
restaurant, pizzeria
tel. 75.7974465
AIC

Revolution Restaurant
Via Juri Gagarin

restaurant, pizzeria
tel. 0755170367

€, AIC

FERENTILLO

Ai Tre Archi
S.S. Valnerina 29

restaurant, pizzeria
tel. 744.780004

AIC

Piermarini
Via F. Ancaiano, 23
Notes: Closed Mondays.

restaurant
tel. 0744780714

€€-€€€€, AIC

Vecchio Mulino Monterivoso
Case Sparse, 5

hotel, restaurant, pizzeria
tel. 0744780772

€-€€€€, AIC

FIGHILLE

L'Isola Che Non C'è
Loc. Petriolo

restaurant, pizzeria
tel. 0758593336

AIC

FOLIGNO

Delfina Palace Hotel
Via Romana Vecchia

hotel, restaurant
tel. 74.2692911
www.delfinapalacehotel.it

AIC

Maison del Celiaco
Via Monte Acuto, 53

bakery, sandwich shop
www.maisondelceliaco.it

€

MeTeMagno TVB
P.zza don Minzoni, 1-3

restaurant
tel. 74.2620452

AIC

Voglia di Pizza
Giacomini, 44

pizzeria
tel. 0742342371   www.vogliadipizzaglutenfree.com

€-€€, AIC

FOLIGNO - TREVI

Ristozoo
Via Popoli snc

restaurant, pizzeria
tel. 742.679099

AIC

FOSSATO DI VICO

De Gusto
Via del Rigo 26

restaurant, pizzeria
tel. 75.9190113

AIC

GIOVE

Mychef Giove Est
A1 Roma - Milano

mychef
tel. 744.99293
www.mychef.it

€, AIC

GUALDO CATTANEO- S.TERENZIANO

Il Buongustaio
Piazza Vittorio Emanuele

restaurant
tel. 0742.930033/347.3661689

AIC

GUALDO TADINO

Da Clelia
Via G. Matteotti, 80 e Loc.Valsorda

restaurant
tel. 075913261

AIC

GUBBIO

Agriturismo Villa Dama
Loc. Torre dell'Olmo

agritourism, restaurant
tel. 75.925613

AIC

Alla Balestra
Via della Repubblica, 41
Notes: Closed Tuesdays.

restaurant, pizzeria
tel. 0759273810

€-€€€€, AIC

Aquilone (Campi Scuola)
Str. di Vignoli 3 - Torre Calzolari

agritourism
tel. 75.9271105

AIC

Piede (J. Roglieri)

Contessa S.S. Contessa 10	restaurant, pizzeria tel. 75.9277256	AIC
Dulcis in Fundo Corso Garibaldi 2	restaurant, pizzeria tel. 75.9273376	AIC
Faro Rosso Fraz.Montanal do 69	agritourism, restaurant tel. 75.925801	AIC
Hotel dei Consoli Via dei Consoli, 59	hotel, restaurant tel. 75.9220639	AIC
Hotel Sporting Via Bottagnone	hotel, restaurant tel. 75.9220753	AIC
L'Arte Golosa	gelato (€, AIC)	Via Europa, 63- Fraz. Cipolleto
Locanda del Gallo Loc. S. Cristina	agritourism tel. 75.9229912	AIC
Parco Coppo Monte Ingino	restaurant, pizzeria tel. 75.9272755	AIC
San Benedetto Piazza Empedocle	restaurant, pizzeria tel. 75.9220489	AIC
San Francesco e il Lupo Via Cairoli, 24	restaurant, pizzeria tel. 0759272344	AIC

MERCATELLO

Locanda le Noci agritourism, restaurant AIC
Vocabolo Molinella, 1 tel. 75.8783271 www.locandadellenoci.it

MONTECASTRILLI

Relais dei Principi restaurant, pizzeria AIC
Via dello Scalo, 9 tel. 744933244

MONTEFALCO

L'Alchimista restaurant, wine bar AIC
Piazza del Comune 14 tel. 742.378558

MONTORO - NARNI

Villa Pina B&B B&B AIC
Str. Castelluccio Amerino 5 tel. 366.9361468 www.villapinaumbria.it

NARNI

Grano e Sale pizzeria €-€€, AIC
Via Flaminia Ternana, 145 tel. 0744715519 www.granoesale.it

Il Gattamelata restaurant AIC
Via Pozzo della Comunità tel. 744.717245

Il Parco dei Cavalieri restaurant, pizzeria AIC
Strada Flaminia Ternana 510 tel. 744.744399

La Rocca restaurant, hotel AIC
S.S. Flaminia Ternana, 508 tel. 744.744521

Tenuta Marchesi Fezia restaurant, pizzeria, B&B AIC
Loc. San. Bartolomeo - Narni Scalo tel. 744.750324 www.tenutamarchesifezia.com

ORVIETO

Antica Cantina (Osteria delle Donne) restaurant AIC
Piazza Monaldeschi 18 tel. 0763.344746/329.6509966

PIEGARO

Millenovecento Pub restaurant, pizzeria, pub AIC
Loc. Canneto 109 -Castiglion Fosco tel. 75.835208 www.millenovecentopub.com

PIETRALUNGA

Bio Agrit./ Fatt. Didattica La Cerqua agritourism AIC
Via San Salvatore tel. 75.9460283 www.cerqua.it

La Cima agritourism, restaurant AIC
Vocabolo Fontinelle tel. 75.9460272 www.agriturismolacima.it

PONTE S. GIOVANNI

Le Olive B&B AIC
Via A. Manzoni, 391 tel. 3282646821

SAN GIUSTINO

Green restaurant, pizzeria AIC
Loc.Uliano 3 tel. 75.8560391

Il Covo del Contrabbandie re restaurant, pizzeria AIC
Via della Repubblica tel. 75.8560427

Il Dongione restaurant AIC
Via Largo Crociani, 6 tel. 75.856567

Starbene San Giustino sandwich shop €-€€, AIC
Via G.O Bufalini 13 tel. 3667312229

SAN SISTO

Caffè La Rosa	bar	€, AIC
Viale S. Sisto 188	tel. 75.5289792	

SAN TERENZIANO

Alla Casella	restaurant	€€-€€€€, AIC
Via Collazzone, 11/2	tel. 074298989	

SANGEMINI

Il Colle	restaurant	AIC
Viale Garibaldi 6	tel. 744.630428	

Meeting Coffee	gelato (€, AIC)	Via Ternana, 1/c

Soc. Agric. Vallantica	restaurant, wine bar	€€€€, AIC
Loc. Valle Antica, 280	tel. 0744243454	

SELCILAMA - SAN GIUSTINO

Il Musicista	restaurant, pizzeria	AIC
Voc. Osteriaccia 1	tel. 75.85835	

SIGILLO

Taverna del Gobbo	restaurant	AIC
Via Petrelli 16/A	tel. 366.5940225	

SPELLO

Borgo della Marmotta	agritourism	AIC
Loc. Poreta, 1	tel. 0743274137	www.leterrediporeta.it

Caffè Porta Consolare	gelato (€, AIC)	P.zza Kennedy, 7/8

SPOLETO

Gi.Gio's	restaurant, pizzeria, tavola calda, bar	AIC
V.le Trento e Trieste 147/a	tel. 743.221161	

H Clitunno/Rist. S. Lorenzo	inn	€€-€€€€, AIC
P.zza Sordini, 6	tel. 0743223340	
Notes: Closed Tuesdays.		

La Ginestra	pizzeria	€-€€, AIC
Loc. Pompagnano	tel. 743.4701	

Le Logge	restaurant, pizzeria	AIC
V.le Martiri della Resistenza, 51	tel. 0743225225	

Ristogiocando/ Italgonfiabili	restaurant, pizzeria	AIC
Via U. La Malfa 21 - Loc. Madonna di Lugo	tel. 348.5595253	

Ristorante del Mercato	restaurant	AIC
Piazza del Mercato 29	tel. 743.45325	

S. Pietro	restaurant, pizzeria	AIC
Loc. S. Pietro	tel. 074346788	
Notes: DS pizza point. Closed Tuesdays.		

Taverna La Lanterna	restaurant	AIC
Via della Trattoria, 6	tel. 74349815	

Trattoria il Capanno	restaurant	AIC
Torrecola di Spoleto	tel. 0743.54119/3358237537	

SPOLETO - CASTEL RITALDI

Locanda di Rovicciano	restaurant	AIC
Via la Penna 9	tel. 743.51679	

TAVERNELLE DI PANICALE

Break Bar — gelato, bar (€, AIC) — Via della Resistenza 21

Mr Over
Via Palladio — restaurant, pizzeria — AIC
tel. 75.832732

TERNI

Agrit. Fontana della Mandorla — agritourism — AIC
Str. Fontana della Mandorla 112 — tel. 744.40071

Andrea — gelato (€, AIC) — Via Mancini, 6

Antico Ponte del Toro
Via Ponte del Toro 23 — hotel, restaurant, resort — AIC
tel. 744.67636

Best Western - Garden Hotel - Rist.Melograno hotel, restaurant — AIC
Viale Bramante 4 — tel. 0744.300375/300041

Cassiopea MMX
Strada di Miranda 55 — restaurant — AIC
tel. 744.279058

Country House Il Pozzo
Strada di Collescipoli, 190 — restaurant, pizzeria — AIC
tel. 74.4813069

Grilli Pasticceria & Food
Via dei Gonzaga 26 — restaurant, pizzeria — AIC
tel. 744.3046

H. del Lago Piediluco - Rist. la Ginestrella hotel, restaurant — AIC
Str. del Porto, Piediluco 71 — tel. 744.36845

Il Forno di Babette
Via G. di Vitalone 41 — sandwich shop, bakery — €-€€, AIC
tel. 744.082921

La Briciola di Pani
Via Mentana 25 — bakery — €, AIC
tel. 744.275579

La Clessidra
Via Masaccio 24/28 — restaurant, wine bar — AIC
tel. 744.433611

Livingstone Pub
Viale Cesare Battisti, 69 — pub, pizzeria — €, AIC
tel. 0744409746 — www.livingstonepub.it

Lu Somaru
Via Cesare Battisti 106 — restaurant — AIC
tel. 744.304787

Pantarhei
Via Cavour 50/52 — restaurant, pizzeria — AIC
tel. 0744.1980941

Placebo
Via Cavour 45 — restaurant — €€, AIC
tel. 744.401216 — www.placeboterni.it

TODI

Le Scalette
Via delle Scalette,1 — restaurant — €€, AIC
tel. 75.8944422 — www.ristorantelescalette.it

TODI - FRAZ. COLLEVALE NZA

H. La Collina di Collevalenza
Viale Madre Speranza 117 — hotel, restaurant — AIC
tel. 75.8870034 — www.lacollinadicollevalenza.com

TORRICELLA-MAGIONE

Caravelle
Via del Lavoro, 59 — pizzeria — €-€€, AIC
tel. 075843330

TRESTINA - UMBERTIDE
Pizza Time   pizzeria   €€, AIC
Fr. Verna - Loc. Banchetti snc   tel. 75.9410448

TUORO SUL TRASIMENO
La Tosca   B&B   AIC
Via Mercato, 14   tel. 075825312

UMBERTIDE
Agrit. Vegetariano/V egano Le Tortorelle agritourism, restaurant   AIC
Fraz. Molino Vitelli, 180   tel. 75.9410949   www.letortorelle.it

Casagrande   restaurant, pizzeria   €€€, AIC
Via Madonna del Moro 30B   tel. 75.9413014

Il Vecchio Granaio   pizzeria   €€€, AIC
Voc. Busternan- Calzolaro 44   tel. 75.9302322   www.ilvecchiogranaio.com

L'Arte del Caffè   bar   €, AIC
Piazza Carlo Marx, 10   tel. 366.3507839

Tankard   pizzeria   €€, AIC
Via R. Morandi - Centro Comm. Fratta   tel. 75.9415388   www.tankard.it

VALFABBRICA
Ca' Mazzetto   agritourism   €€, AIC
Voc. Camazzetto, 22   tel. 0759029409

Ferrara (M. Roglieri)

BOLOGNA AND EMILIA-ROMAGNA

(AIC = participates in the Associazione Italiana Celiachia program)

BOLOGNA

America Graffiti fast food c/o area commerciale Le Piazze sandwich shop €, AIC
Via Pio La Torre,11 c/o area Commericale Le Piazze   tel. 51.705404 www.americagraffiti.it

Bar Pasticc. Ornielli	bar-cafe	€, AIC
Via Battindarno, 354	tel. 0510950461	
Due Lune	restaurant, pizzeria	AIC
Via Nino Bertocchi, 1	tel. 051567569	www.ristoranteduelune.it
La Spiga Amica	bakery	€, AIC
Via Petrarca, 13/2 G	tel. 800601675	www.laspigaamica.it
Master Beer	pub, restaurant, pizzeria	€-€€, AIC
Via Andrea Costa, 158	tel. 051.6140523	www.masterbeer.net
Notes: Gluten-Free menu.		
Novotel Bologna Fiera	hotel, restaurant	€€-€€€, AIC
Via Michelino, 73	tel. 051637771	www.novotel.it
Palazzo Trevi	B&B	AIC
Via Frassinago, 31	tel. 051580230	www.palazzotrevi.it
Pantera Rosa 1 (via C.Tomba)	restaurant, pizzeria	€, AIC
Via Cleto Tomba, 14 A	tel. 0515870544	
Pantera Rosa 2 (via Guelfa)	pizzeria bar	€-€€, AIC
Via Guelfa, 74	tel. 0516011069	
Notes: DS pizza point. Closed Mondays and at lunch.		
Pantera Rosa di Via Zanardi	pizzeria	€-€€, AIC
Via Francesco Zanardi, 189/D	tel. 051.6341538	
Ristorante La Capriata	restaurant	€€-€€€, AIC
Corte Isolani n. 1/E	tel. 51.236932	www.lacapriata.it

| **Star Bene Senza Glutine** | bar, desserts | € |
| Via Angelo Ruffini 6/G/h | tel. 350/5143504 | www.starbenesenzaglutine.it |

Capo Nord	gelato (€, AIC)	Via Murri, 39
Gelateria Iglù	gelato (€, AIC)	Via F. Barbieri, 66/a
Grom	gelato (€, AIC)	Via Massimo D'Azeglio, 13

Carrefour	food store	Via Marilyn Monroe, 2/9
Esselunga	food store	Via Guelfa 13
Esselunga	food store	Via Emilia Ponente 72
Ipercoop	food store	Via M.E. Lepido 184
Ipercoop	food store	Via Beverara 50
Pam	food store	Via Marconi 28/A

THE REST OF EMILIA-ROMAGNA
AGAZZANO

| **Fricandò il Ristolocale** | restaurant | €€€€, AIC |
| P.zza Europa, 26 | tel. 3406970402 | |

Notes: Closed Wednesdays.

ANZOLA DELL'EMILIA

| **I Salici** | agritourism, B&B | €-€€€, AIC |
| Via Suor Orsola Donati, 108 | tel. 051739418 | |

BAGNACAVALLO

| **Gelateria Mambo** | gelato (€, AIC) | Via Mazzini 58 |

BAGNO

| **Villabagno** | agritourism | €€€-€€€€, AIC |
| Via Lasagni, 29 | tel. 0522343188 | |

BELLARIA

| **Aurea** | hotel | €€€€, AIC |
| L.re Colombo, 21 | tel. 0541345665 | |

| **Club Hotel Angelini** | hotel | €€€€, AIC |
| Via Pirano, 3 | tel. 0541345001 | |

Notes: Closed October-March.

BELLARIA IGEA MARINA

| **Albergo Serenità** | B&B | AIC |
| Via Fratelli Cervi, 3 | tel. 0541.346541 | |

| **Capitan Bagati** | restaurant, pizzeria | €€€, AIC |
| Viale Pinzon,10 | tel. 0541340034 | www.capitanbagati.it |

| **Imperiale** | hotel | €€€€, AIC |
| Via Panzini, 73 | tel. 0541344122 | www.nellyhotels.com |

| **Taverna da Bruno** | restaurant, pizzeria | €€€-€€€€, AIC |
| Via Panzini, 150 | | |

| **Villa Lucia** | B&B | AIC |
| Via Ovidio, 31 | tel. 0541331428 | |

Notes: Closed October-March.

BERTINORO

| **Autogrill Bevano Est** | autogrill | €, AIC |
| A14 Ancona - Bologna | tel. 0543.440813 | |

| **Autogrill Bevano Ovest** | autogrill | €, AIC |
| A14 Bologna - Ancona | tel. 0543.440822 | |

BORGO VAL DI TARO

La Bottega del Chisolino restaurant, pizzeria, bar €€, AIC
Via Torresana, 4 tel. 525.90522
www.facebook.com/pages/LA-BOTTEGA-DEL-CHISOLINO/41398950965

CÀ DI LUGO - LUGO

Osteria del Tempo Perso restaurant, pizzeria €, AIC
Via Fiumazzo, 176 tel. 054573069

CADELBOSCO SOPRA

Gelateria K2 gelato (€, AIC) Via Matteotti n.2/d

CADEO

Relais Cascina Scottina/R.Ant.Ost.della Pesa hotel, restaurant €€€€, AIC
Str. Del Riglio - Loc. Scottina tel. 0523504232 www.osteriadellapesa.it

CALDERARA DI RENO

Itaca restaurant, pizzeria €-€€€, AIC
Via Roma, 81/a tel. 051720383 www.pizzeriaitaca.it

CAMPAGNOLA EMILIA

Toro Blanco c/o Multiristorante La Bussola Spanish restaurant/pizzeria € - €€, AIC
Via Reggiolo, 22 tel. 0522663508 www.ristorante-labussola.it

CAPRARA CAMPEGINE

Il Porto restaurant €€-€€€, AIC
Via Nenni, 2/b tel. 0522676625
Notes: Closed Sundays.

CARPI

Cortina gelato (€€, AIC) Via Maiella, 29
Notes: They also have crêpes.

Il Delfino pizzeria, tavola calda €, AIC
Via Don L.Sturzo,36 tel. 59.65186 www.pizzeriaildelfino.com/la-pizzeria

Sapori di Carpi gastropub €€-€€€, AIC
Via Aldo Moro, 6 - 6/B tel. 59.694124 www.saporidicarpi.it

CASALECCHIO DI RENO

Autogrill Cantagallo autogrill €, AIC
A1 Bologna - Firenze tel. 51.593864

CASALGRANDE

Gianni restaurant, pizzeria €€€, AIC
Via del Bosco, 14 tel. 0536823379 www.gianniristorante.it
Notes: Closed Monday-Tuesday.

CASTEL DI CASIO

La Prossima agritourism restaurant, pizzeria €-€€, AIC
Via Prostima, 2 tel. 053442572 www.laprossima.com

CASTEL MAGGIORE

La Barattina restaurant €€-€€€, AIC
Via S. Giuseppe, 19 tel. 51.705734 www.ristorantelabarattina.it

CASTELLARANO

L'Angolo gelato (€, AIC) Via Respighi, 9

CASTIGLIONE DEI PEPOLI

Mychef Roncobilaccio Est mychef €, AIC
A1 Firenze - Milano tel. 534.9795 www.mychef.it

CATTOLICA

L'Anfora
Via Rossini, 16
agritourism,restaurant, pizzeria
tel. 0541953702
€€€-€€€€, AIC

Pizza e Pasta
Via Largo della Pace, 3/5
pizzeria
tel. 0541831166
€ - €€, AIC
www.pizzascuola.com

Tradizioni di Famiglia
Via Mazzini, 38
gastropub
tel. 346.3673842
€ - €€, AIC
www.tradizionidifamiglia.it

CERASOLO DI CORIANO

Pizz'Osteria da Mazza
Via Ausa, 138
restaurant, pizzeria
tel. 0541759060
€-€€, AIC
www.cerasoloausa.net

CERVIA

Borgomarina
gelato (€, AIC)
Via Nazario Sauro, 92

Ca' D'oro
Viale Italia, 92
hotel
tel. 054471939
AIC
www.hotelcadoro.net

Gli Angeli
Via Capinera, 20
B&B
tel. 339.4830281
AIC
www.bebgliangeli.it

Re Sale e Regina Salina
L.re D'Annunzio, 26
restaurant, pizzeria
tel. 0544970442
€€, AIC
www.emmehotels.com

CESENA

Dolce Paradiso
gelato (€, AIC)
V.le Giacomo Matteotti, 124

I Girasoli
Via Emilia Levante, 2223
restaurant, pizzeria
tel. 0547303737
€-€€, AIC
www.ristoranteigirasoli.it

Il Portico
Via Rio Maggiore, 57
restaurant, pizzeria
tel. 0547.333039
€-€€€€, AIC
www.ilportico-ristorante.com

Zero Farina
Via Ravennate, 2846
bakery
tel. 329.5780105
€, AIC

CESENATICO

Al Cenacolo
V.le Trento, 68
Notes: Closed Tuesdays.
restaurant, pizzeria
tel. 0547672820
€-€€€€, AIC
www.ristorantealcenacolo.com

Bagno Piscina 4 Venti
Via Ferrara spiaggia di levante
Notes: At the beach.
tavola calda, bar
tel. 547.75567
€, AIC
www.bagno4venti.com

Cà Nostra
Corso Garibaldi, 60
www.miositoweb.com/ristorante-cesenatico
restaurant, pizzeria
tel. 0547.481522
€€, AIC

Globus
Via Dante, 1
hotel
tel. 0547680700
€€€€, AIC
www.nellyhotels.com

Hotel Vera
Via Ippolito Nievo, 2
hotel, B&B
tel. 054780342
AIC
www.hotelvera.info

Il Jelato di Jessica
gelato (€, AIC)
Viale Carducci, 46/A

COLOMBARO DI FORMIGINE

Antica Pieve
Via Maestri del Lavoro, 16
restaurant, pizzeria
tel. 059553040
€€, AIC

Al Ponticello
Via Cavour, 39

COMACCHIO
B&B
tel. 0533314080

AIC
www.alponticello.it

La Dolce Vita
P.zza del Popolo, 29

COPPARO
bar
tel. 0532.863715

€, AIC
www.dolcevitapasticceria-fe.com

Star Bene Senza Glutine
Corso Mazzini 25/B

CORREGGIO
bar, desserts
tel. 340.6525284

€
www.starbenesenzaglutine.it

Ponte di Ferro
Via Madrara, 1

COTINGNOLA
pizzeria
tel. 0545992464

€ - €€, AIC
www.pontediferro.net

Villa Leri
Via Canepa, 172

CROCE DI MONTECOLOMBO
hotel, restaurant
tel. 0541985262

€€€€, AIC
www.villaleri.it

Gelateria OK

FAENZA
gelato (€, AIC)

Via F.lli Rosselli, 6/2

Jack
Via Firenze, 561

restaurant, pizzeria
tel. 054643071

AIC

Self service Bontavola
Piazzetta Carlo Zauli,1

restaurant
tel. 546.21722

AIC

Albergo K 2
Via Giardini, 281

FAIDELLO-FIUMALBO
hotel, restaurant, bar
tel. 053673913

€€€-€€€€, AIC

Lo Chalet
Via Giardini, 281

FANANO
restaurant, pizzeria
tel. 053668442

€, AIC

Al Ciocco
Via Palloncino, 2

FARNETA DI MONTEFIORINO
hotel, restaurant
tel. 0536974018

€€, AIC
www.alciocco.com

Notes: Closed Monday and month of November.

Albergo Annunziata
P.za Repubblica, 5

FERRARA
hotel
tel. 0532201111

AIC
www.annunziata.it

Astra Hotel
Viale Cavour, 55

hotel
tel. 0532206088

AIC
www.astrahotel.info

Notes: Will serve GF breakfast only.

Carlton
Via Garibaldi, 93

hotel
tel. 0532211130

AIC
www.hotelcarlton.net

Dolcemela
Via Sacca, 35

B&B
tel. 0532769624

AIC
www.dolcemela.it

Le Stanze di Torcicoda
Vicolo Mozzo Torcicoda,9

B&B
tel. 0532.1993033

AIC
www.lestanze.it

Locanda Borgonuovo
Via Cairoli, 29

B&B
tel. 0532211100

AIC
www.borgonuovo.com

Bella Napoli   restaurant, pizzeria   €, AIC
Via M.Boiardo 5   tel. 0532205015
Notes: DS pizza point. Closed Wednesdays.

L'Orlando   restaurant   €, AIC
Via Aldighieri, 3   tel. 0532.202693   www.lorlando.it

Grom   gelato   €, AIC
P.zza Trento e Trieste   www.grom.it

FIDENZA

Il Tondino   agritourism   €€-€€€, AIC
Via Tabiano, 58   tel. 052462106

Sanafollia   restaurant   €€-€€€, AIC
Via B. Bacchini, 23

FILO

Antica Trattoria Vallone   restaurant, pizzeria   €€-€€€, AIC
Via Porto Vallone, 11   tel. 0532.802050   www.trattoriavallone.it

FINALE EMILIA

Pasta per Celia   bakery   €, AIC
Via Stazione, 1   tel. 346.4006185

FIORENZUOLA D'ARDA

Autogrill Arda   autogrill   €, AIC
A1 Milano - Bologna   tel. 0523.985311

FOCOMORTO

F.lli Rizzieri 1969   gastropub   €, AIC
Via Ponte Ferriani,1   tel. 532.65092   www.1969macelleriarizzieri.com

FONTANELICE

Agriturismo La Taverna   agritourism   €€-€€€, AIC
Via Casolana, 53   tel. 054292714
Notes: Closed Monday-Wednesday.

FONTANELLATO

Scacciapensie ri   restaurant, pizzeria   €€-€€€, AIC
Loc. Cannetolo, 25   tel. 0521.821350   www.villascacciapensieri.it

FONTEVIVO

L'Abbazia   B&B   AIC
Via P. P. Pasolini, 19   tel. 0521672472

FORLI

Del Corso   restaurant, pizzeria   €-€€, AIC
Corso della Repubblica, 209   tel. 054332674

Dolce Ro   gelato (€, AIC)   Corso Giuseppe Garibaldi, 61

Hotel della Città   hotel, B&B   AIC
Corso della Repubblica,117   tel. 054328297   www.hoteldellacittà.it

Hotel Masini   hotel   AIC
C.so Garibaldi, 28   tel. 054328072

Los Locos   restaurant, pizzeria   €-€€, AIC
Via dell'Appennino, 697   tel. 0543480735

Mangia Pizza pizzeria €, AIC
Via dell'Appennin o, 287 tel. 0543.405212

Piada 52 restaurant €, AIC
Via Dragoni, 52 tel. 340.3712548 www.piada52.it

Ristorante Tennis Villacarpena restaurant AIC
Via Brando Brandi, 69 tel. 0543.402344
www.facebook.com/pages/Ristorante-Tennis-Villa-Carpena/507753002569209
Notes: Restaurant within a tennis village.

SGlab bakery €, AIC
Via Nazario Sauro, 5-7 tel. 0543.092812 www.sglabforli.it
Notes: Everything is gluten-free.

FORLIMPOPOLI
America Graffiti Fast Food sandwich shop €, AIC
Via Emilia per Forlì, 1387 tel. 0543744945

FORMIGINE
Gelateria Alaska gelato (€, AIC) Via S. Antonio, 8/D 8/E

Harlow restaurant, pizzeria €, AIC
Via Quattro Passi, 21 tel. 0595750204
Notes: DS pizza point. Closed Tuesdays for dinner.

FORNOVOTARO
Ristorante Bel Sit restaurant €€€, AIC
Via Nazionale, 167 tel. 0525400243 www.ristorantebelsit.net

FUNO DI ARGELATO
C'è pizza per te 2 pizzeria €, AIC
Via Galliera, 112 tel. 051.8659415

GAIANO
Chantilly gelato (€, AIC) Via Nazionale, 26

GAZZOLA
La Locanda restaurant €€€-€€€€, AIC
Loc. Tuna, 48 tel. 0523978103 www.trattorialocanda.pc.it
Notes: Closed Thursdays.

GUASTALLA
La Mandragola restaurant €€€€, AIC
Via Sacco e Vanzetti, 2/g tel. 0522219810
Notes: Closed Monday-Tuesday.

GUIGLIA
Locanda del Parco restaurant €€-€€€€, AIC
Via Fondovalle, 3892 tel. 059.795920 www.locandadelparco.com
Notes: Everything is gluten-free.

IGEA MARINA
Internazionale hotel €€€€, AIC
V.le Pinzon, 72 tel. 0541331447 www.internazionalehotel.net
Notes: Closed October-April.

Missouri hotel €€€€, AIC
Via Tibullo, 28 tel. 0541331730 www.hotelmissouri.net

IMOLA
Milana pizzeria €, AIC
Via della Milana, 21 tel. 054242200

Pit Stop   restaurant, pizzeria   €-€€€, AIC
Via Pisacane, 69/d   tel. 054228884   www.pitstoppizzeria.it

LEMIGNANO DI COLLECCHIO

Timeout   restaurant, pizzeria   € - €€€€, AIC
Via Spezia, corner of Via Antolini   tel. 0521804503   www.ristorantetimeout.it

LIDO ADRIANO

Bar Blue   gelato (€, AIC)   V.le Virgilio, 56/58

LIDO DI SAVIO

Ai Pioppi   restaurant   €€-€€€€, AIC
Via Marina, 5   tel. 0544948000

LIDO ESTENSI

Bagno Astra   restaurant bar   €€€-€€€€, AIC
Via Spiaggia, 13   tel. 0533327953

Logonovo   B&B   AIC
Viale delle Querce, 109   tel. 0533327520   www.hotellogonovo.it

Mammamia   gelato (€, AIC)   Viale Carducci 116

LIDO POMPOSA COMACCHIO

Gelateria K 2   gelato (€, AIC)   P.zza Trento e Trieste

LONGIANO

Borgonovo   inn, restaurant, pizzeria   €-€€€€, AIC
Via A. Moro, 1   tel. 054757357   www.ristorantealbergoborgonovo.com
Notes: Closed Tuesdays.

LUGO

Tatì   pizzeria   €, AIC
V.le degli Orsini, 5   tel. 054525901

MARINA ROMEA

Boca Barranca   pizzeria   €-€€, AIC
Viale Italia, 301   tel. 0544.447858   www.bocabarranca.it
Notes: At the beach.

MARZABOTTO

Agrit. Rustico La Quercia   agritourism   €-€€, AIC
Via Quercia, 22   tel. 0516775397   www.lallegroturismo.it

MEDICINA

Il Murello   agritourism   €€, AIC
Via Fiorentina, 3780   tel. 0516962054   www.agriturismoilmurello.it
Notes: Closed Monday-Thursday

Paggio Simone   bakery   €, AIC
Piazza Garibaldi, 30/31   tel. 51.850828   www.paggiosimone.it

Pizzissima Italia   pizzeria   €, AIC
Via Argentesi, 24/c   tel. 051.0343968
www.it-it.facebook.com/pizzissimaitaliasrl

MILANO MARITTIMA

Hotel Fenice   hotel   AIC
Via XVII Traversa, 9   tel. 0544.994325
www.alberghimilanomarittima.com/ita/hotel-fenice-milano-marittima

Albergo Sabrina
V.le Tirrenia, 7
Notes: Closed October-March.

MIRAMARE DI RIMINI

hotel
tel. 0541372213

€€€€, AIC

Hotel Carlo
Via Regina Margherita,72

hotel
tel. 0541.372477

AIC
www.hotelcarlo.it

La Dolcetteria
Via Oliveti, 68c/70

bakery
tel. 333.9572725

€, AIC

MIRANDOLA

Il Gelatino

gelato (€, AIC)

Piazza della Costituente, 29

MISANO ADRIATICO

I Due Fratelli
Via Scacciano, 15

restaurant, pizzeria
tel. 0541606363

€-€€€€, AIC

L'Angelo Azzurro
S.S. Adriatica, 11

restaurant, pizzeria
tel. 0541615341

AIC

Morotti
Via Gabriele D'Annunzio, 17

hotel
tel. 0541.615560

AIC
www.hotelmorotti.it

MODENA

Anissa
Via Mar Mediterraneo, 6

pizzeria
tel. 059252392

€-€€, AIC

Caffè con tè
Via Baccelli, 46/48

restaurant, tavola calda, bar
tel. 340.5530867

AIC
www.caffeconte.com

Fusorari cibi&viaggi
P.le Torti, 5

restaurant
tel. 0594270436

AIC

Grom

gelato (€, AIC)

Largo di Porta Bologna, 40

La Moretta
tel. 380.6950313

gelato (€, AIC)   V.le Martiri della Libertà,18/A
www.gelaterialamoretta.it

La Scintilla

gelato (€, AIC)

Via Giardini, 306-308

Le Macine
Via P. Giardini, 739

pizzeria
tel. 059344646

€, AIC
www.lemacineristorante.it

Le stelle di Adua
Via Biagio Pascal, 123
Notes: Everything gluten-free.

bakery
tel. 059.8756288

€, AIC
www.lestellediadua.com

Osteria Stallo del Pomodoro
Largo Hannover, 63

restaurant, wine bar
tel. 059214664

€€€€, AIC

Pisano

gelato (€, AIC)

Via Pisano, 40/44

Raphael Caffè
Via Vignolese, 92

tavola calda
tel. 347.1807136 www.facebook.com/raphaelcafemodena

€, AIC

Slurp

gelato (€, AIC)

V.le Trento Trieste, 50

Star Bene Senza Glutine
Via Vignolese 870

bar, desserts
tel. 59.374047

€
www.starbenesenzaglutine.it

Starbene senza glutine caffè
Via Vignolese, 870/A

bar, tavola calda
tel. 59.374047

€, AIC
www.starbenesenzaglutine.mo.it

MONTE COLOMBO

I Muretti	agritourism, B&B	€€€, AIC
Via Sarciano, 5	tel. 0541985146	www.imuretti.net

MONTECCHIO EMILIA

La Grattugia	restaurant	€€€, AIC
Via Montegrappa, 30	tel. 0522871520	

Notes: Closed Thursdays.

MONTECENERE DI LAMA MOCOGNO

Bacio del Cimone - Prosciutteria	restaurant	€, AIC
Via Torre, 5	tel. 053641662	

MONZONE DI PAVULLO

Casa Minelli	agritourism	€€, AIC
Via per Montecenere, 30	tel. 053641580	

NONANTOLA

La Bodeguita	restaurant, pizzeria	€-€€, AIC
Via Costa, 6/1	tel. 059546858	

Pizza Matta	pizzeria	€, AIC
Via Mavora, 4/2	tel. 59.547786	

PARMA

Al Petitot	restaurant, pizzeria bar	€€-€€€, AIC
Via P. Torelli, 1/a	tel. 0521235594	

Celì	sandwich shop, gastropub	€, AIC
Via Jenner, 2/D	tel. 0521.710272	www.senzaglutineparma.it

Gelateria Due di Fiori	gelato (€, AIC)	Via G. Sidoli, 33/d
Gelateria OK	gelato (€, AIC)	Via Valenti, 1/c
Grom	gelato (€, AIC)	Via XXII Luglio, 3

Il Cortile	restaurant	€€-€€€, AIC
Borgo Paglia, 3	tel. 0521285779	

Notes: Closed Sundays.

La Vela	pizzeria	€, AIC
Via Montanara, 85	tel. 0521.962478	

www.facebook.com/pages/La-Vela-Ristorante-Pizzeria/164960630187276

Mychef San Martino Est	mychef	€, AIC
Al Milano - Napoli	tel. 0521.604248	www.mychef.it

Officina Gastronomica	sandwich shop, bakery	€, AIC
Via Pò, 9	tel. 0521.967327	www.officinagastronomicaparma.net

Star Bene Senza Glutine	bar, desserts	€
Via Braglia 1/D	tel. 521.240554	www.starbenesenzaglutine.it

PAVULLO NEL FRIGNANO

Da Martino	restaurant, pizzeria	€, AIC
Via Fondovalle Panaro, 39	tel. 053648062	

PIACENZA

Buon per te - Bontà fresche di Nonna Luisa bakery		€, AIC
Via Millo, 51/53	tel. 0523.1998789	www.buonperte.com

Cone Island — gelato (€, AIC)
Via Farnesiana 8/c

Il Grillo — pizzeria — tel. 0523.593393
Emilia Parmense,58
€, AIC
www.pizzeriailgrillo.it

Ludoteca Jungle Village — bar — tel. 366.7131308
Via Emilia Parmense, 21
Notes: For little kids.
€, AIC
www.junglevillagepc.com

Pausa Caffè — bar — tel. 348.5639011
Via P. Cella, 51
€, AIC
www.facebook.com/pages/Pausa-Caff%C3%A8/515601301833273

Pizzeria Bella Napoli — pizzeria — tel. 0523480038
Via Emilia Pavese,98
€, AIC
www.bellanapolipiacenza.it

Trattoria del Borgo — restaurant — tel. 0523484176
Via Trebbia, 22
€€€ - €€€€, AIC
www.tdb-trattoriadelborgo.it

PIANORO

Il Poggiolo — agritourism, B&B — tel. 0516510208
Via Gorgognano, 4
€€-€€€, AIC

PIEVE DI CENTO

Minelli — restaurant/pizzeria — tel. 05175466
Via Ponte Nuovo, 21
€€ - €€€, AIC
www.ristorantepizzeriaminelli.it

PODENZANO

I Cucinieri — bakery — tel. 0523.070266
Via Roma, 65
€, AIC
www.icucinieripiacenza.com

PORTO GARIBALDI

Gelateria del cuore — gelato (€, AIC)
Piazza tre Agosto, 1/A

PUIANELLO

Il Pomodorino — pizzeria — tel. 0522880374
Via C. Marx, 29/B
€, AIC

PUNTA MARINA TERME

Bagno Vela — restaurant — tel. 0544438789
Lungomare C. Colombo, 24
€€-€€€, AIC
www.bagnovela.it

Bar Centrale — tavola calda, bar — tel. 0544.437244
Viale dei Navigatori, 29
€, AIC

H. Ambra/Rist. Eulalia — hotel, restaurant, pizzeria — tel. 0544437108
V.le delle Ondine, 11
€-€€, AIC
www.ristoranteeulalia.it

Pizzeria Cento Pizze — pizzeria — tel. 0544.437321
Via delle Nasse, 21
€, AIC
www.centopizze.com

QUARTO DI GOSSOLENGO

Molto Pizza — restaurant, pizzeria — tel. 0523557132
Via Terracini, 10
€-€€, AIC

RAVENNA

Al 45 — restaurant — tel. 0544.212761
Via Paolo Costa, 45
€€-€€€, AIC
www.al45.it

America Graffiti Fast Food c/o Cinema City sandwich shop — tel. 0544.461097
Viale Secondo Bini, 11
€, AIC
www.americagraffiti.it

Gluten-Free Italy by Region

Cine Pizza Via Secondo Bini, 7	pizzeria tel. 0544.464251	€, AIC
Cube Via Masotti, 2	hotel tel. 0544464691	€€€€, AIC
Il Brigantino Via Marconi, 57	restaurant, pizzeria tel. 0544402598	€€, AIC www.ilbrigantino.org

REGGIO EMILIA

Ad Bed and Breakfast Via Scaruffi, 14/3	B&B tel. 3358155624	AIC
Anna & Ricca C.so Garibaldi, 2	B&B tel. 0522432719	AIC
Piedigrotta 2 Via Emilia Ospizio, 50	restaurant, pizzeria tel. 0522.552637	€-€€, AIC www.nuovapiedigrotta.it
Star Bene Senza Glutine Via F.lli Cervi n. 130/c	bar, desserts tel. 0522/082224	€ www.starbenesenzaglutine.it
Twiga Via Fratelli Cervi, 40/b	pizzeria tel. 0522791029	€, AIC
West Pacific	gelato (€, AIC)	Via Kennedy, 17/h

REGGIO EMILIA-CANALI

La Razza Via Monterampino, 6	agritourism tel. 0522599342	€€€, AIC

RENAZZO-CENTO

La Pergola Via Tassinari, 30	restaurant, pizzeria tel. 051909124	€, AIC

Notes: DS pizza point. Closed Mondays and at lunch.

RICCIONE

22 Garibaldi Home Via Garibaldi, 22	B&B tel. 0541.600683	AIC www.riccionebedandbreakfast.com
Bouganville Via Virgilio, 28/30	restaurant, pizzeria tel. 0541692622	€-€€€, AIC www.ristorantebouganville.it
California Burger Via Bellini, 9	sandwich shop tel. 3425755353	€, AIC
Cremeria Vanilla	gelato (€, AIC)	Viale Dante, 114/A
Niagara V.le Tasso, 40	hotel tel. 0541648664	AIC www.hotelniagara-riccione.it

Notes: Closed October-Easter.

Nuovo Fiore	gelato (€, AIC)	Viale Ceccarini, 1
Sirena Passeggiata Goethe, 10	restaurant tel. 0541660416	€€-€€€€, AIC

Notes: Closed October-Easter.

Trieste Via Manzoni, 7/9	hotel tel. 0541646352	AIC www.hoteltriestericcione.com

RIMINI

Bikini V.le Cristoforo Colombo, 4	hotel tel. 054125700	AIC

Corallo V.le Vespucci, 46	hotel, restaurant tel. 0541390732	AIC www.hotelcorallorimini.com
Da Biagio Via Circon.ne Meridionale, 28	osteria, pizzeria tel. 0541782403	€-€€€€, AIC
Fratelli La Bufala Via Caduti di Nassirya	restaurant tel. 0541380639	€ - €€, AIC www.fratellilabufala.eu
Grom	gelato (€, AIC)	P.zza Cavour, 11
La Brocca via Caduti di Marzabotto, 11	pizzeria, restaurant tel. 0541770796	€, AIC www.labroccarimini.com
La Piazzetta	gelato (€, AIC)	Via Saffi, 4
Matiss Via Della Fiera, 103	restaurant, pizzeria tel. 0541776060	€-€€€, AIC

RONCOLE VERDI
Le Roncole
Via della Processione, 179 — restaurant, B&B — tel. 0524930015 — €€-€€€, AIC

S. ANDREA BAGNI
Andrea's
Via Circonvallazione, 51 — restaurant, pizzeria — tel. 0525431818 — €, AIC

S. EGIDIO
La Rocchetta
Via Rocca, 69 — agritourism — tel. 0532725824 — €€€-€€€€, AIC

S. GIOVANNI IN MARIGNANO
Party Pizza
Via Galleria Marignano, 12 — pizzeria — tel. 0541955065 — €, AIC

SAN CARLO
La Pace Bar Pizzeria Trattoria
Via Statale, 63 — restaurant, pizzeria, trattoria, bar — AIC

SAN GIORGIO PIACENTINO
Il Pallino Rosa
Via Firenze, 16 — bakery — tel. 348.3465567 — €, AIC
www.facebook.com/pages/Pallino-Rosa-pasta-fresca-senza-glutine/439591816083341

Val di Luce
Godi di San Giorgio Piacentino — restaurant, pizzeria — tel. 0523.530100 — €-€€, AIC
www.ristorantevaldiluce.it

SAN GIOVANNI IN MARIGNANO
Star Bene Senza Glutine
Via Della Resistenza, 22 — bar, desserts — tel. 541.97459 — €
www.starbenesenzaglutine.it

SAN GIOVANNI IN PERSICETO
La Fattoria
Via Crevalcore 84 - loc. Amola — pizzeria — tel. 051827072 — €, AIC

SAN GIUSTINO
Star Bene Senza Glutine
Via Ottavio Giovanni Bufalini, 13 — bar, desserts — €
www.starbenesenzaglutine.it

SAN MAURO PASCOLI
Bio Pizza
P.zza Giorgi, 29 — pizzeria — tel. 0541818413 — €, AIC

SANTA MARIA DEGLI ANGELI - ASSISI

| **Star Bene Senza Glutine** | bar, desserts | € |
| Viale della Repubblica n. 8/a | tel. 075/8043627 | www.starbenesenzaglutine.it |

SANTARCANGELO DI ROMAGNA

Bio Pizza pizzeria €, AIC
Via Emilia, 3009 tel. 0541.624820

Vicolo di Brused osteria €, AIC
Via Battisti, 23 tel. 0541.622990 www.biopizza.org

SANTERNO

Vecchiacanala restaurant €€€€, AIC
Via Canala, 355 tel. 0544417245

SANT'ILARIO D'ENZA

Gusto&Sapore pizzeria €, AIC
Via della libertà, 22 tel. 0522.902268

Portami via bakery €, AIC
Via della libertà, 23 tel. 0522.472731 www.portamivia.net

SASSUOLO

Aragosta restaurant, pizzeria €-€€€€, AIC
Via Pia, 183 tel. 0536805153

Harlow Sassuolo pizzeria €, AIC
Via Ancora, 378 tel. 0536806422 www.pizzeriaharlow.it

SAVIGNANO SUL RUBICONE

Sweet Line gelato (€, AIC) P.zza Giovanni XXIII, 8

SESTOLA

Al Poggio hotel, restaurant €€-€€€, AIC
Via Poggioraso, 88 tel. 053661147

TAGLIATA DI CERVIA

Ranch restaurant €€€-€€€€, AIC
Viale Italia, 368 tel. 0544987355

TOSCANELLA DI DOZZA

Millevoglie pizzeria €, AIC
Via 1° Maggio, 12 tel. 0542673509

UMBERTIDE

Star Bene Senza Glutine bar, desserts €
Via Fratta, 44 tel. 392.1010452 www.starbenesenzaglutine.it

VERGATO

Gelateria artigianale Le Streghe gelato (€, AIC) Galleria I Maggio, 91

VIGNOLA

Cucinando bakery, deli €, AIC
Via della Pace, 127 tel. 59.765563 www.cucinandoavignola.com

L'Artigiano gelato (€, AIC) Via N. Bruni,166

VILLA VERUCCHIO

Kiosko il Vincanto café, bar €, AIC
Via Aldo Moro, 105 tel. 0541.676717

Nuovo Tarabacco pizzeria €, AIC
Via Casale, 340 tel. 0541.670672

Pizzeria Osteria De Sgrazjid   restaurant, pizzeria   €, AIC
Via Casale, 392-396   tel. 0541.670279
www.pizzeriaosteriadesgrazjid.it/ristorante.php

VISERBA DI RIMINI
Aurora   hotel   €€€€, AIC
Via Dati, 182   tel. 0541738337   www.haurora.it
Notes: Closed November-April.

VISERBELLA
Cadiz   hotel   €€€€, AIC
Via S. Cenci, 1   tel. 0541721713   www.hotelcadiz.it
Notes: Closed October-March.

ZOLA PEDROSA
C'è Pizza Per Te   pizzeria   €, AIC
Via Risorgimento, 432/8c   tel. 051756905
Notes: Closed Mondays, Sunday lunch.

Nuovo Parco dei Ciliegi   restaurant, pizzeria   €€, AIC
Via Gessi, 2   tel. 051750759   www.parcodeiciliegi.it
Notes: DS pizza point. Closed Tuesdays.

ZOLA PREDOSA
Mychef La Pioppa Ovest   mychef   €, AIC
A14 Bologna - Taranto
tel. 051.6160273   www.mychef.it

Bicicletta (M. Roglieri)

NAPLES AND CAMPANIA

Neopolitan water buffalo make the best mozzarella (U. Benninger)

(AIC = participates in the Associazione Italiana Celiachia program)

NAPOLI

Al Pruneto
Discesa Coroglio, 101/102
restaurant, pizzeria
tel. 081.7690744
AIC

Arcobaleno di Sapori
Via G. Tropeano, 28/30
sandwich shop, bakery
tel. 081/7704881
€, AIC

Birrzeria Re Carlo
Larghetto S. Antonio Abate, 1
restaurant, pizzeria
tel. 081.19979725
AIC

F.lli Pellone
Via G.Leopardi, 239
Notes: Closed Mondays.
pizzeria
tel. 0815934602
€, AIC

Holiday Inn Naples
Centro Direzionale Isola, E/6
hotel, restaurant
tel. 0812250111
€€
www.holidayinn.com/Naples

Hotel delle Terme di Agnano
Via Agnano Astroni, 24
hotel, restaurant
tel. 0817622180
€€
www.hoteltermeagnano.com

La Bufalina
Via U. Masoni, 31
pizzeria
tel. 081.7518890
€, AIC

La Caraffa
Via Piave, 41/47
pizzeria
tel. 0816403030
€, AIC

La Ruota
Via Nicola Rocco, 16/18
pizzeria
tel. 081.7805678
€, AIC

La Taverna di Bacco Via Sementini, 28/32	restaurant, pizzeria tel. 0815466119	€€, AIC www.latavernadibacco.com
Mama. Eat (2 locations) Via E. Alvino, 118 Via Manzoni, 6A/8 Notes: Closed Mondays and at lunch.	restaurant, pizzeria, pub tel. 081.5787833 tel. 0817148696	AIC
Mammina Via Partenope, 15/18	restaurant, pizzeria tel. 081.2400001	AIC
Mascagni Via Mascagni, 42/48	restaurant, pizzeria tel. 081.5602900	AIC
Menhir Via Giotto, 14,16,18 Notes: Closed Mondays at dinner, Sundays at lunch.	pub tel. 0815566945	€, AIC
Oliva da Concettina ai Tre Santi Via Arena alla Sanità, 7/b	pizzeria tel. 081.290037	€, AIC
Pizzazzà Via Michelangelo Caravaggio, 33	pizzeria tel. 081.7146941	€, AIC
Pizzeria La Ruota Via Nicola Rocco, 16/18	pizzeria tel. 0817805678	€, AIC www.pizzerialaruota.com
Rosso Pomodoro Napoli Centro Piazza Trieste e Trento, 7/8	pizzeria tel. 081.412791	€, AIC
Royal Continental Via Partenope, 38	hotel, restaurant tel. 0812452068	€€€-€€€€, AIC www.royalcontinental.it
Siani Senza Glutine Via Domenico Fontana 47/a	bakery tel. 081.5585332	€, AIC
Siani senza Glutine V.le Kennedy, 333	sandwich shop, bakery tel. 081.18901965	€, AIC
Sorbillo Via dei Tribunali, 38 Notes: Closed Sundays.	pizzeria tel. 0810331009	€, AIC www.sorbillo.eu
Gelat. Del Gallo Notes: Closed Wednesdays.	gelato (€, AIC)	Via A.C. De Meis, 60/62
Gelateria Della Scimmia **Gelatosità**	gelato (€, AIC) gelato (€, AIC)	P.zza Carità, 4 Via Mario Fiore, 2/a

THE REST OF CAMPANIA
CAPACCIO

Oleandri Via Poseidonia, 177	resort, hotel tel. 828.8518	AIC www.oleandriresort.com

S. GIORGIO

Italian Bakery Via Europa, 6	bakery tel. 345.71361	€, AIC

SAN GIORGIO

Tutto Senza Via Giovanni XXIII,	bakery tel. 81.36554	€, AIC

ACERRA

Gelatosità	gelato (€, AIC)	Via A. Diaz, 7/9
Primavera	restaurant, pizzeria	€-€€, AIC
Via A. De Gasperi, 30	tel. 0816588002	
Totò e i Sapori	pizzeria	€, AIC
Via S. Gioacchino, 73	tel. 081.5206424	

ACQUAVELLA DI CASALVELINO

Spina Rossa	agritourism	€€, AIC
Loc. Pantaleo	tel. 3406007508	

ACQUAVENA DI ROCCAGLORIOSA

U' Trappitu	restaurant, pizzeria	AIC
Via Del Mare, 51	tel. 0974.980167	

AFRAGOLA

Pachà	crêperie	€, AIC
Via Cinque Vie, 24	tel. 3278856811	www.cornetteriapacha.it
Rosso Pomodoro	pizzeria	€, AIC
Via S. Maria La Nova	tel. 081.3198509	

AGROPOLI

Anna	restaurant, pizzeria, inn	€€€-€€€€, AIC
Via S.Marco, 28-32	tel. 0974823763	
B&B Anna	B&B	AIC
Via S. Marco, 32	tel. 0974823763	www.affittacamereanna.it

AIELLO DEL SABATO

La Locandina	restaurant, pizzeria	€€, AIC
Via Ternana, 1/c	tel. 0825666620	www.villacalvo.it

AIROLA

Antovin	restaurant, pizzeria	€, AIC
Via Caudisi, 11	tel. 0823711439	www.ristorantepizzeriaantovin.com

ALBORI DI VIETRI SUL MARE

Il Cavaliere dei Conti	agritourism	€€€, AIC
Via Case Sparse	tel. 089210791	www.ilcavalieredeiconti.it

AMALFI

Hotel La Bussola	hotel, restaurant	€€-€€€, AIC
Via Lungo Mare dei Cavalieri, 16	tel. 089871533	www.labussolahotel.it
Hotel Santa Caterina	hotel, restaurant, pizzeria	€€€€
S.S. Amalfitana, 9	tel. 089871012	www.hotelsantacaterina.it

AMOROSI

La Piana	hotel, restaurant, pizzeria	€€, AIC
Via Telese, 296	tel. 0824970177	

ANACAPRI

Hotel Bella Vista	hotel/restaurant	
Via Orlandi 10	tel. 0818371463	www.bellavistacapri.com

Notes: GF breakfast. Restaurant will serve GF food.

La Rondinella	caprese/pizza	€€
Via Orlandi 295	tel. 0818371223	

Notes: GF pasta. Reservations recommended.

La Pignata in Bellavista	**ARIANO IRPINO**	
C.da Sterda, 19	restaurant, pizzeria	AIC
	tel. 0825.872433	www.ristorantelapignata.it
Locanda San Cipriano	**ATENA LUCANA**	
Via Serroni snc	restaurant, pizzeria	AIC
	tel. 0975.511447	www.locandasancipriano.it
Blueorange	**ATRIPALDA**	
Via Roma, 110	restaurant, pizzeria	€€, AIC
	tel. 0825627339	
Cose da Mat	**AVELLINO**	
Via Circumvallazione, 118	bakery	€, AIC
	tel. 0825.781815	
Hotel de la Ville	hotel, restaurant	AIC
Via Palatucci,20	tel. 0825.780911	www.hoteldelavilleavellino.it

Mangiamoci su restaurant, pizzeria AIC
Via Luigi De Nitto snc c/o Città Ospedaliera tel. 0825.31097
www.facebook.com/mangiamocisuavellino

Mastrogio'	tavola calda	AIC
C.so Umberto I, 71	tel. 0825.460367	
Springfield	pizzeria	€, AIC
Via C. Colombo, 31	tel. 3490626515	
The Happy Chef	sandwich shop	€, AIC
Circumvallazione, 118/f	tel. 08253199	www.happychef.it
Vecchia Fontana	restaurant, pizzeria	AIC
C.so Umberto I, 32	tel. 0825.756209	
Da Mimmo	**AVERSA**	
Via S. di Giacomo,52	pizzeria	€, AIC
	tel. 081.8903016	
Gastrò	pizzeria	€, AIC
Via Torrebianca, 78	tel. 0818905591	www.gustogastro.it
Il Magnifico	osteria	€-€€, AIC
Via Filippo Saporito, 102	tel. 0815002093	
Infinity	sandwich shop	€, AIC
V.le della Libertà, 156	tel. 333.2288397	
Punto Pizza	restaurant, pizzeria	€, AIC
Piazza V. Emanuele, 50	tel. 0818903920	
Smile Gel	gelato(€, AIC)	P.zza Vittorio Emanuele, 35
Notes: Also has crêpes.		
Baios - Il Gabbiano	**BACOLI**	
Via Cicerone, 21	hotel, restaurant	€€€-€€€€, AIC
	tel. 081868796	
Cala Moresca	hotel, restaurant	€-€€€, AIC
Via Faro, 44	tel. 0815235595	www.calamoresca.it
Gennaro 2	**BAGNOLI**	
Via Lucio Silla, 35	restaurant, pizzeria	AIC
	tel. 0816100855	

	BARONISSI	
I Love Pizza	pizzeria	€, AIC
Via T. Sanseverino, 51	tel. 089953360	

	BARRA	
Scusate il Ritardo	restaurant, pizzeria	AIC
Via Bartolo Longo, 249	tel. 081.5961829	

	BATTIPAGLIA	
Arienzo	bakery	€, AIC
V.le Primo Baratta, 14	tel. 0828.1994139	

Centro Congressi San Luca	hotel, restaurant, pizzeria	€€, AIC
Via S.S. 18 - Km. 76, 5 M.no Braggio	tel. 0828342533	www.sanlucahotel.it

La Fabbrica dei Sapori	pizzeria	AIC
Via Spineta, 84/C	tel. 0828630021	

Pizza Art	restaurant, pizzeria	€-€€€, AIC
Via Rosario, 47	tel. 08281840582	www.pizzaart.eu

Pizza e Sfizi	pizzeria	€, AIC
Via Silvio Pellico, 7	tel. 333.2518793	

Positano	pizzeria	€, AIC
Via Amerigo Vespucci, 1	tel. 0828371285	

Tenuta Marrandino	pizzeria	€, AIC
Via Fosso Pioppo, 5	tel. 0828.047059	

Victoria	pizzeria	€, AIC
Via M. Ripa, 14	tel. 0828.302587	

	BELLONA	
Cotton Hill	restaurant, pizzeria	€€€, AIC
Via Nazionale Triflisco, 3	tel. 0823960617	www.cottonhills.it

	BELTIGLIO DI CEPPALONI	
Zanzibar	bar	€, AIC
Via Roma	tel. 0824.46770	

	BENEVENTO	
Da Claudio	restaurant, pizzeria	€, AIC
C.da S. Chirico	tel. 082429374	www.daclaudio.it

	BOSCO DI SAN GIOVANNI A PIRO	
La Locanda di Romeo	hotel, restaurant	€€-€€€, AIC
Via Provinciale, 33	tel. 0974980004	www.romeo-bosco.com

	BRACIGLIANO	
La Taverna dei Briganti	restaurant, pizzeria	€€€, AIC
V.le Springfield Mass, 10	tel. 3293490990	

	CAPACCIO PAESTUM	
TraleSpighe	bakery	€, AIC
Via Nazionale S.S. 18, 119/121	tel. 0828.821544	

	CAPACCIO SCALO, PAESTUM	
La Basilica Cafè	pizzeria	€, AIC
Via Magna Grecia, 881	tel. 828811301	www.labasilicacafe.it

CAPODICHINO

Autogrill Aeroporto Napoli Capodichino Autogrill   €, AIC
Via dell'Aeroporto di Capodichino   tel. 081.5993220

CAPODRISE

Marconi   bakery, sandwich shop   €, AIC
Via Greco, 1   tel. 338.1179570
www.facebook.com/pages/Pizzeria-Marconi-Celiachia-/184108851601979

Novotel Caserta /Novotelcafé   hotel, restaurant   €€€€, AIC
SS. 87 Sannitica km. 22,600   tel. 0823826553   www.novotel.com

CAPRI

Gelateria Buonocore Raffaele   gelato (€, AIC)   Via Vitt. Emanuele, 35
Notes: Closed Tuesdays.

Punta Tragara   hotel/restaurant
Via Tragara 57   tel. 0818370844   www.hoteltragara.com
Notes: GF breakfast, dinner with advance notice. Closed Nov. – Mar.

Villa Brunella   hotel/seafood restaurant
Via Tragara 24   tel. 0818370122   www.villabrunella.it
Notes: closed Nov.-March.

CARDITO

Appost' Accussi'   pizzeria   €, AIC
Via P. Donadio, 262   tel. 081.8345496

Charlot   gelato (€, AIC)   P.za Madonna d. Grazie, 9

CASALNUOVO DI NAPOLI

Hotel Rea/Rist. Convivio   hotel, restaurant, pizzeria   €€€, AIC
Via Nazionale delle Puglia, 62   tel. 0818421263   www.hotelrea.it

La Sequoia   restaurant, pizzeria   AIC
V.le dei Ligustri, 13   tel. 0818429851

Mister Pizz   restaurant, pizzeria   AIC
Via Napoli, 49   tel. 081.3441610

CASAVATORE

Pizzeria Iorio   pizzeria   €, AIC
G. Marconi, 123/125   tel. 081.7382626

Tutta 'Nata Storia   pizzera, trattoria   AIC
Via Locatelli, 34   tel. 081.0120973

Un Mondo Senza Glutine   bakery   €, AIC
Via Locatelli, 25/27   tel. 081.0401278

CASELLE IN PITTARI

La Pietra Azzurra   restaurant, pizzeria   €, AIC
Via Caporra, 64   tel. 0974988779   www.ristorantelapietrazzurra.it

CASERTA

Alba   gelato (€, AIC)   P.zza Cattaneo, 7

Antica Hostaria Massa   restaurant, pizzeria   AIC
Via Mazzini, 55   tel. 0823.456527

Dogana Golosa   restaurant   €-€€€€, AIC
S.S. Sannitica Km.113 loc. Vaccheria   tel. 0823301508   www.doganagolosa.it

Gluten-Free Italy by Region

Embè Via Tescione, 173	restaurant/pizzeria tel. 08231543751	€€€, AIC www.embediscopub.it
Zero Glutine Via Ricciardelli, 48	bakery tel. 0823.1970249	€, AIC

CASERTAVECCHIA

Caserta Antica Via Tiglio, 75	B&B tel. 0823371158	AIC www.hotelcaserta-antica.it
La Castellana Via Tescione, 174	restaurant tel. 08231540497	€, AIC
La Tana del Lupo Via Lupara, 1	restaurant, pizzeria tel. 0823371333	€€, AIC www.allatanadellupo.it

CASORIA

Graffe & Co Via S. Salvatore, 1	creperie tel. 392.6603805	€, AIC
Juancarlos Via D. Colasanto, 32/34	pizzeria, pub tel. 0815844868	€, AIC
Pizzeria Carducci Via Giosuè Carducci, 19	pizzeria tel. 081.7573311	€, AIC

CASTEL SAN GIORGIO

Salerno Food Via Palmiro Togliatti, 11	bakery tel. 081.5162518	€, AIC

CASTELLAMMARE DI STABIA

Il Mago dello Spiedo Via Annunziatella, 7	pizzeria, sandwich shop tel. 0818704064	€, AIC
Monzu' Via E. De Nicola, 35	restaurant, pizzeria tel. 081.8721022	AIC
Re Di Pi...zze Via Bonito, 45	bakery tel. 334.9746551	€, AIC

CASTELNUOVO CILENTO

Anna dei Sapori Via S. Venere, 1 Fraz. Velina	agritourism tel. 0974.63928	AIC www.annadeisapori.it

CASTELVENERE

Fattoria Ciabrelli Via Sannitica	agritourism tel. 0824940565	€€, AIC www.ciabrelli.it

CASTIGLIONE DEL GENOVESI

Il Riccio Via V. Genovesi	restaurant, pizzeria tel. 089881641	€€-€€€, AIC

CAVA DE' TIRRENI

Alba Chiara Via L. Palmentieri, 1	restaurant, pizzeria tel. 089.2960099	AIC
Caffetteria Remo Via Vittorio Veneto, 282	bar tel. 089.340059	€, AIC
Made in Italy C.so Mazzini, 111	restaurant, pizzeria tel. 089345248	AIC www.madeinitalycava.it

Montecaruso Hotel
Via S. Felice,snc S.Lucia

hotel, restaurant, pizzeria
tel. 089467817

€€-€€€€, AIC
www.montecaruso.it

CERASO

La Petrosa
Via Fabbrica, 25

agritourism
tel. 097461370

€€-€€€, AIC
www.lapetrosa.it

Osteria del Notaro
Via Isca, 19

restaurant, pizzeria
tel. 097461294

€, AIC
www.cilentohouse.it

CERCOLA

Del Pino
Via Don Minzoni, 225

restaurant, pizzeria
tel. 0817331145

€-€€€€, AIC
www.gruppoleonessa.it

CIMITILE

Maidomo
Via Enrico De Nicola, 24

restaurant, pizzeria
tel. 081.19532820

AIC

CIRCELLO

Antica Trattoria Bacco
C.so Municipio, 121/a

restaurant, pizzeria
tel. 0824937720

€€, AIC
www.anticatrattoriabacco.com

CONCA DELLA CAMPANIA

Agriturismo La Palombara
Via I° Novembre, 149

agritourism
tel. 0823923580

€€€, AIC
www.lapalombara.com

CUSANO MUTRI

Mastrillo
Via Giocagni,15

restaurant, pizzeria
tel. 0824862205

€€, AIC

DRAGONEA DI VIETRI SUL MARE

Il Limoneto
Via Raccio, 3

restaurant, pizzeria
tel. 089.210358

AIC

ERCOLANO

Gianni Al Vesuvio
Via Vesuvio, 10

restaurant, pizzeria
tel. 0817395684

€€€, AIC
www.giannialvesuvio.com

Le Nuvole Restaurant
Via Roma, 45

restaurant
tel. 0817322002

€€€, AIC

Villa Signorini Relais
Via Roma, 43

hotel, restaurant
tel. 0817776423

AIC
www.villasignorini.it

FELITO

L'Occhiano
Loc. Difesa Lombi

pub, pizzeria
tel. 0828945255

€€-€€€, AIC
www.ristorantepizzerialocchiano.com

FISCIANO

Belvedere
Via Del Centenario, 82

restaurant, pizzeria
tel. 089878996

€€€, AIC

Rosso Pomodoro
Via Faraldo, 11/23

restaurant, pizzeria
tel. 089.826081

AIC

FOGLIANISE

La Tripolina
Via Roma, 15

pizzeria
tel. 0824.871481

€, AIC

Gluten-Free Italy by Region

FORIO D'ISCHIA

Bosco Hotel
Via San Gennaro, 46

hotel, restaurant
tel. 081909132

AIC
www.hotelalbosco.it

Da Leopoldo
Via Scannella, 12 - Loc. Panza

restaurant, pizzeria
tel. 081907086

AIC

Hotel Terme Castaldi
Via Monterone, 70

hotel
tel. 081997101

€€€€, AIC
www.hotelcastaldi.com

Villa La Cesa
Via Parroco D'Abundo, 129

B&B
tel. 081907512

AIC
www.appartamenticesaischia.com

FORIO-PANZA ISCHIA

La Forastera
Via Forte, 31

restaurant, pizzeria
tel. 081907281

€€, AIC

FRATTAMAGGIORE

Black Burger
Via V. Emanuele, 167

pub
tel. 339.3525163

AIC

PalaPizza
Via Vittoria, 36

pizzeria
tel. 081.8322040

€, AIC

Gastrò
Via Veneto 38/44

pizzeria
tel. 0818804936

€, AIC

Il Rustichiere
Via Padre Mario Vergaro, 10/12

restaurant, pizzeria
tel. 0818804693

€€, AIC

Pinguino Reale

gelato (€, AIC)

Via Padre Mario Vergara, 201

FRATTAMINORE

Da Ciro
Via F. Turati, 40

restaurant, pizzeria
tel. 081.8363181

AIC

FRIGENTO

Fontana Madonna
C.da Fontana Madonna

agritourism
tel. 082544647

€€, AIC
www.fontanamadonna.it

Le Delizie Steakhouse
Via Pagliara, 156

restaurant, pizzeria
tel. 0825440357

€€, AIC

FURORE

Hostaria di Bacco
Via Giovan Battista Lama, 9

hotel, restaurant
tel. 089.830360

AIC

GIFFONI SEI CASALI

Al Vecchio Rifugio
Via Malche, 64

restaurant, pizzeria
tel. 089880141

€€-€€€, AIC
www.alvecchiorifugio.it

Popilia
Via Serroni, 45

restaurant
tel. 089880129

€-€€€, AIC

Villa Regina
Via Serroni, 45

B&B
tel. 089880129

AIC

GIUGLIANO IN CAMPANIA

Alexander Pizza
Via Casacelle, 50/Parco Regina

pizzeria
tel. 0813307010

€, AIC

La Capricciosa
Via Degli Innamorati, 149

pizzeria
tel. 081.5069936

€, AIC

Lido Varca d'Oro
Via Orsa Maggiore
Notes: Self-service.

restaurant, pizzeria, tavola calda €, AIC
tel. 0815091214

Nick
Via Ripuaria, 304

pub, sandwich shop €, AIC
tel. 081.3347517

GRAGNANO
Ai Giardini dei Cesari
Via Pass.ta Archeol.ca Varano

gelato €, AIC
tel. 081.8710234

L'Angelo Rosso
Via Cappella della Guardia, 23

restaurant/pizzeria €€, AIC
tel. 0818794132 www.langelorosso.it.gg

GROTTAMINARDA
A Tempo Perso
Via Valle snc

pizzeria €, AIC
tel. 0825.426204

Villa Sant'Andrea
Ctr Sant'Andrea snc

restaurant, pizzeria AIC
tel. 334.9864853

GROTTOLELLA
La Cantinella
Via della Repubblica, 14

restaurant, pizzeria €€, AIC
tel. 0825671077 www.lacantinella.av.it

MADDALONI
A'ddo' Napulitano
Via Napoli, 80/86

restaurant, pizzeria €-€€€, AIC
tel. 0823402642 www.addonapulitano.it

MAIORI
Al Mare Restaurant e Bar
Via G. Capone, 63

restaurant, pizzeria bar €€-€€€, AIC
tel. 3089852668

Casa Mariannina
Via Scala Santa, 1

B&B AIC
tel. 089.853609 www.casamariannina.com

La Casa d'Amare
Via Orti, 40

B&B AIC
tel. 089.851743 www.lacasadamare.it

Meublè Casa Mannini
Via Casa Mannini, 2

B&B AIC
tel. 331.6261044 www.casamanninimaiori.it

Pensione Vittoria
Via F. Cerasuoli, 4

B&B AIC
tel. 089877652 www.hotel-vittoria.it

MARANO
Adde' Figliole
Via Giovanni Falcone, 36

pizzeria €, AIC
tel. 08119255102

MARINA DI CAMEROTA
La Locanda di Romeo
Via Lungo Mare Trieste

restaurant, pizzeria €€, AIC
tel. 0974551143 www.romeo-bosco.com

Villaggio Alberg. Da Pepè
Via delle Sirene, 41

village restaurant €€€€, AIC
tel. 0974932461 www.villaggiodapepe.net

MASSA LUBRENSE
Emilia
Via Reola, 12

restaurant, pizzeria €€-€€€, AIC
tel. 0818080643

Hotel Piccolo Paradiso
P.zza Madonna della Lobra, 5

hotel, restaurant €€, AIC
tel. 0818789240 www.piccolo-paradiso.com

Tico Tico
Via Caruso, 3

META
restaurant, pizzeria €€, AIC
tel. 0815321837

MIRABELLA ECLANO
Villa Assunta restaurant AIC
Via Capo di Gaudio, snc tel. 0825.476169

MOIANO
Dal Guappo restaurant, pizzeria €, AIC
Via Nuova S.Pietro, 69 tel. 0823711225

Stella Maiuri agritourism €€, AIC
Via Nuova S.Pietro, 69 tel. 3392050508

MOLINARA
That's Amore restaurant, pizzeria €€€, AIC
C.da Gregaria, 97 tel. 0824994059 www.thatsamoremolinara.it

MONTANARO DI FRANCOLISE
Camelot restaurant, pizzeria AIC
Via Passaro e Romano, 61 tel. 335.1852822

MONTESARCHIO
Il Castello hotel, restaurant €€, AIC
Via Vitulanese, 188 tel. 0824834690

MONTEVERDE
Al Giardino restaurant, pizzeria €, AIC
Via Fontana, 4 tel. 3805453055 www.algiardino.eu

MONTORO INFERIORE
La Cantina dell'Arte restaurant €€, AIC
Via Risorgimento, 53 tel. 08251728820 www.lacantinadellarte.com

MONTORO SUPERIORE
Arco di Magliano restaurant, pizzeria €€€, AIC
Via Magliano tel. 0825523515

MUGNANO DEL CARDINALE
Dell'Ulivo restaurant, pizzeria €€, AIC
Via dell'Uguaglianza, 3 tel. 0818257650 www.ristorantepizzeriadellulivo.it

NAPOLI - MARIANELLA
Club Degli Amici pizzeria €, AIC
Via E. Scaglione, 242 tel. 081.5853576

NAPOLI-POSILLI PO
La Gaiola restaurant, pizzeria AIC
V.le Virgilio,1 tel. 081.3653180

Rosiello restaurant AIC
Via S. Strato,10 tel. 081.7691288

NAPOLI-RIVIERA DI CHIAIA
Umberto restaurant, pizzeria AIC
Via Alabardieri,30/31 tel. 081.418555

NAPOLI-SAN GIOVANNI A TEDUCCIO

Le Ancelle
Via Ferrante Imparato, 25
pizzeria, trattoria
tel. 3772462733
€, AIC

NAPOLI-VOME RO

Bier Garten
Via Mattia Preti, 10/a-b
pub
tel. 081.5568932
€, AIC

Ciao Piada
Via Massimo Stanzione, 14/I
pub
tel. 081.19178942
€, AIC

NAPOLI-VOMERO

Gorizia
Via Albino Albini, 18/20
pizzeria
tel. 0815604642
€, AIC
www.pizzeriagorizia.it

NOCERA INFERIORE

Antico Borgo
Via Vescovado, 49
Notes: Closed Mondays.
restaurant, pizzeria
tel. 081920114
€€€, AIC

L'Uliveto
Via Poggio San Pantaleone snc
agritourism
tel. 081.928400
AIC
www.agriturismouliveto.it

Madison
Via Isaia Gabola, 53
Notes: Closed Mondays.
restaurant, pizzeria
tel. 0815153622
€, AIC

Rist. Pizz. Nocera
Via Marcello De Luca, 29
restaurant, pizzeria
tel. 0968.938090
AIC

Y Cabrera
Via Martinez Y Cabrera, 18/24
restaurant, pizzeria
tel. 081.0486961
AIC

NOCERA SUPERIORE

Caramari
V.le del Santuario, 7
restaurant, pizzeria
tel. 0815143740
€€, AIC

L'Angolo del Gusto
Via Indipendenza, 68
restaurant, pizzeria
tel. 081.19505245
AIC

Luna Galante
Via Santacroce, 13
Notes: Closed Mondays.
restaurant
tel. 0815176065
€€€-€€€€, AIC

Madison Nocera Superiore
Via Croce Mallone, 82
pizzeria
tel. 081.0201667
€, AIC

NOLA

Braciami Ancora
Vulcano Buon Isola Amalfi
restaurant, pizzeria
tel. 335.7362926
AIC

NOVI VELIA - VALLO DELLA LUCANIA

La Chioccia D'Oro
Via Pietra dei Correnti
restaurant
tel. 0974.70004
AIC

NUSCO

Hotel Colucci
Via Passaro, 11
hotel, restaurant
tel. 082764071
€€, AIC
www.hotelcolucci.it

OTTAVIANO

Maxi'o
Via Papa Giovanni XXIII, 14
pizzeria pub
tel. 0818278900
AIC

	PADULA	
La Certosa	hotel, restaurant	€€, AIC
Viale Certosa, 41	tel. 097577046	www.certosa.it
	PAGANI	
La Botte	pizzeria	€, AIC
Via A. Califano, 14/16	tel. 0815155440	
	PALINURO	
Pizzeria Degli Amici dal 1973	pizzeria	€, AIC
Via Indipendenza, 166	tel. 3475506376	
Villaggio Arco Naturale Club	resort, hotel, restaurant	AIC
Via Arco Naturale snc	tel. 0974.931157	
	PELLEZZANO	
Taverna Antica Filanda	restaurant, pizzeria	€€, AIC
Via Filanda, 8	tel. 089481578	
Notes: Closed Mondays.		
	PELLEZZANO - COPERCHIA	
Il Girasole	pizzeria	€, AIC
P.zza Giovanni Paolo II, 8	tel. 089.566540	
	PIANA DI MONTE VERNA	
Agriturismo Le Ghiandaie	agritourism	€€, AIC
Via Polizzano, 2	tel. 0823861216 www.agriturismoleghiandaie.net	
	PIANO DI MONTORO INFERIORE	
La Botte	restaurant, pizzeria	AIC
Via Ferrovia, 3	tel. 3473206241	
	PIMONTE	
Il Trifoglio	restaurant, pizzeria	AIC
Via Piano, 24	tel. 349.3856341	
	PISCIOTTA	
Villaggio La Maree	resort, restaurant	AIC
Via Fossa della Marina, 25	tel. 0974.973242	
	POLLA	
Santa Chiara	restaurant, pizzeria	€€, AIC
Via Annia	tel. 0975391470	www.ristoranteschiara.com
	POMPEI	
Osteria Da Peppino	restaurant	€€-€€€€, AIC
Via Duca d'Aosta, 39	tel. 0818504821	
Notes: Closed Tuesdays.		
Pompeo Magno	restaurant, pizzeria	€€, AIC
Via S. Abbondio, 155	tel. 0818598050	www.pompeomagno.it
	PONTECAGNANO	
La Basculla	pizzeria	€, AIC
Via Roma, 25	tel. 089849030	www.labasculla.com
La Regina Scalza	pizzeria	€, AIC
Via Tevere, 18	tel. 089.848156	
Motiè	pizzeria	€, AIC
P.zza Risorgimento, 9	tel. 089.383114	

Primavera	pizzeria	€, AIC
Via Dei Navigatori	tel. 3395068161	

PORTICI

Gelateria del Gallo	gelato (€, AIC)	P.zza S. Ciro, 24/26
Gelateria del Gallo	gelato (€, AIC)	Via Libertà, 115
La Locanda della Regina	restaurant, pizzeria	AIC
C.so Garibaldi, 89	tel. 081.482792	
Pizza Verace	pizzeria	€, AIC
Via Gravina, 12	tel. 081.7769095	
Pizzeria Vesuvio	pizzeria	€, AIC
Via B. Croce, 44	tel. 081475728	

POSITANO

Da Bruno restaurant
Corso Colombo, 157 (up the hill from the main street)   tel. 08 9875392
Notes: GF Pasta. English spoken.

Hotel Villa Gabrisa	restaurant	
Via Pasitea, 227	tel. 089811498	www.villagabrisa.it
Il Fornillo	restaurant	€€€
Via Pasitea 266	tel. 08 9811954	
Notes: English spoken. GF pasta.		

Le Tre Sorelle restaurant   €€
Del Brigantino 27-31 (across from beach)   tel. 089 875452
www.ristorantetresorelle.it
Notes: GF pasta. English spoken.

POZZUOLI

A' Ninfea	restaurant	AIC
Via Provinciale Lucrino Averno, 1	tel. 081.8042925	
Anema e Cono	gelato (€, AIC)	C.so Umberto I, 59
La Cucina degli Amici	restaurant	€€€, AIC
C.so Umberto I, 17	tel. 0815269393	www.lacucinadegliamici.it
Menhir	pub (€, AIC)	Via Pendio S. Giuseppe, 13

PRAIANO

La Cala delle Lampare	restaurant	€€€€, AIC
Via Campo, 5	tel. 089874333	
Tritone	hotel	€€€€, AIC
Via Campo, 5	tel. 089874333	www.tritone.it
Locanda Costa Diva	hotel, restaurant	
via Roma, 12	tel. 089 813076	www.hotelspraiano.com

QUARTO

L'Arcadia	restaurant	€€€€, AIC
Via Cuccaro, 29	tel. 0815873802	www.arcadiaristorante.it

RAVELLO

Al Ristoro del Moro	restaurant	€€€-€€€€, AIC
Via della Repubblica, 10	tel. 089857901	www.alristorodelmoro.it
Notes: Closed Tuesdays.		
Hotel Graal	hotel, restaurant	€€€-€€€€, AIC
Via della Repubblica, 8	tel. 089857222	www.hotelgraal.it

Hotel Rufolo Via San Francesco, 1	hotel, restaurant tel. 089.857133	AIC www.hotelrufolo.it
Parsifal Via Gioacchino d'Anna	hotel, restaurant tel. 089857144	€€, AIC www.hotelparsifal.com
Villa Giordano Via Trinità, 14	inn, restaurant tel. 089857255	€€€€, AIC www.giordanohotel.it
Villa Maria Via Santa Chiara, 2	hotel, restaurant tel. 089857255	€€€€, AIC www.villamaria.it

S. ANGELO - ISOLA D'ISCHIA

Casa Giuseppina Via G. di Iorio, 7- Succhivo	hotel, restaurant tel. 081907771	€€, AIC wwwischiacasagiuseppina.com
Romantica Via Ruffano,11	hotel tel. 081999216	

S. ANGELO D'ISCHIA

Hotel Ferdinando Via Fondolillo, 4	hotel tel. 081999269	AIC

S. GIORGIO DEL SANNIO

Ricci Park Hotel Via Vitulanese, 188	hotel, restaurant, pizzeria tel. 0824338461	€-€€€, AIC

S. GIOVANNI A PIRO - SCARIO

Palazzone Loc. Palazzone snc	agritourism tel. 0974.986530	AIC

S. GIUSEPPE VESUVIANO

Sicilia Via Masseria Perillo, 6	sandwich shop tel. 335.1442316	€, AIC

S. MARZANO SUL SARNO

L'Oasi della Pizza Via Gramsci, 123	pizzeria tel. 3313880076	€, AIC

Notes: DS pizza point. Closed Tuesdays.

S. SEBASTIANO AL VESUVIO

Funiculì Via Figliola, 12	restaurant, pizzeria tel. 0815742627	€, AIC www.funiculifunicula.it

S.AGATA DÈ GOTI

Antico Borgo P.zza Trieste, 9	restaurant/pizzeria tel. 0823717389	€€, AIC www.ristoranteanticoborgo.org
Ape Regina C.da Palmentana	agritourism tel. 082395668	€€€, AIC www.agriturismoaperegina.it
Biancaneve e i Sette Nani Ctr Castrone, 25	agritourism tel. 0823.953181	AIC www.lafattoriadibiancaneve.it
Il Girasole Via Macere, 5	agritourism tel. 349761239	€-€€, AIC
Eden Via S. M. Scozzese, 5	agritourism tel. 0823.953027	AIC
Normanno	gelato (€, AIC)	Via Roma

Agorà Via Chiesa, 79	**S.MARTINO SANNITA** agritourism tel. 0824337422	€-€€, AIC
Strapizzami Via S. Antonio	**SALA CONSILINA** pizzeria tel. 3277607619	€, AIC
Villa delle Acacie Contrada Sagnano	agritourism tel. 0975545076	€, AIC www.agriturismovilladelleacacie.it
Al Campetto Via Sant'Angelo di Ogliara	**SALERNO** pizzeria tel. 089281640	€, AIC
Arienzo Via A. Guglielmini, 7/9	bakery tel. 089.797729	€, AIC
Bar Castorino Via Del Carmine, 23	bar tel. 089.226891	€, AIC
Bar Pedro Via Ventimiglia, 41	bar tel. 089.756364	€, AIC
Brera Via Lungo Mare Clemente Tafuri, 1	restaurant tel. 0897042027	AIC
Caffè Da Totò Via Generale A. Diaz, 39	bar tel. 089.220057	€, AIC
Celiafree Via XX Settembre, 29	bakery tel. 089.725402	€, AIC
Cico's Via Picarelli, 70 loc. Pastena	restaurant, pizzeria tel. 3207645154	AIC
Ciripizza Via F. Conforti, 16-18	pizzeria tel. 089.8426800	€, AIC
Grand Hotel Salerno L.re Clemente Tafuri, 1 Notes: this hotel has five restaurants.	hotel, restaurant, B&B tel. 0897041111	€€-€€€€, AIC www.grandhotelsalerno.it
Il Giardino degli Dei Via S. Eustachio, 44/48	pizzeria tel. 089301127	€, AIC
La Bodeguita Via Silvio Baratta, 16	restaurant, pizzeria tel. 089.9956212	AIC
La Tombola Via S. Marano, 5	restaurant, pizzeria tel. 089229589	€€, AIC
Line Restaurant Cafè C.so Vittorio Emanuele, 176	bar, tavola calda tel. 089.241713	€, AIC
Novotel Salerno Est Arechi Via Generale Clark, 49	hotel, restaurant tel. 089.9957111	AIC www.novotel.com
Trattoria del Padreterno P.zza Flavio Gioia, 12	trattoria tel. 089.239305	AIC
Pathos Via Giugliani, 43	**SAN GENNARELLO DI OTTAVIANO** restaurant, pizzeria tel. 081.8274183	AIC

Gluten-Free Italy by Region

SAN GIORGIO A CREMANO

Pizzeria Galante Tutino pizzeria €, AIC
Via A. Gennaro Galante, 22 tel. 081.472566

Tutto Gelato gelato (€, AIC) Via Pittore, 188

SANTA MARIA CAPUA VETERE

La Loggetta restaurant, pizzeria AIC
P.zza Mazzini, 13 tel. 0823.898417

SANT'ANASTASIA

La Dolce Vita pizzeria €, AIC
Via Romani, 68 tel. 0815303418
Notes: Closed Wednesdays.

SANT'ANTONIO ABATE

Caruso restaurant, pizzeria €€, AIC
Via Scafati, 251 tel. 0818735743

SAPRI

Lucifero restaurant, pizzeria AIC
Trav. C.so Garibaldi, 6 tel. 0973603033

SAVIANO

The Drugstore pub €, AIC
C.so Garibaldi, 79 tel. 347.3465396

SCAFATI

B&B Il Fauno B&B AIC
Via Domenico Catalano, 97 tel. 3349332434 www.bbfauno.it

Il Bugigattolo restaurant, pizzeria AIC
Via D. Catalano, 68 tel. 081.8636297

Il Giardinetto osteria, pizzeria €€€, AIC
Via A. Manzoni, 56 tel. 0818599335 www.ristoranteilgiardinetto.com

Serafino restaurant, pizzeria AIC
Via Buccino, 28/30 tel. 0818638330

Masseria del Procaccia agritourism €€, AIC
Via Procaccia, 1 tel. 0824971366

SOMMA VESUVIANA

Gelatopoli gelato (€, AIC) Via Aldo Moro, 22/24

International Restaurant restaurant, pizzeria €€€, AIC
Via Aldo Moro, 182 tel. 0818997052
Notes: Closed Wednesdays.

Locanda del Cavaliere restaurant, pizzeria €, AIC
Via Santa Maria del Pozzo, 2 tel. 0815317444

Rose Rosse restaurant AIC
Via S.Maria a Castello, 93 tel. 0818931364 www.restaurantroserosse.it
Notes: Closed Tuesdays.

Villa La Sorgente restaurant AIC
Via S. Maria delle Grazie a Castello, 127 tel. 081.8932597

186 *The Gluten-Free Guide to Italy*

SORRENTO

Bar Syrenuse — bar — €€
Piazza Tasso Via Sant'Antonino, 14   tel. 818 075582   www.barsyrenusesorrento.it
Notes: gluten-free menu.

Hotel Conca Park — hotel, restaurant — AIC
Via degli Aranci, 13 bis   tel. 0818071621   www.concapark.com

Hotel Michelangelo — hotel
C.so Italia, 275   tel. 0818784844   www.michelangelohotel.it

I Giardini di Tasso — restaurant — €€€
Via Santa Maria della Pieta 30   tel. 08 18074145

Il Buco Ristorante — restaurant — €€€€
2a rampa Marina Piccola, 5 (Piazza S.Antonino)   www.ilbucoristorante.it

La Fenice — restaurant, pizzeria — €€, AIC
Via degli Aranci, 11   tel. 0818781652
Notes: Closed Mondays.

La Residenza — hotel, restaurant — €€€€
Via Rota, 1   tel. 0818774698   www.laresidenzasorrento.it

Old Taverna — restaurant
Via Fuoro, 23   tel. 0818781442   www.oldtavernasorrentina.it
Notes: Gluten-free menu.

Parco dei Principi — hotel, restaurant — €€€€
Via Rota, 1   tel. 0818784644   www.hotelparcoprincipi.com

Ristorante Ruccio — restaurant — €€€
Piazza Marinai d'italia 33, Sorrento Peninsula   tel. 08 18074069   www.ristoranteruccio.com

Villa Rubinacci — restaurant, pizzeria — €-€€€€
Via Correale, 25   tel. 0818073357

SPERONE

Golosità — creperie — €-€€, AIC
C.so Umberto I, 70/72   tel. 338.7525964

SQUILLE DI CASTEL CAMPAGNANO

L'Ape e il Girasole — agritourism — AIC
Loc. Selvanova   tel. 0823.1764551

STELLA CILENTO

I Fornari — agritourism, B&B — €€, AIC
Loc. Fornari, 2   tel. 0974909204

STRIANO

Il Golosone — restaurant, pizzeria — AIC
Via Palma, 458   tel. 081.5137063

TELESE TERME

L'Orso Bianco — gelato (€, AIC)   Via G. Tanzillo, 13/15

TERZIGNO

Il Cratere — restaurant, pizzeria — €€, AIC
Via Panoramica, 124   tel. 0815299090

Palm Garden — restaurant, pizzeria — €€€, AIC
C.so A. Volta, 262   tel. 0815298956   www.ristorantepalgarden.com

TEVEROLA

Il Magnifico
Via Roma, 161/163
osteria
tel. 0815048251
€-€€, AIC

TORRE DEL GRECO

Franco
Via Nazionale, 410
restaurant, pizzeria
tel. 0818471970   www.ristorantepizzeriafranco.com
€-€€, AIC

La Smorfia
Via E. De Nicola, 57
pizzeria
tel. 081.8492558
€, AIC

TORRECUSA

Rosso Pomodoro
Zona Industriale Torre Palazzo
pizzeria
tel. 0824.876217   www.rossopomodoro.com
€, AIC

TORRETTE DI MERCOGLIANO

Pink Panther
Via Nazionale, 160
restaurant, pizzeria
tel. 082568236473
€€, AIC

TORRIONE - SALERNO

Celiamix
P.zza M. Ricciardi, 9
tavola calda, bar
tel. 089.754718
€, AIC

TRAMONTI

Al Valico di Chiunzi
Via Chiunzi, 91
restaurant, pizzeria
tel. 089.876165
AIC

Costiera Amalfitana
Via Falcone, 21 - fraz. Pietre
restaurant, pizzeria, agritourism   €-€€, AIC
tel. 089856192   www.costieraamalfitana.it

VALLESACCARDA

Oasis Sapori Antichi
Via Provinciale, 8
restaurant
tel. 082797021
€€€€, AIC

VICO EQUENSE

Nonna Rosa
Via Privata Bonea, 2
restaurant
tel. 0818799055
€€€€, AIC
www.osterianonnarosa.it
Notes: Closed Wednesdays, Sunday nights.

Sale e Pepe
Via Filangieri, 87
pizzeria, sandwich shop
tel. 3398142500
€, AIC
www.salendpepe.com

VIETRI SUL MARE

Il Principe e la Civetta
Via Mazzini, 135
restaurant
tel. 897632201
€€€, AIC
www.ilprincipeelacivetta.com

La Fattoria
Via Iaconti 2/a (Dragonea)
restaurant
tel. 089210518
€€€, AIC

L'Argonauta c/o California Beach restaurant
Via G. Pellegrino
€€€, AIC

VOLLA

Leonessa
Via R. Sanzio
hotel, restaurant
tel. 0817748916
€€€€, AIC
www.hotelleonessa.com

Uomini in piazza (M. Roglieri)

BARI AND PUGLIA

(AIC = participates in the Associazione Italiana Celiachia program)

BARI

Al Capriccio
Via G. Capruzzi, 36
pizzeria
tel. 80.553108
€€, AIC
www.alcapriccioristoepizza.it

Corte di Torrelonga
Strada Torrelonga, 10
reception hall
tel. 0805461876
€€€€, AIC
www.corteditorrelonga.it

Da Bari Napoli
Via Piccinni 187/189
pizzeria
tel. 0809905452
€, AIC
Notes: DS pizza point. Closed Saturdays and Sunday at lunch.

Est
Via Toma, 81
restaurant
tel. 80.9904796
€€, AIC
www.vineriaest.it

Frulez
P.zza Umberto I, 14
restaurant
tel. 80.5239827
€€, AIC
www.frulez.it

Galu
Vle Papa Giovanni XXIII, 16/18
pizzeria
tel. 0805614739
€, AIC
Notes: Closed Wednesdays, and everyday at lunch.

Il Braciere
Via S. Visconti, 29
restaurant
tel. 0805239638
€€€-€€€€, AIC
Notes: Closed Sundays, month of August at lunch.

La Tana
Via Giovanni Amendola, 29
pizzeria
tel. 80.5559574
€, AIC

Le Veronique
Via Hahnneman, 4
pizzeria
tel. 0805461822
€€, AIC
Notes: Closed Sundays.

Gluten-Free Italy by Region

Lido S. Francesco alla Rena	pizzeria	€€, AIC
Via Verdi, 59/61	tel. 0805341542	
Opera Prima	pizzeria	€, AIC
Via Pietro Nenni, 9/7	tel. 0805024244	

Notes: Closed Mondays, month of August.

| **Pic Nic** | restaurant, pizzeria | €€€, AIC |
| Via Pietro Colletta, 36 | tel. 0805615131 | www.ristorantepicnic.it |

Notes: Closed Mondays.

| **Sheraton Nicolaus Hotel** | hotel, restaurant | €€€, AIC |
| Via C.A. Ciasca, 27 | tel. 0805682111 | |

| **Taverna Pane e Vino** | restaurant | €-€€, AIC |
| Via Re David, 14 | tel. 0805566187 | www.tavernapaneevino.it |

Notes: Closed June-September.

| **Villa Romanazzi Carducci** | hotel, restaurant | AIC |
| Via Capruzzi,326 | tel. 80.54274 | www.villaromanazzi.it |

| **Zonno Ricevimenti** | restaurant | €€€€, AIC |
| Molo S. Nicola, 5 | tel. 0805212470 | |

Notes: Closed Mondays and month of August.

Pasticceria Portoghese	gelato (€, AIC)	Via G. Modugno, 29/d
Piccinni	gelato (€, AIC)	Via Piccinni, 131
Yogo Land 2	gelato (€, AIC)	C.so Vitt. Emanuele, 9

BARI-PALESE

| **Vittoria Parc Hotel** | hotel | €€€, AIC |
| Via Nazionale, 10/f | tel. 0805306300 | www.vittoriaparchotel.com |

BARI-S.SPIRITO

| **La Tana dell'Artista** | pizzeria | €€, AIC |
| Lung. Cristoforo Colombo 212/d | tel. 0805331682 | |

Notes: Closed Tuesdays.

ACQUAVIVA DELLE FONTI

| **Villa dei Fiori** | restaurant, pizzeria | €€€, AIC |
| Prov.le 127 per Santeramo in Colle | tel. 080769293 | |

| **Gelateria Pastore** | gelato (€, AIC) | Via Roma, 40 |

ALBEROBELLO

| **La Chiusa di Chietri** | hotel, restaurant, reception hall | €€-€€€€, AIC |
| S.S. 172 dei Trulli Km.29, 800 | tel. 0804325481 | www.lachiusadichietri.it |

| **La Foggia** | restaurant, pizzeria | €-€€€€, AIC |
| Via Don F. Gigante, 4 | tel. 0804325927 | |

Notes: DS pizza point. Closed Mondays.

ALBERONA

| **Da Liberato** | restaurant | €€, AIC |
| Loc. Fornaci | tel. 881.592368 | www.ristorantedaliberato.it |

| **La Villetta** | restaurant | €€, AIC |
| Via Minerva, 12 | tel. 881.592042 | |

ALLISTE

| **Antica Terra** | B&B | AIC |
| P.zza Municipio, 14 | tel. 0833599389 | |

190 *The Gluten-Free Guide to Italy*

Cafè dei Napoli	gelato (€, AIC)	P.zza Municipio, 11
	ALTAMURA	
Gelat. Cenzino	gelato (€, AIC)	V.le Martiri, 79
Notes: Closed Thursdays.		
Tre Archi	restaurant, pizzeria	€€€-€€€€, AIC
Via San Michele, 28	tel. 0803115569	www.trearchi.it
Notes: Closed Wednesdays.		
	ANDRIA	
Assapora	tavola calda	€, AIC
Via Piero della Francesca, 95	tel. 883.892911	
Imperiale	pizzeria	€, AIC
Via L. Bonomo, 11	tel. 0883557717	
Notes: DS pizza point. Closed Sundays.		
La Puglia in Tavola	store, restaurant	€, AIC
Via Castel del Monte, 23	tel. 883.545788	www.lapugliaintavola.it
Officina del Gelato	gelato	€, AIC
Via Vaglio, 28	tel. 393.0008656	www.officinadelgelato.eu
	ARADEO	
Antica Tenuta Cornacchia	restaurant	AIC
Contrada Spina	tel. 0836552902	
Notes: Closed Tuesdays.		
Araknos	pizzeria	€€, AIC
Via Bosco ang. Via Grandi, 148	tel. 836.552965	www.araknosrestaurant.it
Villa Silmona	B&B	AIC
Contrada Tre Masserie	tel. 3284182714	www.villasilmona.it
	ARPINOVA-FOGGIA	
Posta Bassi	agritourism, pizzeria	AIC
Via Manfredonia, km 196,200	tel. 0881700155	www.postabassi.it
Notes: DS pizza point. Closed Mondays.		
	ASCOLI SATRIANO	
Il Tramonto	restaurant, pizzeria	€, AIC
Via Stazione, 20	tel. 0885662393	
Notes: Closed Mondays.		
	AVETRANA	
Il Balconcino	restaurant, pizzeria	€, AIC
Via Piave, 13	tel. 389.81737	www.ilbalconcino2011.it
Masseria La Grottella	restaurant reception hall	AIC
Via Ariosto, 42	tel. 0999707452	
Notes: Closed Mondays.		
	BARLETTA	
Al Duomo	restaurant, pizzeria	€€€€, AIC
Via Duomo, 29	tel. 0883332816	
Notes: Closed Wednesdays.		
Al Pomodorino	pizzeria	€€ - €€€, AIC
Via Cialdini, 47	tel. 0883880273	www.ilpomodorino.it
Antica Cucina	restaurant	AIC
Via Milano, 73	tel. 088352171	

Bagno 27	restaurant	€€, AIC
Vicinale delle Salinelle, 24/26 - Lit. di Ponente	tel. 883.510197	www.bagno27.com
Calici di Bacco	restaurant, pizzeria	€€, AIC
Via Cialdini, 7	tel. 883.765858	www.calicidibacco.it
Crèpes à Porter	crêperie	€, AIC
Via Duomo, 3	tel. 3497190791	
Dolce Amore	gelato (€, AIC)	Via Imbriani, 10
Ginevra	restaurant	€€€-€€€€, AIC
Litoranea di Ponente	tel. 0883532262	www.ristoranteginevra.com
Notes: Closed Mondays.		
Guardami	pizzeria	AIC
V.le Regina Elena, 33	tel. 883.347177	
Il Brigantino	restaurant, pizzeria	€€€-€€€€, AIC
V.le Regina Elena, 19	tel. 0883533345	
Madness Caffè	bar	€€, AIC
C.so Garibaldi, 131	tel. 883.885805	
Nuovo Centaro	restaurant, pizzeria	€€, AIC
Via Andria, 30	tel. 330902812	
Notes: Closed Wednesdays.		
Public House Clarence	pizzeria	AIC
Via Cialdini, 8	tel. 883.891393	www.publichouseclarence.it
Taverna Brancaleone	osteria	€€€€, AIC
Via Antonio di Gilio, 4	tel. 0883390622	
Tenuta San Francesco	hotel, restaurant	AIC
S.S. 16 Km 736	tel. 883.639001	www.tenutasanfrancesco.it
Veleno Fish Restorart	restaurant	€€€€, AIC
Via Cialdini, 21	tel. 0883532880	
Notes: Closed Wednesdays.		

BISCEGLIE

Borgo Antico	pizzeria	€, AIC
Via La Marina, 49	tel. 3474144322	
Casale San Nicola	hotel, restaurant	AIC
Carrara Reddito La Notte	tel. 80.3961901	www.casalesannicola.it
Fermata Facoltativa	pizzeria	€, AIC
Carrara Le Coppe, 2	tel. 0803986055	
Notes: Closed Mondays.		
Gelat. Cavour	gelato (€, AIC)	Via Cavour, 53/55
Il Gelatiere	gelato (€, AIC)	Via G. Bovio, 67/69
La Fontana	pizzeria	€, AIC
P.zza Vittorio Emanuele, 27	tel. 3478851430	
Notes: Closed Mondays.		
La Piccola Botte	trattoria, pizzeria	€€-€€€, AIC
Via G. Bovio, 200	tel. 0803922627	

BITONTO

Arcobaleno	pizzeria	AIC
Via Dante, 43	tel. 082919099	

Garden Plaza Via Abbaticchio, 2/6 Notes: Closed Mondays.	restaurant, pizzeria tel. 0809903180	€-€€€, AIC
Gizero Via Carlo Rosa, 12,14,16	restaurant, pizzeria tel. 0802473798	€€, AIC
La Dolce Vita Via Togliatti, 106	restaurant, pizzeria tel. 0803718509	€-€€€, AIC
Lo Spuntino Via G. Matteotti, 176	pizzeria tel. 80.3752422	€€, AIC

BITRITTO

Petit Roy C.so Mazzini, 34	pizzeria tel. 080631339	€€, AIC

BRINDISI

Forum Cafè Via Lanzillotti, 3 c/o Tribunale	bar tel. 831.435413	€, AIC
Ge Yo' C.so umberto, 8	ice cream, crêpes tel. 831.560406	€, AIC
Gruit Via Carmine, 120	restaurant, pizzeria tel. 831.56278	€-€€€, AIC www.gruit.it
Il Botteghino C.so Roma, 35	pizzeria tel. 831.529962	€€, AIC
Penny Via S. Francesco, 5	restaurant tel. 0831563013	€€€€, AIC

CAGNANO VARANO

Villaggio 5 Stelle-Garga no Club C.da Pagliai dei Comb.ti, km 34.500	resort tel. 884.917583	AIC

CANOSA DI PUGLIA

Twins Via Lavello, 42	restaurant, pizzeria tel. 883.6621	AIC

CAPRARICA DI LECCE

Masseria Stali Via Cisterna Vecchia	agritourism tel. 349.7439463	AIC

CARMIANO

Salento Via Veglie, 16	pizzeria tel. 327.3367745	AIC

CAROSINO

Osteria del Pero Via Roma	osteria tel. 99.5925371	€€, AIC

CAROVIGNO

Il Timone Via dei Tamerici s.n	hotel, restaurant tel. 0831987900	€€€€, AIC www.hoteltimone.it
Isola Verde C.da Morandi, 9	hotel, restaurant, pizzeria tel. 0831990140	€€, AIC
Riva Marina Resort Via della Pineta loc. Specchiolla	village, restaurant tel. 0831095700	€€€-€€€€, AIC www.rivamarinaresort.it

Drying Clothes (M. Roglieri)

CARPIGNANO SALENTINO

Hotel Le Muse	hotel, restaurant	AIC
Pr.le 212 Carpignano S.-Cursi	tel. 836.580001	

CASAMASSIMA

Rossopomod oro c/o Centro Comm. Auchan pizzeria	€€, AIC
Via Noicattaro	tel. 80.4578335	

CASARANO

Araknos	pizzeria	€€, AIC
Via Nardò, 22	tel. 320.8439913	

CASSANO DELLE MURGE

Come una Volta	restaurant, pizzeria	€-€€€, AIC
Via Mellitto c.da Parete	tel. 3296571959	

Notes: Closed Mondays, and Tuesdays at lunch.

CASTELLANA GROTTE

Il Piatto Fumante	restaurant, pizzeria	€€-€€€, AIC
SS.237 per Monopoli, km.11	tel. 0804965630	www.ilpiattofumante.it

Notes: Closed Tuesdays.

Park Hotel La Grave	hotel, restaurant, reception hall	€€€-€€€€, AIC
S.C. Ferrone, 6	tel. 0804965443	

Notes: Closed Mondays.

Villa Angela	B&B	AIC
Via Vecchia Conversano, 14	tel. 0804967421	

CASTELLANETA MARINA

Alborea	resort	AIC
S.S. 106 Km 466	tel. 99.8201	

Bar Europa	pizzeria(€, AIC)	Via Mare dei Vapori, 1

Calanè S.S. 106 Km 466	resort tel. 99.8201	AIC
Il Valentino S.S. 106 Km 466	resort tel. 99.8201	AIC
Kalidria S.S. 106 Km 466	resort tel. 99.8201	AIC
Ticho's Lungomare Eroi del Mare	hotel, restaurant tel. 99.8430815	AIC

CASTRO

Antico Murisciu Via Luigi Schifano, 78	B&B tel. 349.0879332	AIC

CASTRO MARINA

Panoramico Via Panoramica, 100	hotel, restaurant, reception hall tel. 0836943007	€€€-€€€€, AIC

CEGLIE MESSAPICA

Caelia C.da Circiello	B&B tel. 0831380977	AIC
Montevicoli V.le Aldo Moro, 64	restaurant, pizzeria tel. 0831381323	€€, AIC www.montevicoli.it
Tre Trulli C.da Montevicoli, 115	hotel, restaurant tel. 831.381311	AIC

CELLAMARE

L'Antico Arco C.so Roma, 31	pizzeria tel. 80.465628	€-€€, AIC

CERIGNOLA

Al Caminetto Contrada Quarto, 5	restaurant, pizzeria tel. 0885418488	€-€€, AIC
Hotel Il Quadrifoglio S.P. 143 Km 0.600	hotel, restaurant tel. 885.424154	AIC www.ilquadrifogliohotel.it
Villa Demetra S.S. 16, 18	B&B tel. 885.418988	AIC www.villademetra.it

CISTERNINO

Désirée C.da Sisto, 18	restaurant, pizzeria tel. 0804317760	€€€, AIC www.ristorantedesiree.com
Gluten Free Shop P.zza Marconi, 9	bar, tavola calda tel. 80.4446857	€-€€, AIC
Lo Smeraldo C.da Don Peppe Sole, 7	hotel, restaurant tel. 80.4448044	AIC www.hotellosmeraldo.com

CONVERSANO

Dalis Pizza & Wine Via Palmiro Togliatti, 47	pizzeria tel. 0804950228	€, AIC
Il Sapore Perfetto Via Machiavelli, 27	pizzeria/restaurant tel. 0804956353	€, AIC www.ilsaporeperfetto.it
Savì Via S. Giacomo, 26/28	crêperie tel. 0804957140	€, AIC www.savicreperia.it

Caffè Duomo
gelato (€, AIC)

CORATO

Via Duomo, 107

New Palace Sempione
Via Ruvo, 101
restaurant, pizzeria
tel. 360.931217
AIC
www.newpalacesempione.it

Parco Serrone
Via S. Magno, 4
hotel
tel. 0808984441
AIC
www.hotelparcoserrone.com

CORIGLIANO D'OTRANTO

Pappa & Ciccia
Via Roma, 35
pizzeria
tel. 0836320545
€, AIC

CRISPIANO

Al Borgo Antico
Via Paisiello, 34
B&B, restaurant
tel. 099611460
AIC

Saracino
C.so Umberto, 207
restaurant/pizzeria
tel. 099611455
€ - €€, AIC

Tutto Buono
Via Monte Calvario, 89
pizzeria
tel. 340.3666203
€ - €€, AIC
www.tuttobuono.it

CURSI

Alogne
Via Alogne, 4
restaurant
tel. 836.332975
AIC

Central Bar
gelato (€, AIC)
P.zza Pio XII, 13

CUTROFIANO

Sangiorgio Resort
Via prov.le Noha-Collepasso
hotel, restaurant
tel. 0836542848
€€€€, AIC
www.sangiorgioresort.it

ERCHIE

Antica Osteria
Via Oria
restaurant, pizzeria
tel. 3477075097
€€, AIC

Da Lucio (sede invernale)
Via Roma, 36
pizzeria
tel. 3457956628
€, AIC

FOGGIA

Al Celone
Via S. Severo Km 4
agritourism
tel. 881.206903
€€-€€€, AIC
www.alcelone.it

Al Primo Piano
Via P. Scrocco, 27
restaurant
tel. 0881708672
€€-€€€, AIC

Alta Marea
Via Napoli, Km.28,00
restaurant, reception hall
tel. 0881310477
€€€€, AIC

Corte Corona
Via degli Aviatori km.3
restaurant
tel. 0881612378
€-€€€€, AIC

Funghi e Tartufi della Puglia
Via Monfalcone, 8/12
restaurant
tel. 0881776183
€€€€, AIC

La Locanda di Hansel
Via A.Ricci,59
restaurant
tel. 0881773871
€€, AIC

Le Due Palme
V.le Fortore, 69
pizzeria
tel. 0881725716
€, AIC

Lo Scrigno
Via XXV Aprile, 22
restaurant
tel. 881.708404
AIC

Le amiche a cena (M. Roglieri)

Osteria La Giara
Via Saverio Altamura, 34

osteria
tel. 881.20692

AIC

Pino Giorgio
Via Delli Carri, 17/21

restaurant, pizzeria
tel. 0881709890

€, AIC

Pizzeria del Parco
Via Rovelli, 2

pizzeria
tel. 328.2752967

€-€€, AIC

Villa dei Gourmets
Trav.Viale Virgilio

hotel, restaurant, pizzeria
tel. 0881632815

€€€-€€€€, AIC

Gabrielino Gelaterie Artigiane
Gelateria Gabrielino
Gelateria Naturale

gelato (€-€€, AIC)
gelato (€-€€, AIC)
gelato (€-€€, AIC)

C.so Garibaldi, 119
P.zza Umberto Giordano, 65
P.zza Italia, 7

FRANCAVILLA FONTANA

La Buona Luna
Via Vittorio Alfieri, 23

restaurant, pizzeria
tel. 3936732455

AIC

GAGLIANO DEL CAPO

Il Carpaccio
P.zza Falcone e Borsellino s.n.

pizzeria
tel. 0833547174

€, AIC

GALATINA

Gelateria Eros

gelato (€-€€, AIC)

P.zza S. Pietro, 9

Il Covo della Taranta
C.so Garibaldi, 13

pizzeria
tel. 3299842820

€, AIC

La Campina te Don Paulu
Via Carlo Alberto dalla Chiesa

agritourism
tel. 3805065970

€€, AIC

Malibu'
Via Largo Tevere, 24

pizzeria
tel. 3341596819

€, AIC

Sole e Luna
Via Roma,11

trattoria
tel. 836.567268

AIC

GALLIPOLI

Eskada
Via Filomarini, 7
pizzeria
tel. 3479105669
€, AIC
www.eskada.it

Il Buongustaio
Via Isabella d'Aragona, 32
trattoria
tel. 833.266343
AIC
www.facebook.com/pages/Il-Buongustaio-Trattoria-Gallipoli-LE/114917535190257

Venti e Mari
P.zza Fontana Greca, 3
B&B
tel. 3496222139
AIC
www.ventiemari.it

GINOSA

Biffy
Via Montescaglioso sn
restaurant, pizzeria
tel. 3470878277
€€, AIC

Valle Rita
C.da Girifalco
agritourism
tel. 0998271824
€€€-€€€€, AIC

GINOSA MARINA

Mille Pini
V.le Mille Pini, 1
hotel
tel. 99.8277001
AIC
www.millepinihotel.it

GIOIA DEL COLLE

Gioia di Pizza
Via Rossellini, 1
pizzeria
tel. 80.3483698
€€€, AIC
www.gioiadipizza.it

GIOVINAZZO

Al Cantagallo
Via Molfetta 18-20
pizzeria
tel. 0803941104
€, AIC

Al Porticciolo
Via L.re Marina Italiana, 1
Notes: Closed Tuesdays.
restaurant
tel. 0803948289
€€€, AIC

Fondaco de' Guelfi
S.S.16 - C.da Torre S.Matteo
agritourism
tel. 0803948008
€€€, AIC

Gran Bar Pugliese
P.zza Vitt. Emanuele, 62
gelato
tel. 080.3942056
€, AIC
www.granbarpugliese.com

Ice Cream Planet
gelato (€-€€, AIC)   P.zza Garibaldi (chiosco Villa C.le)

Riva del Sole
Via Devitofrancesco, 31/C
hotel, restaurant, pizzeria
tel. 0803943166
€€€, AIC

GRAVINA IN PUGLIA

Bar Le Rose
gelato (€-€€, AIC)
Via Potenza, 9

La Lanterna
Viale Orsini, 19
restaurant, pizzeria
tel. 0803264394
€, AIC

GROTTAGLIE

La Piccola Rudie
Via Aldo Moro, 21
restaurant, pizzeria
tel. 0995622823
€€, AIC

Pizza Fast
Via Calò, 49
pizzeria
tel. 0995639902
€, AIC

LECCE

Estia Banqueting
Via Leuca, 90
restaurant
tel. 0832289652
€€, AIC

Fiori di Zucca Via Forlanini, 26	trattoria tel. 0832230313	€€, AIC www.trattoriafioridizucca.it
Grand Hotel Tiziano e Dei Congressi hotel, restaurant Viale Porta D'Europa	tel. 832.272111	AIC www.grandhoteltiziano.it
La Pagghiara Via Taranto, 64	restaurant, pizzeria tel. 832.240659	AIC lapagghiara@libero.it
Osteria della Divina Provvidenza Via Rubichi, 4	restaurant tel. 08321792078	€€€, AIC
Ramses II Via Di Vaste, 80	pizzeria tel. 832.305955	€€, AIC www.ristoranteramsesii.it
Sottozero Via G. Giusti, 21	gelato (€-€€, AIC) www.gelateriasottozero.com	
Tentazioni	gelato (€-€€, AIC)	Viale Leopardi, 56
Volo Restaurant V.co della Saponea, 15	restaurant tel. 0832246815	€€€, AIC www.volorestaurant.it

LESINA MARINA-GARGANO

Acapulco 2 V.le Centrale, 49	restaurant, pizzeria tel. 0882995079	€-€€€, AIC

LEUCA

Osteria del Pardo Via Doppia Croce Notes: Closed at lunch.	osteria tel. 0833758603	€€, AIC www.hosteriadelpardo.com

LEVERANO

Stuzzicami Vero Salentino Via Ancona s.n.	restaurant, pizzeria tel. 08321790143	€€, AIC

LUCERA

Palazzo D'Auria Secondo P.zza Oberdan, 3	restaurant, pizzeria, B&B tel. 0881530446	€-€€€, AIC www.palazzodauriasecondo.it

MAGLIE

Il Viandante Via Dante Alighieri, 9	B&B tel. 366.4350443	AIC www.ilviandantebeb.it
Il Visitatore Via Cav. Di Vitt. Veneto, 6	B&B tel. 836.312672	AIC www.ilvisitatore.it
La Cascina Via S. Antonio Abate, 41 Notes: Closed Mondays and at lunch.	restaurant, pizzeria tel. 0836424712	€€, AIC

MANDURIA

Gelateria Miola	gelato (€, AIC)	Via per Maruggio, 96
Lanternella Pub Corte Paradiso, 2	restaurant, pizzeria tel. 0999711354	€-€€€€, AIC www.lanternellapub.it
Relais Reggia Domizia SS 7 Manduria-Sava c.da Pozzo Capo	restaurant tel. 0999745111	AIC

MANFREDONIA

Da Tommasino	gelato (€, AIC)	V.le dell'Arcangelo

Gluten-Free Italy by Region

| **Regio Hotel Manfredi** | hotel | AIC |
| S.P. 58 Km.12 | tel. 0884530122 | www.regiohotel.it |

MARGHERITA DI SAVOIA

| **Canneto Beach 2** | restaurant, pizzeria, wine bar, B&B | €€€€, AIC |
| Via Amoroso, 11 | tel. 883.651091 | www.ristorantecannetobeach2.com |

| **Grande Hotel Terme** | hotel, restaurant | €€€€, AIC |
| C.so Garibaldi, 1 | tel. 0883656888 | |

MARTINA FRANCA

| **Al Focolare** | pizzeria | €, AIC |
| Via Pergolesi, 66 | tel. 0804838762 | |

| **La Rotonda** | restaurant/pizzeria | €€ - €€€€, AIC |
| Villa Comunale Garibaldi | tel. 0804807052 | |

| **Villa Carmine** | restaurant, pizzeria | €-€€€€, AIC |
| Villa Carmine s.n. | tel. 0804838910 | |

MASSAFRA

| **L'Orsa Maggiore** | restaurant, pizzeria | €€, AIC |
| Via Cirillo, 19 | tel. 0998801229 | |

MATINO

| **Lu Riale** | pizzeria | €, AIC |
| Via San Michele, 7 | tel. 3382857252 | |

MATTINATA

| **Gabrielino** | gelato | €, AIC |
| Via Garibaldi, 3 | tel. 884.559444 | www.gabrielino.it |

| **Hotel Ristorante Apeneste** | hotel, restaurant | AIC |
| P.zza Turati, 3 | tel. 884.550743 | www.hotelapeneste.it |

MINERVINO

| **Masseria Barbera** | agritourism | €€€€, AIC |
| S.P.le 230 km. 5,850 | tel. 8'083692095 | www.masseriabarbera.it |

MINERVINO MURGE

| **La Tradizione Cucina Casalinga** | restaurant | €€€, AIC |
| Via Imbriani, 11/13 | tel. 0883691690 | www.osterialatradizione.net |

MODUGNO

| **De Amicis** | restaurant, pizzeria | €-€€€€, AIC |
| P.zza De Amicis | tel. 0804037930 | |

| **De Gustibus** | pizzeria | €, AIC |
| Via Sanremo, 14 | tel. 80.5320676 | |

MOLA DI BARI

| **Dolcevoglia** | gelato (€, AIC) | Via C. Colombo, 42 |

| **Le Case di Sottovento** | B&B | AIC |
| Via di Vagno, 63-69 | tel. 0804741886 | www.lecasedisottovento.it |

MOLFETTA

| **Antica Gelat. Cipriani** | gelato (€, AIC) | Banchina S. Domenic, 55 |

Notes: They also have crêpes. Closed Thursdays.

| **Bufi** | restaurant | €€€€, AIC |
| Via Vitt. Emanuele,15-17 | tel. 0803971597 | |

Dentro le Mura
C.so Dante, 42
pizzera, trattoria
tel. 80.3349989
€€€-€€€€, AIC
www.dentrolemura.com

I Monelli
Via Madonna dei Martiri, 108
pizzeria
tel. 0809648792
€, AIC
www.pizzeriaimonelli.it

Il Vecchio Gazebo
Via Marconi, 18
restaurant, pizzeria
tel. 0803344877
€-€€€, AIC

Melficta
P.zza G. Garibaldi, 49
pizzeria/restaurant
tel. 0803358191
€, AIC

Mezzopieno
C.so Dante, 106
restaurant, pizzeria
tel. 80.334109
€-€€, AIC

MONOPOLI

A Crepétt
Via Caporale Contento, 2/f
sandwich shop
tel. 0802470353
€, AIC

Bar della Stazione
L.go Stazione
pizzeria, bar
tel. 80.9306032
€-€€, AIC

Delicatesse
Via Marina del Mondo
restaurant, pizzeria
tel. 0804107238
€, AIC

Hakuna Matata (ex Upendi)
Via Rocco Scotellaro, 8/10
Notes: Closed Tuesdays.
osteria, pizzeria
tel. 0802373911
€, AIC

Il Guazzetto
Via dell'Erba 39/41
restaurant
tel. 0804107175
€€€, AIC

L'Abbraccio di Morfeo
Via Lepanto, 101
B&B
tel. 080'08872867
AIC

Oltremare
via Fracanzano,1
restaurant, pizzeria
tel. 80.937186
AIC

San Domenico
Via San Domenico
trattoria
tel. 080937192
€€-€€€, AIC

Victorian Pub
C.da Vagone, 345
restaurant, pizzeria
tel. 0806901838
€, AIC

Yogomania
Notes: They also have crêpes.
gelato (€, AIC)
Via Rattazzi, 1

MONTERONI DI LECCE

Lo Scacciapensieri
Via A. De Gasperi
hotel, restaurant
tel. 0832321884
€€, AIC

MOTTOLA

Pizza Taxi
Via F.lli Bandiera, 65
pizzeria
tel. 99.886301
€€, AIC

Villa Petruscio
Via S. Allende,158
reception hall
tel. 0998866214
€€€€, AIC

NOCI

Miramonte Party
Str. Prov.le per Castellaneta, km 1
Notes: Closed Mondays.
restaurant
tel. 0804978005
€€€€, AIC
www.miramonteparty.com

Luigi the Pizza Guy Makes the Best GF Pizza

Cremeria L'Arca

NOICATTARO
gelato (€, AIC)

Via P. Nenni, 16/5

Nuova Sala Paradiso
Via Piano Paradiso, s.n.

ORSARA DI PUGLIA
restaurant
tel. 0881964763

€€€€, AIC

Hotel Novelli
S.S.16 Km 695+132

ORTANOVA
restaurant, pizzeria, bar
tel. 885.787432

AIC
www.hotelresortnovelli.com

OSTUNI

Cremeria alla Scala
Piaz.ta don Elio Antelmi, 17

gelato
tel. 338.8221451

€, AIC
www.cremeriaallascala.com

Hostaria San Filippo
C.so Vitt. Emanuele, 218

restaurant
tel. 0831334546

€€-€€€, AIC

La Dolce Vita

gelato (€, AIC)

Via Cav. Di Vitt. Veneto, 15

Piccolo Hotel Villa Rosa
Via per Martina Franca, km.1

B&B
tel. 0831332615

AIC
www.villarosaostuni.it

OSTUNI MARINA

Masseria S. Lucia
S.S. 379 Km. 23,5

hotel, restaurant
tel. 08313560

€€€€, AIC

PALESE

Mychef Aeroporto Civile di Bari Palese mychef
tel. 80.5308201   www.mychef.it

€, AIC

PALMARIGGI

Sciarabba'
Via Roma, 45

restaurant, pizzeria
tel. 0836354497

€-€€€, AIC

Allo Scrigno
Via Salentina, 113

Bakayokò
Via Isonzo, 2

Le Veneri
Via Coltura, 70

Lo Sturno
Via Immacolata, 2

Prima o poi
Via G.ni Vinci, 62

Aquilino
Vico Galliani, 15a

Club Village Maritalia
Baia di Peschici
Notes: Closed October-April.

Gelateria Pinagel

Gusmay Resort
Loc. Manacore

Casa Salcone
Via Canalicchio, 28

Marsavè

Casa Dorsi
Via Porto, 58

Donna Gina
Via Cala Porto, 7/9

Irvi's Caffè

L'Arciere
Via Cosimo Basile, 18

Petali Rosa
P.zza S. Antonio

Specchia Sant'Oronzo
Contrada Fratta
Notes: Closed Wednesdays.

Villa degli Aranci
Via Caduti di tutte le Guerre, 5/7

Vingtsept Relais & Suite
Via G. Matteotti, 29

Isola Lo Scoglio
P.zza N. Sauro

PARABITA
B&B
tel. 0833509947

pizzeria pub
tel. 08331828283

restaurant
tel. 3453363901

trattoria
tel. 0833593477

B&B, restaurant, pizzeria
tel. 0833595006
PATÙ
B&B
tel. 3489288087

PESCHICI
hotel
tel. 0884963399

gelato (€, AIC)

hotel
tel. 0884911016

PIETRA MONTECORVINO
restaurant/pizzeria
tel. 0881555743

gelato (€, AIC)
POLIGNANO A MARE
B&B
tel. 0804251168

restaurant
tel. 0804240914

gelato (€, AIC)

bar
tel. 338.9742217

B&B
tel. 80.4249478

restaurant, pizzeria
tel. 0804240386

restaurant, pizzeria
tel. 0804249161

B&B
tel. 80.4241361
PORTO CESAREO
restaurant
tel. 833.569079

AIC
www.salentiamoci.it

€€, AIC
www.bakayoko.it

€€-€€€, AIC

€€, AIC

€, AIC

AIC
www.aquilino.it

€-€€, AIC

C.so umberto I, 7

€-€€, AIC

€ - €€, AIC
www.casalcone.com

P.zza Martiri del Terrorismo, 16

AIC
www.casadorsi.com

€€€€, AIC
www.donnagina.it

Via Martiri di Dogali, 62

€, AIC

AIC
www.bebpetalirosa.it

AIC
www.specchiasantoronzo.it

AIC

AIC
www.vingt-sept.it

AIC
www.isolaloscoglio.it

Antico Borgo P.zza del Popolo, 32 Notes: Closed Tuesdays.	**PRESICCE** pizzeria tel. 0833722124	€-€€, AIC
Corte Sant'Andrea Via Matteotti, 9/I	B&B tel. 3498321729	AIC www.corteterrasignura.it
Corte Terra Signura Via Matteotti, 68	B&B tel. 3283731355	AIC www.corteterrasignura.it
Il Grillo V.le dei Micenei - Lit. Salentina	**PULSANO** hotel, restaurant tel. 0995333925	€€€€, AIC
Le Arcate Via Paisiello, 31	pizzera, trattoria tel. 99.5338265	€€, AIC
Agribiotrulli C.da Madonna del Rosario, 58	**PUTIGNANO** agritourism tel. 3206918541	€€, AIC www.agribiotrulli.it
Caffè Verdi	gelato (€, AIC)	Via Giuseppe Verdi, 11
Dimora Lama d'Inferno Sc. Lama d'Inferno, 13	B&B tel. 80.4031635	AIC www.dimoralamadinferno.it
Premiata Pizzeria Via Carlo Rosselli, 32	restaurant, pizzeria tel. 0804058523	€€, AIC
Park H. Villa Americana Via Grossi, 23	**RODI GARGANICO** hotel, restaurant tel. 884.96639	AIC www.villaamericana.it
Bar Cardigliano	**RUFFANO** gelato (€, AIC)	Via De Gasperi, 1
Il Mulino Via Carlo Rosselli, 32	**RUTIGLIANO** pizzeria tel. 0804769029	€, AIC www.ilmulinopizzeria.it
Lama San Giorgio Str. Prov.le 84 Rutigliano/Adelfia	agritourism, restaurant, hotel tel. 0804761609	€€€, AIC www.lamasangiorgio.it
L'Arte del Gelo	gelato (€, AIC)	C.so Mazzini, 5
Crem. American Bar	**RUVO DI PUGLIA** gelato (€, AIC)	P.zza Bovio, 15
U.p.e.p.i.d.d.e. Vico S.Agnese, 2	restaurant tel. 0803613879	€€€, AIC
Desideria	**S. CATERINA DI NARDÒ** gelato (€, AIC)	Via Mastro Gioffreda
San Cassano Via Papa Giovanni XXIII, 15	**S. FERDINANDO DI PUGLIA** pizzeria tel. 883.766178	€-€€, AIC
Hotel Corona Via Anna Freud, 5	**S.GIOVANNI ROTONDO** hotel, restaurant tel. 882.457873	AIC www.hotelcorona.fg.it

Hotel le Cese C.da Matine	hotel, restaurant tel. 0882450972	€€€€, AIC
Hotel Sollievo Via S. Gennaro, 4	hotel, restaurant tel. 0882456134	€€, AIC www.hotelsollievo.it
Villa Xenia Via Luigi Pinto,1	B&B tel. 882.454981	AIC www.hotelxenia.com

S.GIORGIO JONICO

Da Boe Via Principe di Piemonte, 180	sandwich shop tel. 99.4008363	€, AIC

www.facebook.com/pages/Da-Boe-PucciaPizza/1481614212081335?hc_location=timeline

Villaggio S.Giovanni Contrada S. Giovanni	hotel, restaurant, reception hall tel. 0995900606	€€€€, AIC

S.SEVERO

Il Carbonaio Via Santa Lucia, 68	restaurant, pizzeria tel. 0882331415	€-€€€, AIC

SAN DONACI

da Peppino Via Pastrengo, 23	restaurant, pizzeria tel. 831.634084	€€, AIC www.dapeppino.vpsite.it
Gargantù Via Giulio Cesare, 4	pizzeria tel. 3286815776	€, AIC

SAN PIETRO IN LAMA

Cantina Don Carlo Via S. Antonio, 10	restaurant, pizzeria tel. 08322632'099	€€€, AIC

S. PIETRO IN BEVAGNA-MANDURIA

Hotel dei Bizantini Via Borraco, 224	hotel, restaurant tel. 0999729823	€€€-€€€€, AIC

S. SEVERO

Ristore Via Togliatti, 54	restaurant/pizzeria tel. 0882228280	€€€, AIC

S. VITO DEI NORMANNI

Cheer's Pub Cafè Via Isonzo, 6	pub tel. 3383295901	€, AIC
Hotel Resort dei Normanni SS. 16 Km 2,7	hotel, restaurant tel. 0831951884	AIC www.hoteldeinormanni.it
Il Vulcano Via Carovigno, 49	pizzeria tel. 333.9792436	€-€€, AIC www.ristoranteilvulcano.com

SANTA MARIA AL BAGNO

Il Covo degli Orsini	gelato (€, AIC)	P.zza Nardò, 21

SANTERAMO IN COLLE

Green Elf Via Fausto Coppi, 16	pizzeria pub tel. 3387019661	€, AIC

SAVELLETRI DI FASANO

Il Veliero P.zza del Porto, 1 Notes: Closed Tuesdays.	restaurant tel. 0804820022	€€€-€€€€, AIC

Poggio del Sole	SELVA DI FASANO restaurant	€€€€, AIC
V.le del Minareto, 51	tel. 0804331386	
	SOLETO	
Caffetteria Orsini	gelato	€, AIC
Via Orsini, 1	tel. 836.663802	www.caffetteriaorsini.it
	SQUINZANO	
Delizie	gelato (€, AIC)	Via A. Diaz, 167
	SUPERSANO	
La Mezzaluna	pizzeria	€-€€, AIC
Via Vittorio Veneto, 27	tel. 0833631687	
Notes: Closed Monday-Wednesday.		
	TALSANO	
H.Bel Sit/R.La Nuova Mandragora hotel, restaurant		€€€, AIC
Via Mediterraneo, 111/a	tel. 0997716362	www.lanuovamandragoraebelsit.com
L'Angolo Nascosto	restaurant, pizzeria	€€, AIC
C.so Vitt. Emanuele	tel. 0997712220	
Victory House Coffee	gelato (€, AIC)	V.le Europa, 121
	TARANTO	
Al Canale	restaurant	€€€€, AIC
Discesa Vasto	tel. 0994764201	
Al Faro	hotel, restaurant	€€€€, AIC
Via della Pineta 3/5	tel. 0994714444	
Bar Pasticc. Principe	gelato (€, AIC)	Via De Cesare, 38
Gelateria del Ponte	gelato (€, AIC)	Via D'Aquino, 110
Marc'Aurelio	restaurant, pizzeria	€-€€€, AIC
Via Cavour, 17	tel. 0994527893	
Pandoro L'angelo senza glutine e non pizzeria		€€, AIC
Via Japigia, 25 a/b	tel. 0997362440	
	TAVIANO	
Irene Marchese	B&B	AIC
Via M. D'Azeglio, 14	tel. 833.911477	www.irenemarchese.it
Santa Lucia	restaurant	€€-€€€, AIC
Via Castelforte, 118	tel. 0833911388	
	TERLIZZI	
Alighieri Eventi	restaurant	€€-€€€, AIC
C.so Dante Alighieri, 15	tel. 80.3514887	www.alighierieventi.it
	TORRE A MARE	
Miramare	gelato (€, AIC)	Via G. Leopardi, 54
TORRE CANNE DI FASANO		
Villa Imperiale	restaurant	€€-€€€, AIC
C.da la Cordara-via del Procaccio	tel. 3338643215	
	TORRE COLIMENA	
Da Lucio (Sede estiva)	pizzeria	€€, AIC
Via dei Dentici	tel. 0999718793	

TORRE SAN GIOVANNI

L'Approdo
C.so Annibale, 68
restaurant, pizzeria
tel. 0833931872
€-€€, AIC
www.approdotrattoria.it

TORREMAGGIORE

La Tana
Via della Costituente, 140
pizzeria
tel. 0882381064
€, AIC

TRANI

Amadeus
Via Statuti Marittimi, 32/34
restaurant, pizzeria
tel. 0883956358
€€, AIC

Bar Gelat. Commercio
gelato (€, AIC)
C.so Vitt. Emanuele, 140

Bodeguita
Via Zanardelli, 27
pizzeria
tel. 0883954303
€, AIC

Donna Rosa
C.so Vitt. Emanuele, 138
pizzeria
tel. 0883764958
€, AIC

Il Melograno
Via Giovanni Bovio, 185
restaurant
tel. 0883486966
€€€€, AIC

Il Paese del Gelato
gelato (€, AIC)
Via S.Giorgio, 5

TREPUZZI

Tre Pozzi
Via P. Giovanni XXIII, 170
B&B
tel. 832.757375
AIC
www.bnbtrepozzi.it

TRICASE

I Fornelli di Teresa
Via Giuseppe Tartini, 34
pizzeria
tel. 833.770312
€-€€, AIC
www.ifornelliditeresa.it

TRIGGIANO

Beverly Hills
Via G. Fortunato, 21/a
pizzeria
tel. 0804688637
€, AIC

TROIA

Fattoria Giuntoli Azienda Agrituristica agritourism
C.da Cisternino
tel. 881.970154
AIC
www.fattoriagiuntoli.it

TUGLIE

Museo della Civiltà Contadina agritourism
Via Venturi, 30/32 -P.zzo Ducale
€, AIC

TURI

Pizza e Crêpe Desirèe
Via Torino
pizzeria
tel. 80.4512933
€, AIC

VEGLIE

Labor. del Gelato Artigianale-Roxy gelato (€, AIC)
Trav. Di Via Isonzo s.n.

VIESTE

Bar Ruggieri
gelato (€, AIC)
C.so L. Fazzini, 89

Borgo Antico
Via Cesare Battisti, 11
restaurant, pizzeria
tel. 0884701377
€-€€, AIC

Box 19
Via S. Maria di Merino, 13
restaurant
tel. 0884705229
€€, AIC

Hotel degli Aranci
P.zza S. Maria delle Grazie, 10
hotel, restaurant
tel. 0884708557
€€€-€€€€, AIC

I Melograni e Vill. Baia degli Aranci hotel, restaurant   €€€-€€€€, AIC
Lungomare Europa, 48   tel. 0884701088

Le Diomedee   restaurant, pizzeria   €-€€, AIC
Loc. Pantano   tel. 0884706472
Notes: Closed October-April.

Maggiore D.A.   gelato (€, AIC)   Via S. Maria di Merino, 40

Spiaggia Lunga   village, restaurant   €€-€€€, AIC
Litoranea Vieste Peschici km. 7   tel. 0884706171
Notes: Closed October-April.

Villa Carla   B&B   AIC
C.da Intresiglio, 47   tel. 884.702783   www.villacarla.it

VILLA CASTELLI

Pazzi Per Pizza   pizzeria   €-€€, AIC
Via Ceglie, 130   tel. 3358009503

I Trulli

Agrigento (J. Kelly)

SICILIA

(AIC = participates in the Associazione Italiana Celiachia program)

ACI SANT'ANTONIO

Ke Bontà	bakery	€, AIC
Via Fleming C.da Colle del Gelsomino	tel. 095.2969488	www.kebonta.it

ACICASTELLO

Acido Lattico	pizzeria	€, AIC
Via Stazione, 32	tel. 0957111001	
Il Timo/Sheraton Catania Hotel	hotel, restaurant	AIC
Via A. da Messina, 45	tel. 095.7114111	www.sheratoncatania.com
La Scogliera	restaurant	€€-€€€, AIC
Via A. Musco, 13/a	tel. 095494634	

ACIREALE

Briciole Senza Glutine	bakery, gastropub, rotisserie	€, AIC
Via delle Terme, 7	tel. 339.7791357/342.7258216	
La Caverna del Mastro Birraio	restaurant/pub	€€, AIC
Via Cristoforo Colombo, sn	tel. 0958035019	www.lacavernadelmastrobirraio.it
Le Quattro Stagioni	pizzeria	€, AIC
Via Marchese di S. Giuliano, 53/57	tel. 0957634196	

ACITREZZA

Pellegrino	pizzeria	€-€€, AIC
P.zza Verga, 6-7	tel. 095276060	

ACQUEDOLCI

La Cascina	restaurant, pizzeria	€€, AIC
C.da Oliveto	tel. 0941726193	www.ristorantelacascina.net

AGIRA

Fud Sud Group c/o Sicily Outlet Vill. restaurant/pizzeria €€€ - €€€€, AIC
C.da Mandre Bianche   tel. 0935594044   www.fudsud.it

AGRIGENTO

Le Caprice   restaurant, pizzeria   €€€, AIC
Via Cavaleri Magazzeni   tel. 0922411364

Terra & Mare   trattoria   €€, AIC
P.zza Lena, 7   tel. 092225413

ALCAMO

G.F.D. di Impellizzeri (Gulliver) restaurant, pizzeria   €€, AIC
C.da S. Gaetano, 1/a   tel. 092424012

AUGUSTA

Red Lions   pizzeria   €-€€, AIC
Lungomare Rossini   tel. 0931994086

AVOLA

La Scogliera   restaurant, pizzeria   AIC
Via Aldo Moro, 121   tel. 348.1494956   www.ristorantelascoglieradiavola.it

BAGHERIA

Dolce Gelato   gelato   €, AIC
Via Alcide De Gasperi, 61   tel. 334.3383808
www.gelateriapasticceriadolcegelato.blogspot.com

BARCELLONA POZZO DI GOTTO

Casa del Dolce   gelato, bar (€, AIC)   Via On. Giacomo Martino, 1

Napoli Mania   pizzeria   €€, AIC
Via Tenente Genovese, 47   tel. 90.9701301

BELPASSO

Feudo Delizia   restaurant   €€, AIC
C.da Segreta   tel. 095918950   www.ristorantefeudodelizia.it

BUONFORNELLO

Ron e Salvo   restaurant, pizzeria   AIC
S.S. 113 km 207   tel. 0918140159

CACCAMO

A' Castellana   restaurant, pizzeria   €€, AIC
P.zza dei Caduti, 2/3/4   tel. 0918148667   www.castellana.it

CALTAGIRONE

I Marchesi di S. Barbara   restaurant   €€€-€€€€, AIC
Via S. Bonaventura, 22   tel. 093322406

La Piazzetta   restaurant, pizzeria   AIC
Via Vespri, 20/a   tel. 093324178

CALTANISSETTA

Al Rustico   pizzeria   €€, AIC
Via Ten. Lilly Bennardo, 11   tel. 934.2335   www.pizzeriaalrustico.com

Al Vecchio Olmo   B&B   AIC
P.zza Marconi, 6   tel. 934.25376   www.bedebreakfastalvecchioolmo.com

Az. di Turismo Rur. Belvedere   agritourism   AIC
C.da Canicassè snc   tel. 0934568166

| **Il Bignè** | gelato (€, AIC) | Via Calabria, 64/66 |

Le Fontanelle — agritourism, restaurant — €€, AIC
C.da Fontanelle — tel. 934.592437
www.agriturismo.8k.com/cl/lefontanelle.htm

M.B. — gelato (€, AIC) — Via E. Vassallo, 67/69

Panineria Calà — sandwich shop — €, AIC
P.zza Repubblica s.n — tel. 0934591278

Totò e Peppino — restaurant, pizzeria — €, AIC
Via Piero Leone s.n. — tel. 0934555037

CAMMARATA
S. Martino de Kamerata — restaurant, pizzeria — €€, AIC
Ugo La Malfa, 10 — tel. 0922905572 — www.ristorantesanmartino.it

CAMPOBELLO DI LICATA
La Madonnina — restaurant/pizzeria — €€, AIC
Via Edison, 162 — tel. 0922870177 — www.ristorantelamadonnina.com

CANICATTÌ
Pasticceria Termini — bar, tavola calda — €-€€, AIC
Via Pirandello, 24, 28, 30 — tel. 0922851519

CAPO D'ORLANDO
Il Torrente — restaurant, pizzeria — €, AIC
Via Torrente Forno, 54 — tel. 0941901970

CARLENTINI
Al Punto Giusto — bar — €-€€, AIC
S.S. 194 KM 18+830 dir. Ragusa — tel. 95.94467

CASA SANTA - ERICE
F.lli Virzì — gelato, bakery — €, AIC
Via Madonna di Fatima, 181 — tel. 923.566133

L'Acquolina in Bocca — sandwich shop — €, AIC
Via Cosenza, 143 — tel. 09231893633

CASTELBUONO
Antico Baglio — restaurant, pizzeria — €, AIC
P.zza Ten. Schicchi, 3 — tel. 0921679512 — www.anticobaglio.it
Notes: DS pizza point. Closed Mondays and Tuesdays.

CASTELLAMMARE DEL GOLFO
Cozzeria Solemare — restaurant — AIC
Via Don Luigi Zangara,5 — tel. 3924570282 — www.ristorantecozzeria.it

CATANIA
Biscottissimi e Cannolissimi — bakery — €, AIC
P.zza Michelang elo Buonarroti, 21 — tel. 348.9938446

Catania City Center — B&B — AIC
Via Naumachia, 103 — tel. 0957232924 — www.cataniacitycenter.com

Delizie Libere — bakery, gastropub, rotisserie — €, AIC
Via Guzzardi, 6/a — tel. 95.432172 — www.liberedelizie.it

La Smorfia — pizzeria, sandwich shop — €, AIC
Via Landolina, 50 — tel. 95.2180605 — www.lasmorfiapizzeria.it

Occhio al Glutine
Via Barriera del Bosco, 349/a

bakery, rotisserie
tel. 347.8818226

€, AIC
www.occhioalglutine.it

Primopiano
Via A. Decurtis, 8

restaurant, pizzeria
tel. 095531028

€€-€€€, AIC

Stecco Natura

gelato (€, AIC)

Via Etnea, 105

CEFALÙ

Via Roma Vecchia
Via Carlo Ortolani Bordonaro, 76

restaurant, pizzeria
tel. 921.820143

€€, AIC
www.ristorante-viaromavecchia.it

COLLESANO

Casale Drinzi
C.da Drinzi

restaurant, pizzeria
tel. 0921.664027

€€-€€€, AIC
www.casaledrinzi.it

COMISO

Punto Caldo
Via R. Livatino, 21

bakery, rotisserie, gastropub
tel. 0932.721196

€, AIC
www.puntocaldo.it

ENNA

Bar Di Maggio
P.zza A. da Messina, 2/4

tavola calda
tel. 093529343

€, AIC

Cucaracha
Via G. Marconi, 16/18

pub
tel. 3475179254

€, AIC

Delizia Bar
P.zza Duomo, 5/6

bar, tavola calda
tel. 0935500549

€, AIC

ENNA BASSA

Netser
C.da Gentilomo

restaurant, pizzeria
tel. 093520418

AIC

ERICE

Ulisse
Via Chiaramonte, 45
Notes: Closed Thursdays.

restaurant, pizzeria
tel. 0923869333

€-€€€€, AIC
www.sitodiulisse

Ulisse Camere
Via Santa Lucia, 2

B&B
tel. 0923860155

AIC
www.sitodiulisse.it

FAVARA

Gluten Bon
Via Francesco Crispi, 64

bakery, rotisserie
tel. 0922.31031

€, AIC
www.facebook.com/glutenbon.favara

Oneiratos
Via Soldato Schifano, 5

B&B
tel. 922.420163

AIC
www.oneiratos.it

FORZA D'AGRÒ

Agostiniana Hotel
Via A. De Gasperi, 54

hotel/restaurant
tel. 0942721608

€€€€, AIC
www.agostinianahotel.com

FURCI SICULO

Fragolina
Via 4 Novembre, 3

B&B
tel. 0942792951

AIC
www.bbfragolina.it

GALATI MAMERTINO

Fattoria Fabio
C.da Sciara

restaurant
tel. 0941434042

€€, AIC

Le Cisterne Via S. d'Acquisto, 10	**GIARRE** restaurant, pizzeria tel. 095965093	AIC
Al Nord Est Piazza della Regione, 1	**GRAVINA DI CATANIA** restaurant, pizzeria tel. 095394797	€, AIC
Agrit. Baglio Vultaggio Via Federico dei Roberto	**GUARRATO** agritourism tel. 0923864261	AIC
Le Giare Via S. Caterina, 17	**ITALA** hotel, restaurant tel. 0909595006	€€-€€€, AIC www.legiare.org
Da Natale Trav Prov.le, 15	**ITALA MARINA** restaurant, pizzeria tel. 090953144	€, AIC
Gli Infiniti Sapori del Gluten Free Via Roma, 82	bakery, gastropub tel. 090.8969412	€, AIC
Sicilia Nostra Via Etnea	**LENTINI** restaurant/pizzeria tel. 0957038582	€ - €€, AIC www.sicilianostra.it
Villa Speranza Via E. Rinaldi, 191	**MARAUSA** restaurant, pizzeria, B&B tel. 0923843162	AIC www.villasperanza.net
Caffè delle Rose	**MARINA DI RAGUSA** gelato (€, AIC)	P.zza Duca degli Abruzzi, 25/26
L'Abbuffata C.da Gaddimeli	restaurant, pizzeria tel. 932.239521	AIC
Armony C.da Ciappola, SS 115	**MARSALA** restaurant, pizzeria tel. 0923966551	AIC
Peppizza C.da Strasatti, 921	restaurant, pizzeria tel. 0923741403	€, AIC www.peppizza.it
Sir Damian Corso Gramsci 143	restaurant, pizzeria tel. 092371168	€, AIC
Baby Luna Via Punica, 1	**MAZARA DEL VALLO** restaurant, pizzeria tel. 0923948622	€-€€€, AIC
La Conchiglia Via S. Quasimodo, 11 Notes: Closed Mondays.	restaurant, pizzeria tel. 0923945333	AIC
Ariston Caffè	**MAZZARINO** gelato (€, AIC)	C.so Vitt. Emanuele, 161
Casa Canalotto Via La Loggia, 4	agritourism tel. 09341900766	€€-€€€, AIC www.casacanalotto.it

Pizzeria Ciancio   pizzeria   €, AIC
V.le della Resistenza, 17/a   tel. 3389991558

                                       MERÌ
L'Arancin o D'oro   tavola calda   €, AIC
Via Dante, 182   tel. 90.9763233

                                       MESSINA
Autogrill Tremestie ri Ovest   autogrill   €, AIC
A20 Messina - Palermo   tel. 90.730269

Gli Antenati   pizzeria/pub   €, AIC
C.so Cavour, 109   tel. 090672430   www.gliantenatipub.it

Le Altre Farine del Mulino   bakery, gastropub, rotisserie   €-€€, AIC
Via I° Settembre, 66   tel. 090.9431962

L'Ossidiana   restaurant   €€€€, AIC
Via dei Verdi, 7/11   tel. 090675899   www.gliantenatipub.it

Number One   restaurant, pizzeria   AIC
Via XXVII Luglio, 79   tel. 090774495   www.numberonemessina.it

Pizza Sprint   pizzeria   €, AIC
Via S. Licandro Piazza XXV Aprile   tel. 09059607

Rossopo modoro   pizzeria   €-€€, AIC
Via S.S. 114 km 4,700 vill. Pistunina   tel. 90.632831

                                       MILAZZO
Sapori di Pane e Più   breads, sandwiches   €, AIC
Via Umberto I, 41 / Via Orsa Maggiore, 16   tel. 340.2494284/324.8286647

                                       MILENA
Le Delizie   gelato (€, AIC)   Via Nazionale, 21/25

                                 MIRABELLA IMBACCARI
Al Canale   bar, tavola calda   €, AIC
Via Roma, 122   tel. 933.991441

La Rondine   restaurant   AIC
C.da Gatta   tel. 933.991139   www.larondineristorante.com

                                       MISILMERI
Alla Botte   pizzeria   €€€€, AIC
Via Mariano Scaduto, 14   tel. 91.873357   www.ristolaveranda.it

                                      MISTERBIANCO
Funny Island c/o Parco Giochi   pizzeria   €, AIC
via Sonnino   tel. 095483676   www.funny-island.com

                                       MODICA
Bye Spike   bakery, rotisserie   €, AIC
Via Fosso Tantillo Pirato, 1   tel. 0932.905525   www.byespike.it

Pietre Nere Resort   hotel, restaurant   AIC
Via Pietre Nere, 142   tel. 932.753051   www.pietrenereresort.it

                                       MONREALE
Il Gelato della Piazzetta   gelato (€, AIC)   Via Roma, 91

Punto ICS
Via Etnea, 93/95

I Giardini di Noto
C.da Fiumara

Donna Rosa
Via Roma, 27

Baglio Cantello
Via Cantello, 2

La Corte di Eolo
Via Antonino Uccello, 1

Al Gelatone

Aromatico Zero Glutine
Via dell'Orsa Minore, 268
Via Trinacria, 40/42

Don Rice
via Giuseppe Pagano, 13

Duetto
V.le Regione Siciliana, 710

Extrò Cafè
Via Terrasanta, 87

Gabibbo
Via Oreto, 351

Gelateria Azzurra
Via Messina Marine, 627

Gelato 2

Il Fedino
Via Mongerbin o, 13

Il Gelatiere

Il Genio dei Sapori
Via Gen. C. A. Dalla Chiesa

Il Marchese del Gatto
Via Vincenzo di Marco, 3/a

King
Via Briuccia, 24

La Dolce Vita
Via Giuseppe Giusti,17

La Gatta Mangiona
Via Danimarca, 21/23

NICOLOSI
restaurant, pizzeria
tel. 95.7910362 — €€, AIC — www.pizzeriapuntoics.it

NOTO
restaurant, pizzeria
tel. 0931839730 — €, AIC

OLIVERI
restaurant, pizzeria
tel. 941.314074 — €-€€, AIC — www.ristorantedonnarosa.it

PACECO
agritourism
tel. 923.526529 — AIC — www.bagliocantello.it

PALAZZOLO ACREIDE
restaurant
tel. 0931883185 — €€, AIC

PALERMO
gelato (€, AIC) — Via Autonom. Siciliana, 98

bakery, rotisserie
tel. 91.2511603
tel. 91.8873028 — €, AIC

tavola calda
tel. 91.507297 — €, AIC

restaurant, pizzeria
tel. 091.590180/328.3342755 — AIC

bar, pizzeria
tel. 91.9801904 — €, AIC — www.extrocafe.com

restaurant, pizzeria
tel. 0916476195 — €, AIC — www.pizzeriagabibbo.it

gelato
tel. 91.6221182 — €, AIC — www.gelateriaazzurra.com

gelato (€, AIC) — Via Alcide De Gasperi, 215

restaurant, pizzeria
www.ristorantepizzeriailfedino.it — AIC

gelato(€, AIC) — Via C. Scobar, 47/49

restaurant/pizzeria
tel. 0917219260 — €€, AIC

bakery
tel. 91.5081525 — €, AIC — www.ilmarchesedelgatto.com

trattoria, pizzeria
tel. 091511098 — €€, AIC

restaurant, pizzeria
tel. 91.300074 — €€, AIC — www.ladolcevitapalermo.it

restaurant, pizzeria
tel. 091.519188 — €€€-€€€€, AIC — www.lagattamangiona.net

L'Arte Bianca Via Giacinto Carini, 22/24	pizzeria tel. 91.670308	€€, AIC www.pizzerialartebianca.it
L'Aurora del Buon Gelato	gelato (€, AIC)	P.zza Tommaso Natale, 66
Naif Via Vann'Antò, 21	restaurant tel. 091346525	€, AIC www.ristorantenaif.it
Piccola Sicilia Via Tenente Giovanni Ingrao, 2	B&B tel. 091.320335	AIC www.piccolasicilia.it
Sesto Canto Via S. Oliva, 26	restaurant tel. 091324543	€€€-€€€€, AIC
Stancampiano Sabrina	gelato (€, AIC)	Via Aquileia, 60/62
Stecco Natura	gelato (€, AIC)	P.zza Castelnuo vo, 14
Trinkhaus Via S. Isidoro, 23/B	pizzeria tel. 0916731010	€-€€, AIC
Villa Costanza Via Pietro Bonanno, 42	restaurant, pizzeria tel. 91.547027	€-€€, AIC www.villacostanza.com
Zero Via Palmerino, 54/a	bakery, rotisserie, gastropub tel. 91.421221	€, AIC

PARTINICO

Villa Teresa C.da Garofalo	restaurant, pizzeria tel. 091908134	€, AIC

PATERNÒ

Antico Forno Verona Corso Italia, 42	bakery, rotisserie tel. 095.843343	€, AIC www.anticofornoverona.com
Capricci di Gola Piazzale Diritti Umani, 6/7	pizzeria tel. 3407296029	€, AIC

PEDARA

La Tettoia Corso Ara di Giove, 129	restaurant, pizzeria tel. 0957800988	€, AIC

PERGUSA-ENNA

Riviera Hotel Villaggio Pergusa	hotel, restaurant, pizzeria tel. 0935541267	€€, AIC www.hotelrivieraenna.it

PIRAINO

Borgo Murauto C.da Salinà Via Murauto	restaurant (vegan, vegetarian) tel. 0941.581235	€€, AIC www.borgomurauto.it

POLIZZI GENEROSA

U Funnacu Largo Regina Elisabetta, 31	pizzeria tel. 921.688119	€€, AIC www.ufunnacu.it

PORTO EMPEDOCLE

Talia Zucchero e Sale Via Malato, 11	creperie, sandwich shop tel. 366.9833938	€, AIC

POZZALLO

Mastro Pizza V.le Europa	pizzeria tel. 932.956763	€€, AIC www.pizzeriamastropiero.com

RAGUSA

Barbecue — restaurant — €€, AIC
Via Fanfulla da Lodi, 5 — tel. 0'0932644963 — www.cremiapasticceria.it

Borgo Monachella — B&B — AIC
C.da Monachella — tel. 333.4338523 — www.borgomonachella.it

Cuccagna In... — restaurant, pizzeria — €, AIC
Via M. Rumor, 8 — tel. 0932255469
Notes: Closed Mondays and month of August.

L'Abbuffata — restaurant, pizzeria — €€-€€€, AIC
C.da Gaddimeli — tel. 0932239521

Limoni di Sicilia (J. Kelly)

RODÌ MILICI

Da Tonino — restaurant, pizzeria — €€, AIC
Via Vittorio Emanuele Orlando, 114 tel. 090.9741358 — www.ristorantedatonino.net

ROSOLINI

Rostipan — bakery, rotisserie — €, AIC
Via Manzoni, 184 — tel. 0931.1883094 — www.rostipan.it

Squillo da Vitaliano e Rosanna — pizzeria — €, AIC
Via Aldo Moro, 8 — tel. 0931859994

S. PIER NICETO MARINA

Eurialo e Niso — restaurant, pizzeria — €€, AIC
C.da S. Biagio, 22 — tel. 90.9910777 — www.eurialoeniso.it

S. TERESA DI RIVA

Le Terrazze — restaurant/pizzeria — €€, AIC
Via Lungomare, 87 — tel. 0942792981

S. VITO LO CAPO

Gardenia — hotel — AIC
Via Dante Alighieri, 3 — tel. 0923972188

Le Plus Bon Miceli	gelato (€, AIC)	Via Savoia, 72
S. Vito Via S. Vito, 26	B&B tel. 0923.972215	AIC
Stecco Natura Via Savoia, 25	gelato tel. 923.972622	€, AIC www.stecconatura.it
Thaam Via Duca degli Abruzzi, 32 www.sanvitoweb.com/thaam/ristorante.htm	restaurant, B&B tel. 0923972836	€€€, AIC
Vento del Sud Via Duca degli Abruzzi, 183	hotel tel. 0923.621450	AIC www.hotelventodelsud.it

S.GIOVANNI GALERMO

Pizzeria Da Nunzio Via S. Giovanni Battista, 74/76	pizzeria tel. 95.420339	€€, AIC www.pizzeriadanunzio.altervista.org

S.GIOVANNI LA PUNTA FRAZ.TRAPP ETO

Bottega Gastrono mica Via Madonna delle Lacrime, 29	pizzeria, tavola calda tel. 95.8188962	€€, AIC

S.ALFIO

Case Perrotta Via Andronico, 2	restaurant, agri+G2961tourism, B&B tel. 095968928	€€€, AIC www.caseperrotta.it

SAN CATALDO

Mediterranea V.le Italia, 73	pizzeria tel. 0934571045	€, AIC

SANTA CATERINA VILLARMOSA

La Variante Via Aldisio, 52	pizzeria tel. 934.679843	€€, AIC

SANTA NINFA

Due Palme S.S. 119 Km.42,700	restaurant, pizzeria tel. 092461044	€€, AIC
Vecchio Casale Via Di Stefano Perez	pizzeria tel. 3476274967	€-€€, AIC

SAPONARA MARITTIMA

Pizzeria Diamante Via Nazionale, 103	tavola calda, pizzeria tel. 090.332768/346.3224249	€, AIC

SCIACCA

Hostaria del Vicolo Vicolo Sammaritano, 10	osteria tel. 092523071	€€€€, AIC

SCORDIA

Punto Zero Glutine Via Garibaldi, 161	bakery, rotisserie tel. 340.8284351	€, AIC

SELINUNTE DI CASTELVETRANO

Gelateria Mozart	gelato (€, AIC)	Zona Artigianale C.da Strasatto

SICULIANA

Sole Mediterraneo Millennium SNC Via Principe di Piemonte, 1	restaurant/pizzeria, resort tel. 0922815210	€€€, AIC www.solemediterraneo.it

Algilà Via Vitt. Veneto, 93	**SIRACUSA** hotel/restaurant tel. 0931465186	€€€€, AIC www.algila.it
Bar Milano Via Giuseppe Di Natale, 16	pizzeria bar tel. 093122457	€€, AIC
Celifree Via Pietro Novelli, 55	bakery, rotisserie tel. 931.442076	€, AIC
Don Chisciotte Viale Teocrito, 69/A	pizzeria tel. 093164324	€€, AIC
Gran Caffè del Duomo Piazza Duomo, 18/19	restaurant, pizzeria tel. 931.21544	€€, AIC
Mentirosa Viale Scala Greca, 409	restaurant, pizzeria tel. 931.75922	€€, AIC

www.facebook.com/PizzeriaPizzoleriaMentirosa

Neapolis V.le Scala Greca, 67/h	B&B tel. 393.5728619	AIC www.neapolisbb.wix.com
Pizza d'Autore Via Polibio, 84	pizzeria tel. 09311852566	€, AIC
Pizzoleria Tica Viale Tica, 96	pizzeria tel. 931.413977	€, AIC
Stecco Natura	gelato (€, AIC)	Via Roma, 41

SORTINO

Nabila Via Santa Sofia, 19	restaurant, pizzeria tel. 093195395	AIC

TAORMINA

Licchio's Bar P.zza S. Caterina, 7	bar, pizzeria tel. 0942.625607	€€€€, AIC
Stecco Natura	gelato (€, AIC)	C.so Umberto, 229

TRABIA

La Tonnara Largo Tonnara	hotel,restaurant, pizzeria tel. 91.8146865	€€€, AIC www.grandhotellatonnara.it

TRAPANI

C'è Pizza per Te Via Vespri, 194/196	restaurant/pizzeria/sandwich shop tel. 092328810	€, AIC www.cepizzaperte.com
Che Pizza! Via Riccardo Passaneto, 64	pizzeria tel. 0923.26633/380.4731476	€, AIC
Da Peppe P.zza Ciaccio Montaldo, 4	pizzeria tel. 096899300	€, AIC
Duca di Castelmonte Via Motisi, 3	agritourism tel. 0923526139	AIC
Gelateria Gino	gelato (€, AIC)	P.zza Gen. Dalla Chiesa, 1
Gelatissimo	gelato (€, AIC)	Via Conte A. Pepoli, 172
Le Plus Bon Miceli	gelato (€, AIC)	Via Giuseppe Garibaldi , 35

Villa Carmen
Via Madonna dell'Indiriz zo, 64

Poggio...del Tempo Perduto
Contrada S. Antonino

Magie di Forno
Corso Vittorio Emanuele, 614

Don Guto 1975
Via Nazionale, 149

La Trizzera
Via Fosse Ardeatine, 59

Aria dell'Etna
Via Nipitelli, 10

Esperia Palace Hotel
Via delle Ginestre, 27/d

La Ginestra dell'Etna
Via delle Ginestre, 27/d

Parco dei Principi
restaurant   €€€€, AIC
Via delle Ginestre, 1
tel. 0957082335
www.ristoranteparcodeiprincipi.it

Villa Mirador
restaurant   AIC
Via Zafferrana - Milo, 23
tel. 0957082890

TRECASTAGNI
B&B   AIC
tel. 95.7800587   www.bebvillacarmen.it

VALDINA
restaurant, pizzeria   €, AIC
tel. 0909977009

VILLABATE
sandwich shop, rotisserie, bakery   €, AIC
tel. 327.3091541 www.facebook.com/MagieDiForno

VILLAGRAZIA DI CARINI
restaurant (Brazilian)   €€€, AIC
tel. 091.8674257/345.4240674

VILLASETA
restaurant, pizzeria   €, AIC
tel. 0922512415

ZAFFERANA ETNEA
B&B   AIC
tel. 349.3162268   www.bebariadelletna.it

hotel   AIC
tel. 95.7082335   www.esperiapalace.com

B&B   AIC
tel. 0957081302   www.ginestradelletna.it

Fish Market (J. Kelly)

Lovers (J.Kelly)

SARDINIA

ALGHERO

Aragon
Via Gramsci, 8

restaurant, pizzeria
tel. 0799731001

AIC

ARZACHENA

Corbezzolo
Piazzetta Fontana - Loc. Baja Sardinia

restaurant, pizzeria
tel. 078999893

€€-€€€, AIC
www.ristorantecorbezzolo.it

Hotel Citti
V.le Costa Smeralda, 197

hotel
tel. 078982662

€, AIC
www.hotelcitti.com

La Rocca
Loc. Pulicinu, box 1392

restaurant
tel. 789.933011

AIC
www.laroccaresort.com

ASSEMINI

Sapore Antico
Via Cagliari, 213

pizzeria
tel. 070940437

€, AIC

BADESI

Resort Le Dune
Loc.tà Li Junchi, snc

hotel
tel. 079610200

AIC

BORTIGIADAS

Golden Gate
SS 127 Km. 53

hotel, restaurant
tel. 079627174

€€, AIC
www.ristorantegoldegate.ory.it

Gluten-Free Italy by Region

BUDONI

La Volpe — restaurant, pizzeria — €-€€€, AIC
Via Agamennone, 9 fraz. Taunanella — tel. 0784837388

CAGLIARI

Antico Caffe — restaurant
P.za Costituzione, 10 — tel. 070658206 — www.charmingsardinia.com
Notes: Notes: closed Tuesday.

B&B Le Tartarughe — B&B
Via Marconi 41/A, Sinnai — tel. 070766253 — www.letartarughe.net

Caesar's Hotel — inn, reception hall — €€€€, AIC
Via S. Freud, 5 — tel. 070340750

da Rita — pizzeria — €, AIC
Via Palestrina, 94 — tel. 0704980444
Notes: Closed Mondays and at lunch.

Dal Corsaro — restaurant — €€€-€€€€
Viale Regina Margherita 28 — tel. 070664318 — www.dalcorsaro.com
Notes: GF pasta with advance notice. English spoken. Reservations necessary.

Flora — restaurant, pizzeria — €€€, AIC
Via Sassari, 45 — tel. 070664735 — www.florasrl.com
Notes: Closed Sundays and the month of August.

Galleria 18 — pizzeria — €-€€, AIC
Viale La Playa, 18 — tel. 070680377
Notes: Closed Saturday at lunch and all day Sunday.

Su Gologone — hotel, restaurant — €€€-€€€€
Loc Su Gologone — tel. 0784287512 — www.sugologone.it
Notes: Special celiac menu. GF breakfast. Reservations preferred.

Tore — restaurant, pizzeria — €, AIC
Piazza Belly, 4 — tel. 3400092174

CANNIGIONE

Hotel Cala di Falco — hotel — AIC
Loc. Cala di Falco — tel. 0789899200
www.hotelcaladifalco.com/sardinia/camere-2.html

CASTELSARDO

Rocca'ja — restaurant, pizzeria — AIC
Via Sedini — tel. 079470164

CASTIADAS

Araxi 'e Mari — restaurant — €€€-€€€€, AIC
Località San Pietro snc — tel. 70.995144 — www.araxiemari.it

Pizza Folle — pizzeria — €, AIC
Loc. Olia Speciosa — tel. 0'0709949091 — www.pizza-folle.it

DORGALI

Il Querceto — hotel/restaurant — €€€ - €€€€, AIC
Via La Marmora, 4 — tel. 078496509 — www.ilquerceto.com

S'Adde — hotel, restaurant, pizzeria — €€, AIC
Via Concordia, 38 — tel. 078494412 — www.hotelsadde.it

Baddy's
Via Cappuccini, 16

IGLESIAS
pizzeria
tel. 0781255029

€, AIC
www.ristorantebaddys.it

L'Aragosta
Via Ciusa, 33

LA CALETTA
hotel, restaurant
tel. 0784810046

€€€-€€€€, AIC
www.laragostahotel.com

Da Mommo
C.so V. Emanuele, 82/a

MAMOIADA
pizzeria
tel. 078456444

€, AIC

Vera Club Costa Rei
Via delle Tuie snc

MURAVERA
resort
www.veratour.it

AIC

Vera Club Suneva
Strada per Capo Ferrato sn

resort
www.veratour.it

AIC

Canne al Vento
Via Biasi, 159

NUORO
restaurant
tel. 0784201762

€€€-€€€€, AIC

Il Rifugio
Via A. Mereu, 28/36

restaurant
tel. 0784232355

€€€, AIC
www.trattoriarifugio.com

Tamatta
c/o Centro Com.le Pratosardo

pizzeria
tel. 0784294147

€-€€, AIC

Barbagia
Via Galvani, 94

OLBIA
restaurant
tel. 078951640

www.ristorantebarbagia.com

Notes: GF pasta. English spoken. Closed Wednesdays.

Caffetteria della Nonna
Via Nazionale, 33 - Loc. Murta Maria

hotel, restaurant, bar
tel. 0789379025

€€€€, AIC
www.speraesole.it

Gallura
C.so Umberto, 145

restaurant
tel. 078924648

€€€€

H. Mercure Olbia Hermaea
Via Puglie, snc

hotel/restaurant
tel. 07891890067

€€€€
www.mercure.com

Cocco e Dessi
Via Tirso, 31

ORISTANO
restaurant
tel. 0783300720

€-€€€
www.coccoedessi.it

Notes: English spoken. Reservations essential.

Mariano IV palace hotel
Piazza Mariano, 50

hotel
tel. 0783360101

www.m4ph.isarose.net

Notes: GF breakfast. GF pasta. English spoken.

Trattoria Gino
Via Tirso, 13

restaurant
tel. 078371428

€€€-€€€€

S'Arzola
C.so Vittorio Emanuele, 82

OROTELLI
pizzeria
tel. 078479303

€, AIC
www.pizzeriasarzola.com

Time's Café
Via Roma, 33

ORTACESUS
pizzeria
tel. 0709804306

€, AIC

OZIERI

Terradoro hotel, restaurant, pizzeria   AIC
Localitá Chilivani   tel. 079758904   www.albergoristoranteterradoro.it
Notes: GFM.

PALAU

H. Cala di Lepre-Delphina Hotels hotel   €€€, AIC
Loc. Cala di Lepre   tel. 0789702142   www.delphinahotel.it
Notes: Closed October-April.

H. Capo d'Orso-Delphina Hotels hotel   €€€€, AIC
Loc. Cala Capra   tel. 0789902000   www.hotelcapodorso.com
Notes: Closed October-May. No GF pizza.

Hotel Altura   hotel, restaurant   €€€-€€€€
Porto Raphael   www.hotelaltura.it
Notes: GF upon request.

Il Paguro   restaurant   €€€€, AIC
Loc. Cala Capra   tel. 0789702036   www.delphina.it
Notes: Closed October-April.

PORTO CERVO

Cervo H. Costa Smeralda Resort hotel, restaurant, pizzeria   €€€€, AIC
Piazzetta di Porto Cervo   tel. 0789931111   www.sheraton.com/cervo

PORTO TORRES

Piazza Garibaldi   restaurant, pizzeria   AIC
Piazza Garibaldi, 13   tel. 079501570   www.piazzagaribaldiportotorres.it

PULA

Baia di Nora   hotel, restaurant   AIC
Loc. Su Gunventeddu   tel. 0709245551   www.hotelbaiadinora.com
Notes: Closed November-March.

QUARTU SANT'ELENA

Colombo   pizzeria   €, AIC
Viale Colombo, 264   tel. 070820608
Notes: Closed Wednesdays.

S. TEODORO

Al Faro   hotel, restaurant, pizzeria   €€-€€€€, AIC
Via del Tirreno Spiaggia La Cinta   tel. 0784865665   www.hotelalfaro.com

S. TERESA DI GALLURA

Resort Valle dell'Erica   hotel/resort   €€€€, AIC
Loc. Valle dell'Erica   tel. 0789750020   www.hotelvalledellerica.com

SASSARI

Andreini   restaurant   €€€€
Via Arduino 45   tel. 079982098   www.ristoranteandreini.it
Notes: GF pasta. Reservations essential. English spoken.

Fainè Da Carlo   pizzeria   €, AIC
SP Sassari Argentiera, 193/A Loc. Bancali   tel. 079309773

I 3 Leoni   pizzeria   €-€€, AIC
Loc. Bancal, 218   tel. 079308041

Tiffany   restaurant, pizzeria   €€-€€€, AIC
Via Carlo Felice, 33   tel. 079272434   www.ristorantetiffany.it

SIAMAGGIORE

Da Renzo
SS. 131 Km.99
restaurant
tel. 078333685
€€€€, AIC
Notes: Closed Sunday evenings and Mondays.

TEMPIO PAUSANIA

Bonvicino
Loc. Bonvicini Ss127 Km 39, 900
restaurant, pizzeria
AIC

Museum
P.zza Gallura, 27
restaurant bar
tel. 079671083
€, AIC
Notes: Closed Sundays.

Pausania Inn
S.S. 133 Km.1
hotel, restaurant
tel. 079634037
€€, AIC
www.hotelpausaniainn.com
Notes: Closed Tuesdays and at lunch.

TORPÈ

Sa Inza
Loc. Santeddu - via Milano, 5
agritourism, B&B
tel. 3282579271
€€-€€€, AIC
www.agriturismosainza.it

TRINITÀ D'AGULTU

Hotel Marinedda Thalasso & SPA hotel
Loc. Isola Rossa
tel. 079694185
€€€€, AIC
www.delphina.it

Hotel Relax Torreruja - Delphina Hotels hotel
Loc. Isola Rossa
tel. 079694155
€€€€, AIC
www.delphina.it

VILLASIMIUS

Chiccheria
Via Vittorio Emanuele II 2
gelato
tel. 331.5694256
€, AIC
www.chiccheria.com

Gli uccelli (D. Kraushaar)

TORINO, PIEDMONT, AND VALLE D'AOSTA

(AIC = participates in the Associazione Italiana Celiachia program)

TORINO

Al Grassi　　　　　　　restaurant　　　　　　　€€€€, AIC
Via Beaumont, 32/c corner of Via Grassi　tel. 0114345430　　　www.algrassi.it

Alma Latina　　　　　　restaurant　　　　　　€€-€€€, AIC
Via Baretti, 8/bis　　　　tel. 11.6692554　　　　www.almalatina.to.it
Notes: Latin, Spanish cuisine.

Antica Trattoria con Calma　restaurant　　　　　€€€, AIC
Strada Comunale del Cartman, 59　tel. 0118980229

B&B Lingotto　　　　　B&B　　　　　　　AIC
Via Rocca de Baldi, 23　　tel. 0116638878

Bar Myosotis　　　　　bar　　　　　　　€, AIC
Via L. Spallanzani, 1/b　　tel. 393.8355486

Cafè & Patisserie　　　bar　　　　　　　€, AIC
Via Filadelfia, 113/b　　tel. 11.19506672　www.facebook.com/cafeepatisserie

Caffetteria Lo Spuntino　bar　　　　　　€, AIC
Via L. Cibrario, 57　　　tel. 338.3853491

Casa Firmino　　　　　B&B　　　　　　　AIC
Str. alla Funicolare, 23/4　tel. 0118987517　　www.casafirmino.it

Circolo La Toga C.so Casale, 287	restaurant tel. 333.7953679	AIC
Cravero Str. Cimitero Sassi, 6/A	bakery tel. 11.8980034	€, AIC www.pasticceriacravero.com
Crazy pizza Via Vandalino, 56/GH	pizzeria tel. 0117732317	€, AIC www.crazypizzatorino.it
Curryzone Via Gioberti, 4	restaurant tel. 0114546875	€€, AIC
Dolcesalato Senza Glutine Via De Sanctis, 111/a	bakery tel. 11.768131	€, AIC www.dolcesalatosenzaglutinetorino.it
Duca 102 C.so Duca degli Abruzzi, 102	restaurant, pizzeria tel. 0115817273	€€€, AIC
Gluti Nostress Caffè Via dei Mille, 32	bar tel. 11.763353	€, AIC www.gluti.it
Gran Caffè Vittoria Via Genova, 6	bar-cafe tel. 0116964448	€, AIC
Hotel Cairo Via la Loggia, 6	hotel tel. 11.3171555	AIC www.hotelcairo.it
Il Gusto di Carmilla Via San Donato, 29	tavola calda tel. 11.4274001	€, AIC www.ilgustodicarmilla.it
Il Vicolo Via Melchiorre Gioia, 3/D	restaurant tel. 011535233	€-€€, AIC
Kipling Restaurant Via Mazzini, 10	restaurant tel. 0118172616	€€€ - €€€€, AIC www.kiplingrestaurant.com
La Barrique C.so Dante, 53/a	restaurant tel. 011657900	€€€€, AIC www.labarriqueristorante.it
La Birba/Il Briccone Via Barbaroux, 25	restaurant tel. 011533376	€€€, AIC
La Medusa P.zza Pasini, 3	restaurant, pizzeria tel. 0118980371	€-€€, AIC www.ristorantelamedusa.com
La Pasta Fresca P.zza Fontanesi, 4	bakery tel. 11.884357	€, AIC www.pastafrescatorino.it
La Strambata Via Ugo Foscolo, 20	restaurant, pizzeria tel. 0116692681	€, AIC www.ristorantelastrambata.com
Las Rosas Via Bellezia, 15/f	restaurant (Mexican) tel. 0115213907	€, AIC www.lasrosas.it
Locanda del Pentegallo Via Alessandro Volta, 3	pizzeria, restaurant tel. 0117640344	€, AIC www.locandadelpentegallo.it
M**Bun (2 locations) C.so Siccardi 8/a Via Rattazzi, 4	sandwich shop tel. 0115617097 tel. 01119704606	€, AIC www.mbun.it www.mbun.it
Maison del Celiaco Via Avet 8 (Zona P.zza Statuto)	bakery, sandwich shop www.maisondelceliaco.it	€
Mescè	shakes and crepes	€, AIC

Via S. Dalmazzo, 4	tel. 11.5824479	www.walkingfood.it/IWF
Noè	restaurant, pizzeria	€, AIC
Via Guala, 120	tel. 0113174520	
Novotel Torino/Novotelcafé	hotel, restaurant	€€€€, AIC
C.so Giulio Cesare 338/34	tel. 0112601211	www.novotel.com
Panperfocaccia	restaurant, pizzeria	€-€€€€, AIC
Via Conte verde, 7/a	tel. 3468520279	www.panxfocaccia.com
Piero's	pizzeria	€, AIC
Via Principe Amedeo, 25	tel. 0118172254	
Pizzeria da Michi	restaurant, pizzeria	€€, AIC
Via S. Donato, 38	tel. 11.4732408	
Pizzeria Pratico	pizzeria	€€, AIC
Via Madonna di Campagna,9	tel. 11.2768409	www.pizzeriapratico.it
Pizzeria Ristoro Qeendici	pizzeria/restaurant	€, AIC
P.zza Peyron, 15/b	tel. 0114370150	
Rist. La Campana/H. Chelsea	restaurant hotel	€€-€€€, AIC
Via XX Settembre, 79/c/e	tel. 0115214011	www.hotelchelsea.it
Ristorante Massimo Hotel il Convento restaurant, hotel		€€€€, AIC
Via Hermada, 3/A	tel. 161.805181	
www.ilconventoditrino.com/?page_id=51&lang=en		
Sapordivino	restaurant	€€, AIC
Via Borgo Dora, 25/h	tel. 0514365104	www.sapordivino.net
Silvano	gelato	€, AIC
Via Nizza, 142	tel. 11.6677262	www.gelateriasilvano.it
Soup & Go	restaurant	€, AIC
Via S. Dalmazzo, 8/a	tel. 0110712763	www.soupandgo.it
Statuto da Carmen	restaurant, pizzeria	€€, AIC
Via Manzoni, 0/f	tel. 051537363	
Notes: Closed Mondays.		
Tratt. Raffaello 5	trattoria	€€, AIC
C.so Raffaello, 5	tel. 0516694723	www.raffaello5.com
Yogurteria Creperia Fyò	gelato, crepes	€, AIC
P.zza Palazzo di Città, 6/d		
Yogurteria Fyò	gelato, crepes	€, AIC
Via Accademia delle Scienze, 2/e		

Grom	gelato (AIC)	P.zza Paleopaca, 1/d
Grom	gelato (AIC)	Via Accademia delle Scienze, 4
Grom	gelato (AIC)	P.zza S. Rita da Cascia, 6/a
Grom	gelato (AIC)	Via Cernaia, 18
La Gelateria da Bobo	gelato (AIC)	C.so Traiano, 2/c
L'Apegaia	gelato (AIC)	Str. S. Mauro, 180/e
Gelateria Nicola	gelato (AIC)	C.so Vittorio Emanuele II, 199/c
Il Gelato Amico	gelato (AIC)	Via S. Massimo, 34

Auchan
supermarket
Corso Romania 160

Carrefour
supermarket
Corso Grosseto 330

Celi@Chia-Food
supermarkets
Via Somalia 30
Piazza Sofia 28/A
Via Crissolo 23
Pam
supermarkets
Corso Cosenza 46/B
Via Salbertrand 67
Corso Traiano 58
Via Nizza 230
Corso Svizzera 52

Turingel
supermarkets
Corso Sebastopoli 147
Via S. Secondo 48
Corso Vercelli 78

Ave Maria (C. Caneparo)

THE REST OF PIEDMONTE

ACQUI TERME

Vineria Angolo Divino Via alla Bollente, 44 Notes: Closed Tuesdays.	restaurant tel. 0144321005	€€, AIC
Spigallegra Via Rodi, 1/a	bakery tel. 0121.376759	€, AIC www.spigallegra.it

ALBA

Al Setaccio Via Crispi, 4	restaurant, pizzeria, bakery tel. 173.592577	€-€€, AIC www.al-setaccio.webnode.it
Bar Roma Via Alberione, 3/b	bar, gelato tel. 173.442127	€, AIC
Hotel i Castelli C.so Torino, 14/1	hotel, restaurant tel. 173.361978	AIC www.hotel-icastelli.com
Panetteria Giacosa C.so Langhe, 68/a	bakery tel. 173.44058	€, AIC www.panetteriagiacosa.net

ALBUGNANO

Le Tre Colline Via Serra, 4	agritourism tel. 0119922038	€€, AIC www.letrecolline.com
Ristorante Al Gottardo Loc. Vezzolano, 1/bis	restaurant, wine bar tel. 11.9922014	€€€€, AIC www.ristorantealgottardo.it

Sunset on Lago Maggiore (D. Impastato)

Terra e Gente
Loc. S. Emiliano, 45

agritourism €€€€, AIC
tel. 11.9920841 www.terraegente.it

ALESSANDRIA

Arcimboldo
Via Legnano, 2

restaurant €€€€, AIC
tel. 013152022 www.ristorantearcimboldo.it

Gelat. Soban

gelato (€, AIC) Via S. Lorenzo, 99

Grom

gelato (€, AIC) Via Milano, 1

Il Forno di Madama Caterina
C.so IV Novembre, 13

bakery, sandwich shop, cupcake shop €, AIC
tel. 333.3286158

Il Girone dei Golosi
Via Vinzaglio, 67

restaurant €€-€€€, AIC
tel. 131.22371 www.gironedeigolosi.com

ALFIANO NATTA

Agriturismo Crealto
Str.da Crealto, 6

agritourism AIC
tel. 345.5686278 www.crealto.it

ALICE CASTELLO

Ranch
Via Cavaglià, 20

restaurant €€, AIC
tel. 161.9091

ALMESE

Nonsolovino
Via Avigliana, 107

restaurant €€€, AIC
tel. 0119359774 www.ristorantenonsolovino.it

ALPETTE CANAVESE

Hosteria Alpina
Via Paganini, 5

hotel, restaurant €€, AIC
tel. 0124809143

ALPIGNANO

Farenheit 451
Via Cavour, 46

restaurant, pizzeria €€, AIC
tel. 0119787379

Torino, Piedmont and Valle d'Aosta

Oasi dello Chef
Viale Vittoria, 18
restaurant
tel. 393.2141194
€€, AIC
www.oasidellochef.altervista.org

ANGROGNA

Rifugio Jumarre
Loc. Vaccera, 266
restaurant
tel. 0121.944233
€€-€€€, AIC
www.rifugiojumarre.it

ARONA

Yogorino di Bonetti Giovanna
gelato (€, AIC)
Corso Cavour, 82

ASTI

Agriturismo il Buon Seme
Frazione Sessant, 240
agritourism
tel. 333.2233491
€€€, AIC
www.ilbuonseme.it

Al Sangiovanni
Via Guttuari, 12
restaurant
tel. 141.231317
€€€€, AIC
www.alsangiovanni.it

Campanarò
Via Secondo Arò, 30
restaurant
tel. 014133252
€€€, AIC
www.campanaro.it

Casa del Ventiniere
Fr. Variglie,81
B&B
tel. 348.3934263
AIC

Grom
P.zza San Secondo, 11
gelato
www.grom.it
€, AIC

La Piola
C.so Alessandria, 150
restaurant, pizzeria
tel. 141.219892
€-€€, AIC
www.pizzeriaristorantelapiola.com

BAGNOLO P.TE

Il Provenzale
Via Cave, 305
restaurant, pizzeria
tel. 0175391510
€€, AIC
www.ristoranteilprovenzale.it

BALME

La Masinà
Loc. Pian della Mussa
agritourism
tel. 3474439384
€€€, AIC
www.agrimasina.com

BARDONECCHIA

Etable
Via Medail, 82
restaurant
tel. 012296973
€€€€, AIC

La Pigna
Fraz. Melezet, 119
hotel, restaurant
tel. 0122880303
€€, AIC
www.hotel-lapigna.it

BARGE

Bar Gazebo
Piazzetta della Madonna s.n.
bar-cafe
tel. 03487030509
AIC

BEINASCO

Mychef Beinasco Nord
Progr. km 2,670 diramaz. x Pinerolo della Tang. Sud di Torino
www.mychef.it
mychef
€, AIC
tel. 11.3496314

BIELLA

Al Buon Ricordo
Viale Matteotti, 17
Notes: Closed Monday-Wednesday.
restaurant
tel. 01523831
€€€-€€€€, AIC

Alice
gelato (€, AIC)
Via Italia, 12

Caffè del Chiostro
Via Q. Sella-Museo del Territorio
restaurant
tel. 0152523112
€-€€, AIC

Caffetteria del Corso Via Italia, 50	bar, tavola calda tel. 01522345	€, AIC
Fra Le Nuvole Via S. Filippo, 17	bakery tel. 015.3700947	€, AIC www.fralenuvolebiella.com
Giordano Via Delleani, 33	pizzeria tel. 015405306	€, AIC
Ristorante Palazzo Boglietti Via Piacenza, 1	restaurant tel. 15.8497995	€€€-€€€€, AIC www.ristorantepalazzoboglietti.it

BORGARO TORINESE

Hotel Atlantic - Rist. Il Rubino Via Lanzo, 163/165	hotel, restaurant tel. 0114500055	€€€€, AIC www.hotelatlantic.com
Mondo Bio Via Lanzo, 107	tavola calda tel. 11.4543424	€-€€, AIC www.spesamondobio.it

BORGO TICINO

Cascina Cesarina Via dei Cesari, 32	agritourism, B&B tel. 032190491	€€, AIC www.cascinacesarina.com

BRANDIZZO

Sòrbole Via Torino, 396	restaurant, pizzeria tel. 11.9137498	€€-€€€€, AIC www.sorbole.it

BRONDELLO

La Torre Via Villa, 35/a	restaurant tel. 017576198 www.ristorantelatorrebrondello.com	€€, AIC

BUBBIO

Agriturismo Mondoaranci o Reg. Stropeta, 100	agritourism tel. 331.4467918 www.agriturismomondoarancio.it	AIC

BUTTIGLIERA D'ASTI

La Gallina Bionda Via Villanova, 62 - Fr.Crivelle	pizzera, trattoria tel. 11.9921314	€€, AIC

CALAMANDRANA

La Corte Fr. Quartino, 6	hotel, restaurant tel. 141.769109	AIC www.agrilacorte.com

CALTIGNAGA

Trattoria Risorgimento Via Risorgimento, 26	restaurant tel. 0321.652125	€€€, AIC www.trattoriarisorgimento.it

CAMINO

Agriturismo Ca' San Sebastiano Via Ombra, 10/12	agritourism tel. 142.9459	€€€, AIC www.casansebastiano.it
Billy Bau Via Rocca, 75- Fraz. Rocca	restaurant tel. 142.469014	€€, AIC www.billybau.com

CAMPIGLIONE FENILE

Locanda del Terzo Tempo Via Edmondo de Amicis, 13/C	trattoria, bar tel. 329.949807	€€€, AIC

CANALE

La Siesta P.zza Europa, 5	pizzeria tel. 3318962126	€, AIC

Lou Lindal
Frazione Preit, 1

CANOSIO
inn, restaurant
tel. 0171998301

€-€€, AIC

Villa Pepa
Via Vico, 13

CAPREZZO
B&B
tel. 0323559039

AIC
www.villapepa.it

CARBONARA SCRIVIA
La Rocca dei vecchi e nuovi sapori pizzeria
Vicolo del castello, 7/a tel. 131.89218

€€, AIC

Il Canonico
Strada Castagnole, 29

CARIGNANO
restaurant
tel. 0119692388

€€€, AIC
www.ilcanonico.it

Trattoria del Porto
Via del Porto, 158

CARMAGNOLA
trattoria
tel. 11.9717937

€€, AIC

Mondo Pizza
C.so Valentino, 38/40

CASALE MONFERRATO
pizzeria
tel. 142.74838

€€, AIC
www.mondopizzacasale.com

Il Ventaglio
Via Martiri della Libertà, 33

CASELLE TORINESE
bakery, gelato, bar
tel. 11.9975676

€, AIC

LA.TI.MI.DA.
Str. Ricaldone di Sotto, 28

CASSINE
agritourism
tel. 0144715371

€€, AIC
www.agriturismolatimida.it

Agriturismo Surì
Via della Chiesa, 3

CASSINE FRAZ. S. ANDREA
agritourism
tel. 0144767079

€€, AIC
www.suri.it

Nero Seppia
Via Alba, 12/e Loc. baraccone

CASTAGNITO
restaurant
tel. 0173212025

€€€€, AIC
www.nero-seppia.it

B&B Cascina Motette
Via Cascina Motette, 46

CASTAGNOLE PIEMONTE
B&B
tel. 0119862621

AIC
www.cascinamotette.it

B&B Edera
Via Garibaldi, 27

B&B
tel. 0119862106

AIC
www.edera.net

Equin'ozio
Fraz. Filia, 70

CASTELLAMONTE
restaurant
tel. 124.513635

€€€, AIC
www.equin-ozio.it

Il Valentino
Strada Castelnuovo Nigra, 21

restaurant
tel. 124.515476

€€€, AIC
www.ristoranteilvalentino.it

Trattoria San Giovanni
Via Centrale, 53 Fraz.S.Giovanni

restaurant
tel. 124.513287

€€-€€€, AIC
www.trattoriasangiovanni.it

Il Nido di Bacco
Via Pro.le 12

CASTELLAR
B&B
tel. 017546603

€€€€, AIC

CASTELLERO

Casale Gentile	agritourism	€€€, AIC
Via Vernetto, 18	tel. 0141669715	www.casalegentile.com

CASTELLO DI ANNONE

Mychef Crocetta Nord	mychef	€, AIC
A21Torino/Alessa ndria/Piacenz a km 48+225	tel. 141.401162	www.mychef.it

CASTIGLIONE TINELLA

Campagna Verde	restaurant	€-€€€, AIC
Via Balbi, 22	tel. 0141855108	

CERES

Valli di Lanzo	restaurant, hotel	€€€-€€€€, AIC
Via Roma, 11	tel. 012353397	www.ristorantevallidilanzo.it

CERESETO

Monferrato Resort	restaurant, agritourism	AIC
Fr. Cascine Franchi	tel. 142.940127	

CERRETTO LANGHE

Trattoria del Bivio	restaurant	€€€-€€€€, AIC
Località Cavallotti, 9	tel. 0173520383	www.trattoriadelbivio.it

CERRIONE

Il Tiglio	agritourism	€€€, AIC
Cascina Ronco	tel. 03348592883	www.iltiglio.it

CERVERE

Primi Dolci	restaurant	€€-€€€, AIC
P.zza S. Sebastiano, 30	tel. 0172474471	www.primidolci.it

CESSOLE

Tenuta Antica S.S.	agritourism	AIC
Reg. Busdone, 2	tel. 144.80113	

CHERASCO

Flyfood	bar, tavola calda	€, AIC
Via del Lavoro,13	tel. 172.474003	
Locanda Pane e Vino	restaurant	€€-€€€, AIC
Via Moglia, 12	tel. 0172489108	

CHIALAMBERTO

La Muanda	agritourism	€€€, AIC
Fraz. Vonzo, 23	tel. 3498490840	www.lamuanda.com

CHIERI

Dolci & Dolci	bakery	€, AIC
Via Orfane,5	tel. 11.9413695	
Grom	gelato	€, AIC
Via Vittorio Emanuele, 59	www.grom.it	
Il Faro di Mara Cirmia	bar	€, AIC
Via Andezeno, 6	tel. 11.4276536	
Sayuri Sushi Bar	restaurant	AIC
P.zza Mazzini, 6	tel. 11.9421197	

Ristorante Boschetto
Via S.Anna, 26 _ Fraz. Boschetto

CHIVASSO
restaurant
tel. 11.9195948

AIC

Pizza Konnection
Via Statale, 39

CINZANO
pizzeria/restaurant
tel. 0172479073

€ - €€, AIC

Il Capriccio di Tiziana
Via Torino,53

CIRIÈ
bar, restaurant
tel. 331.536585

AIC

La Smorfia
Via Robassomero, 70

pizzeria
tel. 11.9205044

AIC

L'Isola che Non C'è
Località Ghe, 1

agritourism
tel. 0119205669

€€, AIC
www.agriturismolisolachenonce.it

Dolci Idee
V.le XXIVMaggio, 5

COLLEGNO
gelato
tel. 11.4152524

€, AIC
www.gelateriadolciidee.it

Pizzeria del Viale
V.le Antonio Gramsci, 4

restaurant, pizzeria
tel. 011786390

€, AIC

Sapori di Casa
V.le Gramsci, 4/C

gastropub, pizzeria, bakery
tel. 11.7910735

AIC
www.gastronomiasenzaglutine.it

La Bussola
Via Mazzini, 42

COSSATO
restaurant, pizzeria
tel. 015921702

€-€€€, AIC

Panta Rei
Via Mazzini, 42

restaurant
tel. 015921084

€€€-€€€€, AIC
www.ristorantepantarei.com

Enoteca Caffè Roma
P.zza Umberto I

COSTIGLIOLE D'ASTI
wine bar
tel. 0141966544

€€, AIC

Belvedere Resort
Fraz. Mozzio, 24

CRODO
hotel, restaurant
tel. 032461055

€€€, AIC
www.belvederemozzio.it

La Cantina in Collina
Via Marconi,9

CUCCARO MONF.TO
agritourism
tel. 0131771111

€€-€€€, AIC

Alpigrill
Via Bra, 1

CUNEO
restaurant
tel. 0171413249

€€-€€€, AIC

Grom

gelato (€, AIC)

P.zza Galimberti, 2

Les Gourmands
Via Statuto, 3

restaurant
tel. 03357548416

€€-€€€€, AIC
www.lesgourmands.it

Mario Senza Glutine
Via Porta Rossa, 3/b

cupcake shop, bakery
tel. 171.613464

€, AIC
www.mariosenzaglutineglutenfree.eu

Agriturismo Oryza
P.zza Castello, 8

DESANA
agritourism
tel. 0161318565

€-€€, AIC
www.oryzariso.it

Gluten-Free Italy by Region

Tenuta Larenzania
Borgata Piandeltroglio, 16

Il Tiglio
Via Deseno, 3/5

La Gelattica

Dalla Padella alla Brace
Via Volta, 31/a

Gli Amici
C.so Matteotti, 25

Pracatinat
Località Pra Catinat

Cascina Monticone
Collina S. Giuseppe, 71

Amici Miei
S.R. 229, 5

Bastian
Str. Stazione, 13

Dolcelatte

Il Drago e la Fata
Via Marconi, 1

Bar di Sotto
C.so Aldo Porro, 22

La Rustica
Via Madonna , 69

L'Artigiana del Gelato

Al Gufo Nero
Via Novara, 162

Cre' Seren
Fraz. S. Rocco, 10

DOGLIANI
hotel, restaurant   €€, AIC
tel. 017371086   www.larenzania.it

DOMODOSSOLA
B&B   AIC
tel. 0324249306   www.bb-tiglio.com

DORMELLETTO
gelato (€, AIC)   C.so Cavour, 94

DRUENTO
restaurant, pizzeria, wine bar   €€, AIC
tel. 011994262   www.ristorantedallapadellaallabrace.net

FAVRIA CANAVESE
hotel, restaurant, pizzeria   €, AIC
tel. 0124360798

FENESTRELLE
inn   AIC
tel. 0121884884   www.pracatinat.it

FERRERE
agritourism   AIC
tel. 328.7431747

FONTANETO D'AGOGNA
restaurant, pizzeria, Gel   €€, AIC
tel. 322.890053   www.ristorantepizzeriaamicimiei.it

FONTANILE
agritourism   AIC
tel. 0141774475   www.agriturismobastian.it

FOSSANO
gelato (€, AIC)   Via Cesare Battisti, 11

hot dogs, pizza, vegetarian   €, AIC
tel. 392.2920327

FUBINE
restaurant, bar   €, AIC
tel. 131.798972

GATTICO
restaurant, pizzeria   €€, AIC
tel. 0322838781

GATTINARA
gelato (€, AIC)   C.so Garibaldi, 76

GHEMME
restaurant   €€-€€€, AIC
tel. 0163840251

GIAGLIONE
agritourism   €€, AIC
tel. 0122629264   www.agriturismogiaglione.it

Orchidea
Via Pontepietra, 34

Ristorante Novarello
Via D. Graziosi, 1

Bargiglio Rosso
Via Garibaldi, 157

La Salinera
Via IV Novembre, 19

La Tagliata
Via IV Novembre, 45

Locanda Vecchio Novecento
Via Corio, 8/a

Coop. Agricola del Duc
Strada del Portone, 197

Grom

Il Sagittario
P.zza Papa Giovanni XXIII, 15

Io e Luna
Fraz. Montebello, 1

Ristorante Pizzeria Eporediese
C.so Vercelli, 132

Ristorante Campana
Via Torino, 33

Bar Ristorante Pizzeria da Frankino
Loc. Quartino, 5

Roma
P.zza Martiri, 8

La Vecchia Fornace
Via Fornaci, 25

I Sapori
Strada Statale, 193

Il Baco da Seta
Via S. Leone, 5

GIAVENO
restaurant
tel. 0119363936
€€€, AIC
www.ristorantepizzeriaorchidea.it

GRANOZZO
restaurant
tel. 338.5835902
AIC

GRINZANE CAVOUR
restaurant, pizzeria
tel. 173.262115
€€-€€€, AIC

restaurant
tel. 0173262915
€-€€, AIC

restaurant
tel. 173.262692
€€-€€€, AIC
www.latagliata.it

GROSSO
restaurant
tel. 0119268614
€-€€, AIC
www.vecchionovecento.it

GRUGLIASCO
agritourism
tel. 0113149929
€€, AIC
www.cascinaduc.it

gelato (€, AIC)   Via Crea, 10 C/O Le Gru primo piano

restaurant/pizzeria
tel. 011701687
€€, AIC

GUARENE
restaurant
tel. 0173611724
€€€€, AIC
www.ioeluna.com

IVREA
restaurant, pizzeria
tel. 125.251038
€€-€€€, AIC

LA CASSA
restaurant
tel. 011.9842946
€€, AIC
www.ilristorantecampana.it

LOAZZOLO
restaurant, pizzeria, bar
tel. 144.83536
€€, AIC
www.frankino.it

LUMELLOGNO
pizzeria
tel. 0321469033
€€, AIC
www.trattoriapizzeriaroma.com

MAGGIORA
agritourism
tel. 0322870086
€€, AIC

MANTA
restaurant, pizzeria
tel. 0175289538
€-€€, AIC

agritourism
tel. 0175289352
€€, AIC
www.ilbacodaseta.com

Il Pithosforo
S.S. Laghi di Avigliana, 171

Il Forno di Nonna Ada
Via Martiri della Libertà, 15

Il Mulino di Chalier
Via Giordani, 52

Per i Golosi
Via Monteverde, 2

Il Giardino Pensile
Piazzetta della Parrocchia, 12

Nuova Gandolfi
Via Gandolfi, 1

Lievito Madre e Puro Latte
Via Garibaldi, 4

Tosa Restaurant House
Str. Genova, 200

Trattoria del Freisa
Via Mosso, 6

La Borsarella
Via del Crhist, 2

Cascina Pian Borga
Località S.Giuseppe, 11
Notes: Closed Monday-Thursday.

Enoteca Caffè Rocca Costantino
P.zza Umberto I, 20

Belvedere
Vicolo San Giovanni, 3

Cascina Vrona
Fraz. Sant'Anna, 6

La Fenice
Via Roma, 38
Notes: Great reviews.

MANTA DI SALUZZO
restaurant, pizzeria €-€€, AIC
tel. 017588174 www.hotelcicerone.it

MATHI
bakery €, AIC
tel. 11.0561884

MATTIE
hotel, restaurant AIC
tel. 0122.238132 www.mulinomattie.it

MONASTERO BORMIDA
bakery, gelato €, AIC
tel. 144.88089

MONASTERO DI LANZO
restaurant € - €€€, AIC
tel. 01234217

MONASTERO DI VASCO
restaurant, pizzeria €€€, AIC
tel. 0174689628

MONCALIERI
restaurant, ice cream shop €€, AIC
tel. 011642673 www.lievitomadrepurolatte.it

restaurant €€€€, AIC
tel. 0116474971 www.tosaristorante.it

MONCUCCO TORINESE
restaurant €€-€€€, AIC
tel. 0119874765 www.trattoriadelfreisa.it

MONDOVI
restaurant €€€, AIC
tel. 017442999 www.laborsarella.it

MONFORTE D'ALBA
agritourism €€, AIC
tel. 0173789212

restaurant, wine bar €€, AIC
tel. 0173707156

MONTÀ D'ALBA
inn, restaurant €€€-€€€€, AIC
tel. 0173976156 www.albergobelvedere.com

MONTEU ROERO
agritourism, B&B €€, AIC
tel. 017390629

MORNESE
restaurant, pizzeria €€, AIC
tel. 342.005852 www.ristorantepizzerialafenice.eu

Will
Via IV Novembre, 43

NETRO
B&B
tel. 338.8921152

AIC

da Zio
Via Superga, 18

NICHELINO
restaurant, pizzeria
tel. 03484207447

€€€, AIC
www.pizzeriadazio.com

Il Giardino dei Sapori
Via Buffa, 79

restaurant, gelato, pizzeria
tel. 11.6807816

€-€€€€, AIC
www.ilgiardinodeisapori.eu

La Romantica
Str.da Alessandria, 13

NIZZA MONFERRATO
restaurant, pizzeria
tel. 141.701129

€€, AIC

Ristorantino Tantì
Via Pio Corsi, 18

restaurant
tel. 141.727338

€€, AIC
www.tanti.it

L'Orologio
Via Roma, 71

NONE
restaurant
tel. 0119904296

€€€, AIC

C'era una Volta
Fr. S. Pietro, 1

NOVALESA
agritourism
tel. 335.7883741

€, AIC
www.corbusier.it

20 Regioni - Bar Cucina Shop
Via Magnani Ricotti, 14/b

NOVARA
restaurant, bar
tel. 0321331504   www.20r.it

€€, AIC

Autogrill Autostrada A4
Torino - Milano

autogrill
tel. 321.691144

€, AIC

Grom
C.so Italia, 13

gelato
www.grom.it

€, AIC

La Piramide
C.so XXIII Marzo, 314

pizzeria, trattoria
tel. 0321402900

€€€, AIC
www.pizzeriaristorantepiramide.com

Pontida
Via Pontida, 6/a

trattoria
tel. 032135045

€€-€€€, AIC

Rist. Sushi bar Long Jin di Yunana
C.so Torino, 52/d

restaurant
tel. 0321031277

€€, AIC
www.longjin.it

Trattoria Cavallino Bianco
Via Vicolo Dell'Arco, 2/A

restaurant
tel. 032139308

€€€, AIC

La Terrazza
Via Garibaldi, 91

NOVI LIGURE
restaurant, pizzeria
tel. 014376688

€€-€€€, AIC

L'ultima Spiaggia c/o Aquarium
Via F.lli Rosselli, 2

restaurant, pizzeria
tel. 0143743789

€, AIC

Mychef Marengo Nord
A26 Genova Voltri Gravellona Toce Km 9.700   tel. 143.417967 www.mychef.it

mychef

€, AIC

Az. Agr. Cascine Bellini
Via Cascine Bellini

OLEGGIO
agritourism
tel. 0321995193

€€€, AIC

Dinamo	restaurant, pizzeria	€, AIC
Via Paganini, 5	tel. 0321998333	

OROPA

Croce Bianca	hotel, restaurant	€-€€€€, AIC
Via Santuario Oropa, 480	tel. 0152455923	

OROPA SANTUARIO

Ristoralp Croce Bianca	hotel, restaurant	€€-€€€, AIC
Via Santuario Oropa, 480	tel. 15.2455923	www.ristorantecrocebianca.it

ORTA S. GIULIO

S. Rocco	hotel	€€€€, AIC
Via Gippini, 11	tel. 0322911977	

OSASCO

La Siepe	B&B	AIC
Via Rovina, 10	tel. 0121541552	
www.bed-and-breakfast.it/en/pagina.cfm?id=22296&idregione=12		

PARODI LIGURE

Al Ghiottone	agritourism	€€€-€€€€, AIC
Via Cadegualchi, 1	tel. 0143681213	
Notes: Closed Monday-Wednesday.		

PAVAROLO

Ristorante del Castello	restaurant	AIC
Via Maestra, 7	tel. 0119408042	www.ristorantedelcastello.com

PECETTO TORINESE

L'Escalier	restaurant, pizzeria	€-€€€, AIC
Via Circonvallazione, 22	tel. 0118609845	www.granclasse.com

PEROSA ARGENTINA

Clara's Lodge	B&B	AIC
Via Monte Grappa, 7	tel. 0121804009	

PERRERO

Il Girasole	B&B	AIC
Borgata Moliera, 3 fraz. Riclaretto	tel. 0121808962	

PIANEZZA

La Fattoria del Gelato	gelato (€, AIC)	Via Grange, 44
La Muradora	agritourism	AIC
ViaGrage, 47	tel. 340.0829526	www.lamuradora.it
Osteria del Musicante	osteria	€-€€€, AIC
Via Caduti per la Libertà, 26/A	tel. 0119661249	www.osteriadelmusicante.com
Severino - Delizie Senza Glutine	sandwich shop, bakery	€, AIC
Via Mombello, 26	tel. 348.0444859	www.deliziesenzaglutine.it

PIEA

Pian Dij Babi	agritourism, B&B	AIC
Via Vallunga, 1	tel. 320.1792756	www.piandijbabi.it

PINASCA

Bella Baita	B&B	AIC
Serre Marchetto, 1	tel. 3479842945	

	PINEROLO	
B&B Casa Carla	B&B	AIC
Via Costagrande, 51	tel. 0121322195	
Charlie Bar	bar-cafe	AIC
P.zza V. Veneto, 7	tel. 012177331	
Perbacco	restaurant	€€, AIC
P.zza S. Donato, 8	tel. 0121397487	
	PINO TORINESE	
Pinocchio	restaurant	€€-€€€, AIC
Via Roma, 3	tel. 011842451	
	PIOBESI D'ALBA	
Tenuta Carretta	restaurant	€€€€, AIC
Località Carretta, 2	tel. 0173619261	www.tenutacarretta.com
	PIOBESI TORINESE	
Caffè Ristorante Albergo Stazione	bar, hotel, restaurant	AIC
P.zza Paracleto, 2	tel. 11.9657372	
Ristorante Hotel Celestino	restaurant, hotel	AIC
C.so Italia, 10	tel. 11.9650343	www.hotelristorantecelestino.it
	POIRINO	
Trau Brusà	pizzeria	€, AIC
C.so Fiume, 79/bis	tel. 0119450368	www.pizzeriatraubrusa.it
	POLLONE	
Il Faggio	restaurant	€€€€, AIC
Via Oremo, 54	tel. 01561252	www.ristoranteilfaggio.it
	POLONGHERA	
La Via del Sale	trattoria	€€, AIC
Via Dellera, 4	tel. 011974413	www.trattorialaviadelsale.com
	PONZONE	
Malò	hotel, restaurant	€€-€€€, AIC
P.zza Garibaldi, 1	tel. 014478075	www.albergomalo.com
	POZZOLO FORMIGARO	
La Locanda dei Narcisi	restaurant	€€€€, AIC
Str. Barbotti, 1 fraz. Bettolle	tel. 0143319822	www.lalocandadeinarcisi.it
	PRAGELATO	
Villaggio Gofree Camping	restaurant, village	€, AIC
Via Nazionale, 2/a fraz. Ruà	tel. 012270045	www.villaggiogofree.com
	PRAGELATO LOC.PLAN	
La Greppia	restaurant	€€€, AIC
Via del Beth, 9	tel. 012278409	
	PRALORMO	
Ristorante Pizzeria dell'Olmo	restaurant, pizzeria	€€€ - €€€€, AIC
Via Alba, 67	tel. 11.9481851	www.ristorantepizzeriadellolmo.com

Lago Maggiore (A. Komorowski)

Lo Scoglio	**PRATO SESIA** restaurant, pizzeria	€-€€€€, AIC
Via Paganini, 5	tel. 0163850581	
La Virginia	**REVELLO** agritourism	€€€ - €€€€, AIC
Via Valle Po, 77	tel. 0175259026	www.lavirginia.it
Tomato Pizza Rivalta	**RIVALTA DI TORINO** pizzeria, restaurant	€, AIC
Via Giaveno, 18 C/O Carrefour	tel. 0119005595	www.tomatopizza.org
Amaranto	**RIVAROLO CANAVESE** restaurant, gastropub	€€, AIC
Via Farina ,3	tel. 124.42585	www.amarantofood.it
Crema & Cioccolato	bar	€€, AIC
C.so Indipendenza, 74 c/o Urban Center	tel. 124.428079	www.rivarolourbancenter.it
Oggi Pizza c/o Urban Center	pizzeria	€, AIC
C.so Indipendenza, 74	tel. 0124420113	
2uepuntozero	**RIVOLI** restaurant	€, AIC
Via Piave, 20	tel. 0119589556	www.2uepuntozero.it
Biogelateria Rivoli	gelato (€, AIC)	Via Stura, 22
M**Bun	fast food	€, AIC
C.so Susa, 22	tel. 11.9534062	www.mbun.it
Pastepartout	bakery	€, AIC
Via Cavalieri Vittorio Veneto, 27	tel. 333.9795996	www.pastepartout.com
Pizzeria Brasserie Un'Altra Volta	restaurant, pizzeria	€, AIC
Via Vittorio Veneto, 109	tel. 017178197	www.pizzeriaunaltravolta.com

ROBILANTE

La Rosa dei Venti
Via Torino, 6/8

ROLETTO
restaurant, pizzeria
tel. 121.54219
€€, AIC
www.larosadeiventiroletto.it

Eremo della Gasprina
Borgata Cappallotti, 2

S. MARIA DI LA MORRA
restaurant
tel. 017350498
€€€, AIC

Stella
Via Prevignano, 7

S. SALVATORE MONFERRATO
restaurant, pizzeria
tel. 0131233107
€€, AIC

Ristorante Albergo Nazionale
Via Sant'Anna, 111

S.GIACOMO DI ROBURENT
hotel, restaurant
tel. 174.227127
€€-€€€, AIC
www.albergonazionale.cn.it

Az. Agrit. Ca' d'Andrei
Via Trento, 2

SAGLIANO MICCA
agritourism
tel. 0152475013
€€, AIC

Fattoria delle Rose
Cascina Emilia, 1

SALUSSOLA
trattoria, agritourism
tel. 0161999955
€€, AIC
www.fattoriadellerose.com

Le Quattro Stagioni d'Italia
Via Volta, 21

SALUZZO
restaurant, pizzeria
tel. 017547470
€€, AIC

Piazza Grande
V.le Tramvie, 3
trattoria, self-service
tel. 175.290675
€-€€, AIC
www.piazzagrandesaluzzo.it

Profumo di Lillà
Via San Pancrazio, 8

SAN GILLIO
B&B
tel. 3496052520
AIC

L'Antico Pioppo La Carolina
Via Badini, 28

SANTENA
agritourism
tel. 11.9454467 www.anticopioppo.it/agriluogo.html
AIC

Gran Baita
Via Cuneo, 23

SAVIGLIANO
hotel, restaurant
tel. 0172712060
€€, AIC
www.granbaitahotel.it

La Sirenetta
Via Solerette, 9/a
pizzeria
tel. 0172377193
€, AIC

Nuovo Monarca
Strada Tetti Olio, 2

SCARNAFIGI
restaurant
tel. 017574420
€€-€€€€, AIC

La Raviola Galante
Via Maiocco, 4

SCURZOLENGO
restaurant
tel. 0141203015
€€€, AIC
www.laraviolagalante.it

La Rosa dei Vini
Loc. Parafada, 4

SERRALUNGA D'ALBA
restaurant, B&B
tel. 0173613219
€€, AIC
www.larosadeivini.com

Ristorante Crea
P.zza Santuario, 7

SERRALUNGA DI CREA
bar, restaurant
tel. 142.940108
€€-€€€€, AIC
www.ristorantedicrea.it

La Marenda Sinoira
Fr. Cesnola, 74 Reg.Cornaley

SETTIMO VITTONE
restaurant
tel. 125.65847

€€, AIC
www.marendasinoira.it

Al Rustico
Via degli Alpini, 16

SOMERARO DI STRESA
restaurant
tel. 32832172

€€€-€€€€, AIC

Ristopizza Nuovi Sapori
Loc. Piano, 56

SOMMARIVA PERNO
restaurant, pizzeria
tel. 017246405

AIC

Antico Ca' d'Gamba
Via B. Bona, 78

SORDEVOLO
restaurant
tel. 0152568813

€€€, AIC

Al Pum Rus
Via Cerano, 1

SOZZAGO
agritourism
tel. 321.70178

€€-€€€€, AIC
www.alpumrus.it

G.H. Des Iles Borromees
C.so Umberto I, 67

STRESA
hotel
tel. 323938938

€€€€, AIC
www.borromees.it

La Palma
C.so Umberto I, 33

hotel
tel. 032332401

AIC
www.hlapalma.it

Regina Hotel
C.so Umberto I, 29

hotel
tel. 323936936

AIC
www.regina-palace.com

Il Pianeta 2000
Via Circonvallazione, 29

TARANTASCA
restaurant/pizzeria
tel. 0171931858

€€, AIC
www.ilpianeta2000.com

Il Melograno
P.zza Vitt. Emanuele III, 9

TERRUGGIA
restaurant
tel. 0142401531

€€€, AIC
www.osteriailmelograno.com

La Civetta
P.zza Pietro Micca, 4

TORRE PELLICE
restaurant
tel. 3336741005

€€, AIC

Mediterraneo
Via Arzani 10/d

TORTONA
restaurant, pizzeria
tel. 0131814782

€, AIC
www.ristorantemediterraneo.net

Gelat. Soban

VALENZA
gelato (€, AIC)

P.zza Gramsci, 23

Fungo Reale
Fraz. Airale, 11

VALLORIATE
hotel, restaurant
tel. 0171717039

€, AIC

Geoffrey's
Via S. Marchese, 38

VENARIA
restaurant, pizzeria
tel. 11.4591646

€-€€, AIC
www.ristorantegeoffreys.com

La Smorfia
Via Verga, 14

pizzeria
tel. 0114246595

€, AIC

Al Binario 20 Viale Roma, 20	**VENARIA REALE** restaurant, pizzeria tel. 11.459808	€-€€€, AIC www.albinario20venaria.it
Trattoria la Terrazza P.zza Martiri, 4	**VENASCA** restaurant, trattoria tel. 175.567167	€€€, AIC www.trattorialaterrazza.it
Edenatura P.zza Mercato, 25	**VERBANIA** restaurant, bar tel. 323404314	AIC www.edenatura.it
Hotel Ancora C.so Mameli, 65	B&B tel. 32353951	AIC www.hotelancora.it
di-Lab Via Vittorio Veneto, 3	**VERCELLI** sandwich shop, gluten-free products tel. 161.214887	€, AIC www.di-lab.it
Grom	gelato (€, AIC)	C.so Libertà, 4
I Due Forni Via Thaon de Revel, 41	restaurant, pizzeria tel. 161.302354	€€€, AIC
Ristorante Vecchia Brenta Via Morosone, 6	restaurant tel. 161.25123	€€€, AIC www.ristorantevecchiabrenta.it
Da Pasquale Via Torino 12	**VERCELLI - CASCINE STRÁ** restaurant, pizzeria tel. 161.313164 www.facebook.com/pasquale.dapasquale	€€, AIC
Due Lanterne Borgata Molino, 15	**VERDUNO** restaurant tel. 172470127	€€, AIC www.ristoranteduelanterne.it
La Cascata Zona Gurej, 1	restaurant tel. 0172470126	€€-€€€, AIC www.lacascata.com
La Tavola del Chiostro P.zza Carlo Emanuele I, 4	**VICOFORTE** hotel, restaurant tel. 17565300	€, AIC www.santuariodivicoforte.com
Ristorante Pizzeria Laura Via Trento, 3/5	**VIGNALE MONFERRATO** restaurant, pizzeria tel. 339.8287447	€€€, AIC
Monte Cimolo Via Bèe, 1	**VIGNONE** restaurant, pizzeria tel. 323551403	€, AIC
La Tavernetta C.so Italia, 4	**VILLADOSSOLA** restaurant tel. 3396511980	€€€, AIC www.tavernettaristorante.com
Il Valdichiesa da Enzo Strada per Chieri, 92	**VILLANOVA D'ASTI** restaurant, pizzeria tel. 3333444941	€€, AIC
La Stella Polare Strada Cappello, 29	agritourism tel. 0141946245	€€, AIC

VILLANOVA SOLARO

Castello dei Solaro
Via Vitale, 4
restaurant €€€€, AIC
tel. 017299365 www.castellodeisolaro.it

VILLASTELLONE

La Cascinetta
Via Tetti Mauritti, 26
agritourism AIC
tel. 342.5548652 www.lacascinetta.wix.com/villastellone

VINOVO

Antica Piazza delle Grida
Via Cottolengo, 109
Notes: Closed Mondays.
restaurant €€, AIC
tel. 0119623036

VISTRORIO

Fior di Zucca
Regione Selva, 30
agritourism €€, AIC
tel. 012576405

VOLPIANO

La Lenza
Regione Selva, 30
restaurant €€, AIC
tel. 0119882385 www.lalenza.it

VALLE D'AOSTA

ANTEY SAINT-ANDRÈ

Au Jardin Fleuri
Fraz. Bourg, 7
agritourism AIC
tel. 348.4818426 www.agriturismoantey.com

AOSTA

Grom
gelato (€, AIC) Via Jean Baptiste de Tillier

BREUIL-CERVINIA

Hotel Edelweiss
Via Guido Rey, 18
hotel, restaurant AIC
tel. 166.949078

BRUSSON

Hotel Laghetto
Rue Trois Villages, 291
hotel, restaurant, bar AIC
tel. 125.300179 www.hotellaghetto.it

CHAMPOLUC

Hotel Cré Forné
Loc. Cré Forné
hotel AIC
tel. 125.307197 www.champoluc.it

CHATILLON

Mychef Chatillon Nord
mychef (€, AIC) Autostrad a Torino – Aosta

COGNE

Les Pertzes
Via Dr. Grappein, 93
restaurant, bar €€€, AIC
tel. 165.749227 www.nigritelles.com

COURMAYEUR

Auberge de la Maison
Via Passerin d'Entreves 16
hotel, restaurant
tel. 165869811 www.aubergemaison.it
Notes: English spoken. GF breakfast and pasta with advanced notice.

Cadron Solaire
Via Roma 122
restaurant
tel. 165844609
Notes: Reservations essential. English spoken.

Hotel Aigle
Strada la Palud, 5 fraz.Entréves
hotel, restaurant AIC
tel. 165.8697

Maison de Filippo restaurant
Fraz. Entreves tel. 165869797 www.lamaison.com
Notes: Very popular restaurant. Reservations essential. English spoken.

Villa Novecento hotel, restaurant
Viale Monte Bianco 64 tel. 165843000 www.villanovecento.it
Notes: English spoken. GF with advance notice.

GRESSAN
Le Bon Plat restaurant €€, AIC
Fraz. Borettaz, 7 tel. 165.251621
www.facebook.com/pages/LE-BON-PLAT/138059293068653

GRESSONEY LA TRINITÉ
Chalet du Lys restaurant, hotel restaurant, hotelres AIC
Loc. Staffal, 14 tel. 0125.366806 www.chaletdulys.it

Romantik Hotel Jolanda Sport hotel, restaurant AIC
Loc. Edelbode n Sup. , 31 tel. 125.36614 www.hoteljolandasport.com

GRESSONEY SAINT JEAN
Lyshaus- Carducci hotel, restaurant AIC
Loc.tà Tschoard e, 1 tel. 125.356643 www.lyshaus.com

LILLIANES
Maison Vallomy B&B AIC
Loc. Vers Chessun, 8 tel. 347.3866874

SAINT MARCEL
Chambre d'Hotes Le Coffret B&B AIC
Loc. Jayer, 32 tel. 0165.778751 www.lecoffret.it/en/le-coffre

SAINT VINCENT
Il Ritrovo restaurant €-€€€€, AIC
Via Roma, 42 tel. 166.510098 www.ilritrovo-restaurant.it

Oasi restaurant, pizzeria €€€€, AIC
Via Cretier, 4 tel. 0166.511577 www.ristorantepizzeriaoasi.eu/en/index.htm

SARRE
Il Pirata restaurant, pizzeria €€-€€€, AIC
Fraz. Arensod, 39 tel. 165.257988 www.dalpirata.it

VALTOURNENCHE
Au Vicariat B&B AIC
Loc. Capoluog o tel. 166.92348 www.vicariat.it

Lo Baracon Dou Téne restaurant €€€€, AIC
Località Cime Bianche tel. 0166.93023 www.baracon.blogspot.com

Rifugio Perucca Vuillermo z B&B AIC
Vallone di Cignana tel. 166.969747 www.rifugioperuccavuillermoz.it

VILLENEUVE
Hotel Valdotain restaurant, hotel AIC
P.zza Assunzion e, 6/7 tel. 0165-95032 www.valdotain.it

Bellezza (D. Kraushaar)

ALTO ADIGE, TRENTINTO, AND THE DOLOMITES

ALTO ADIGE

(AIC = participates in the Associazione Italiana Celiachia program)

BRESSANONE

Harpf
Loc. La Mara, 107

restaurant, pizzeria
tel. 0472851047

€€, AIC
www.harpf.net

CALDARO

Pensione Christl
Via S. Antonio, 23

inn
tel. 0471963173

AIC
www.pension-christl.it

CAMPO TURES

Alphotel Stocker
Via Wiesenhof, 39/41

hotel
tel. 0474678113

AIC
www.hotelstocker.com

Hotel Drumlerhof
Via Municipio, 6

hotel, restaurant
tel. 0474678068

€-€€€€, AIC
www.drumlerhof.com

LAIVES

Grill Raif
Via Kennedy, 258

restaurant, pizzeria
tel. 0471590681

€€, AIC

MAREBBE

Ucia Picio Prè
La Plì, 29

restaurant
tel. 3381406452

€€-€€€, AIC
www.piciopre.it

Pensione Schlaneiderhof
Località Salonetto, 7

MELTINA
inn
tel. 0471668147

AIC
www.schlaneiderhof.com

Schofflmair
Via Tures, 23

MOLINI DI TURES
hotel, pizzeria
tel. 0474678126

€€-€€€, AIC
www.schoefflmair.com

Hartmann
Via Rezia, 308

ORTISEI
hotel
tel. 0471774444

AIC
www.hotel-hartmann.com

Hotel Weiss
Via Venosta, 38

PARCINES
hotel
tel. 0473967067

AIC
www.hotelweiss.it

Happy
Via Roma, 44

POSTAL
restaurant, pizzeria
tel. 0473290057

€€, AIC

Petra
Via Pusteria, 16

S. SIGISMONDO CHIENES
restaurant, pizzeria
tel. 0474569600

€€, AIC
www.pizzeriapetra.it

Acadia Beauty & Relax
Via Puez, 24

SELVA DI VAL GARDENA
hotel
tel. 0471774444

€€€€, AIC
www.acadia.it

Family Resort Rainer
Via S. Giuseppe, 40

SESTO-SEXTEN
hotel, restaurant, pizzeria, catering
tel. 0474710366

AIC
www.hotelrainer.com

Hotel Villa Madonna
Via Ibsen, 29

SIUSI ALLO SCILIAR
hotel
tel. 0471708860

AIC
www.villamadonna.it

Mair am Turm
Via Principale, 3

TIROLO
hotel, restaurant
tel. 0473923307

€€, AIC
www.mairamturm.it

Sporthotel e Resid. Griesfeld
Via St. Johann, 5/6

VALLE AURINA
hotel
tel. 0474671172

AIC

TRENTINO

Al Giardino
Via Ronchiano 1

ALA
pizzeria
tel. 0464671058

€, AIC

Albergo Villa Adria
Via De Cost, 109

ALBA DI CANAZEI
hotel
tel. 462.601291

AIC

Ca' Rossa
Via Linfano, 47

ARCO
restaurant, pizzeria
tel. 464.50642

AIC

El Filò
Via Miralago, 43

BASELGA DI PINÈ
restaurant
tel. 0461553156

€€-€€€, AIC
www.ristoranteelfilo.it

Pasticceria Pinetana Gelateria	gelato (€, AIC)	C.so Roma, 61
	BEDOLLO	
Hotel Pineta Lago delle Piazze	hotel, restaurant tel. 461.556642	AIC
La Laita Via Massenzi 2	B&B tel. 333.6853285	AIC
	BELLAMONTE	
Hotel Sole Via De L'Or, 8	hotel tel. 0462576299	AIC www.hsole.it
	BOLZANO	
Caffè Edicola Degustibus Via Rosmini 51	bar tel. 471.983373	€, AIC
La Lanterna Via Rovigo 14	restaurant, pizzeria tel. 471.502107	AIC
Walthers' P.zza Wolther, 6	restaurant, pizzeria, bar tel. 0471/982548	AIC www.walthers.it
	BRENTONICO	
La Pineta Loc. S. Caterina	B&B, pizzeria tel. 464.395258	€-€€€€, AIC www.pizzeriapineta.it
	BRESSANONE	
Harpf Loc. La Mara 107	restaurant, pizzeria tel. 472.851047	AIC www.harpf.net
	CALDARO	
Hotel Masatsch Pianizza di Sopra 30	hotel, restaurant tel. 471.669522	AIC www.masatsch.it
	CAMPITELLO DI FASSA	
Hotel Relais San Giusto Via Roma 1	hotel, restaurant tel. 462.750331	AIC www.san-giusto.it
	CAMPO TURES	
Alphotel Stocker Via Wiesenhof, 39/41	hotel tel. 474.678113	AIC www.hotelstocker.com
Hotel Drumlerhof Via Municipio, 6	hotel, restaurant tel. 474.678068	AIC www.drumlerhof.com
	CANAZEI	
Hotel Astoria - Rist. De Tofi Streda Roma, 92	hotel, restaurant tel. 462.601302	AIC www.hotel-astoria.net
	CANEZZA DI PERGINE	
Osteria Storica Morelli P.zza Petrini, 10	restaurant tel. 461.509504	AIC www.osteriastoricamorelli.it
	CAVALESE	
Bellavista Via Pizzegoda, 5	hotel tel. 0462340205	AIC www.hotelbellavista.biz
	CAVEDAGO	
Fiore Blu Via de la Viola, 9	restaurant, pizzeria tel. 0461654019	AIC

Hotel alle Rose
Via Tomas 12

hotel
tel. 461.654219

AIC

CENTA S. NICOLÒ

Agritur Maso Rauter
Loc.Rauteri 16

B&B
tel. 461.722257

AIC

Martinelli
Fraz. Doss, 4

agritourism
tel. 0461722125

€-€€, AIC

CLES

Il Giardino
Via Pilati, 16

restaurant, pizzeria
tel. 463.422709

AIC

COMANO TERME

Cattoni Hotel Plaza
Via Cesare Battisti, 19

hotel
tel. 0465701442

AIC
www.cattonihotelplaza.com

Don Pedro
Via C. Battisti, 26

pizzeria
www.pizzeriadonpedro.it

€ - €€, AIC

COREDO

Nardis
Via Moncher, 3

pizzeria
tel. 0463538000

€, AIC

COSTA DI FOLGARIA

Nevada
Via Fontanelle, 47

hotel, restaurant
tel. 0464721495

€€, AIC
www.villaggionevada.it

DARÉ

Le Fontane
Via Civico, 115

restaurant, pizzeria
tel. 0465801601

€, AIC

FAI DELLA PAGANELLA

Agostini
P.zza Italia Unita, 16

pizzeria
tel. 0461583301

AIC
www.pizzeriaagostini.it

FOLGARIA

Az. Agr. La Fonte
Loc. Gruim Mezzomonte

agritourism
tel. 0464720041

€€, AIC
www.la-fonte.org

Cogola Ristorante e B&B
Via Pasubio 135 -Serrada

restaurant, B&B
tel. 464.727156

AIC

ISERA

Agritur Maso Carpenè
Loc. Carpenè 1

agritourism
tel. 335.5926227

AIC

Locanda delle Tre Chiavi
Via Vannetti, 8

restaurant
tel. 0464423721

€€€€, AIC
www.locandadelletrechiavi.it

LAIVES

Res.Rest.Lounge bar Alpenrose
Via San Giacomo, 91

restaurant, hotel, bar
tel. 0471252209

€€€€, AIC

LEDRO - BEZZECCA

Albergo Maggiorina
Via XXIV

hotel
tel. 464.591029

AIC

LEVICO TERME

Alla Loggia dell'Imperator e
Via G.Prati, 27

B&B
tel. 461.706261

AIC

Gluten-Free Italy by Region

Trenti NO glutine Via XXIV Maggio, 16	**LODRONE** bakery tel. 465.880776	€, AIC
Hotel Crozzon Viale Dolomiti di Brenta, 96	**MADONNA DI CAMPIGLIO** hotel, restaurant tel. 465.442222	AIC
St. Raphael Via Torre del Brenta, 1	hotel tel. 0465441570	€€€, AIC
Agriturismo alle Gorghe Strada alle Gorghe, 17	**MEANO** agritourism tel. 0461448268 www.facebook.com/agriturallegorghe	€€, AIC
Pensione Schlaneiderhof Località Salonetto, 7	**MELTINA** hotel tel. 471.668147	AIC www.schlaneiderhof.com
Happy Pomodoro Via Laurin 8/a	**MERANO** restaurant, pizzeria tel. 473.222884	AIC www.pizzeriahappy.com
Al Castagneto da Giorgio Loc. ai Piani, 1	**MEZZO LOMBARDO** restaurant, pizzeria tel. 0461601359	€€€, AIC www.alcastagneto.net
Faloria Piaz de Sotegrava, 18	**MOENA** inn, restaurant tel. 0462573149	AIC www.hotelfaloria.it
Lo Sfizio Piazza de Ramon, 32 Notes: Very favorable reviews.	restaurant, pizzeria, creperie tel. 462.574757	€€, AIC
Schofflmair Via Tures, 23	**MOLINI DI TURES** hotel, pizzeria tel. 474.678126	AIC www.schoefflmair.com
Hotel Des Alpes Via Nazionale, 7	**MOLVENO** hotel tel. 0461586983	AIC www.desalpes.it
Hotel Excelsior Via Nazionale, 41	hotel tel. 0461586921	€€€€, AIC www.molveno-excelsior.it
Comparsa Via Domenica Targa, 49	**MONTAGNAGA DI PINÈ** pizzeria tel. 0461557006	€, AIC
Bosco Incantato Loc. Montevaccino, 1/d	**MONTEVACCINO-TRENTO** pizzeria tel. 0461960826	€-€€, AIC
Alla Nave Fr.Nave San Felice 29	**NAVE SAN FELICE** pizzeria tel. 461.870111	€-€€, AIC
Hartmann Via Rezia, 308	**ORTISEI** B&B tel. 471.774444	AIC www.hotel-hartmann.com

Hotel Grones VIA Stufan, 110	hotel tel. 471.79704	AIC

PARCINES

Hotel Weiss Via Venosta,38	hotel tel. 473.967067	AIC www.hotelweiss.it

PEJO FONTI

Hotel Vioz Via dei Cavai, 10	hotel tel. 463.753146	AIC www.hotelvioz.it
Rosa degli Angeli Via del Fontanino, 2	hotel, restaurant tel. 0463743031	€, AIC www.hotelrosadegliangeli.it

PERGINE VALSUGANA

Antiche Contrade Via al Lago, 11	restaurant, pizzeria bar tel. 0461538228	€€€, AIC www.antichecontrade.com
Giropizza Vip Loc. Valcanover, 13	pizzeria tel. 0461512282	€ - €€, AIC

PINZOLO

Hotel Corona Corso Trento, 31	hotel tel. 465.50103	AIC www.hotelcoronapinzolo.it

POZZA DI FASSA

Rifugio T. Taramelli (m. 2.046) Loc. Valle dei Monzoni	restaurant tel. 360.879719	AIC
Vidor Strada Ruf de Ruacia, 15	pizzeria tel. 0462760022	€, AIC www.campingvidor.it

RISCONE

Hotel Petrus Aichner H. & Co. KG Reinthalstr. 11	hotel, restaurant tel. 474.548263	AIC

RIVA DEL GARDA

Agritur Eden Marone Via Marone, 11	agritourism tel. 0464521520	€€€, AIC www.edenmarone.com
Hotel Villa Enrica Via Brione 1/A	B&B tel. 464.551254	AIC www.hotelvillaenrica.com
La Berlera Loc. Ceole, 8/b	restaurant tel. 0464521149	€€€-€€€€, AIC www.laberlera.it
Villa Nicolli V.le Cattoni, 5	hotel tel. 0464552589	AIC www.hotelvillanicolli.com

ROVERETO

Bar Botti Corso Verona, 76/A	restaurant, pizzeria tel. 0464432521	€, AIC
Cherry Gelateria Pasticceria Via Roma 24	gelato, bakery tel. 335.83425	€, AIC

S. CRISTINA

Smart Hotel Saslong Via Pallua, 40	B&B tel. 471.774444	AIC www.saslong.eu

S.SIGISMONDO CHIENES

Petra
Via Pusteria, 16
restaurant, pizzeria — AIC
tel. 0474.569600/348.7094907 www.pizzeriapetra.it

S.ORSOLA TERME

Malga Agritur Cambroncoi
Loc. Cambroncoi
agritourism — AIC
tel. 329.8016326 www.hotel-malgacambroncoi.it

SAN CANDIDO

Acquafan
Via Hueber, 2
restaurant, pizzeria — AIC
tel. 474.914102

SAN CRISTOFORO AL LAGO - PERGINE VALSUGANA

La Darsena
Via dei Pescatori, 47
restaurant, pizzeria — AIC
tel. 328.0364129

SAN LORENZO IN BANALE

Rifugio Silvio Agostini Val D'Ambiez (m. 2.410) restaurant — AIC
Val D'Ambiez
tel. 465.734138

SELVA DI VAL GARDENA

Acadia Beauty & Relax
Via Puez, 24
hotel — AIC
tel. 471.774444 www.acadia.it

Boutique Hotel Nives
Via Nives, 4
hotel, restaurant — AIC
tel. 471.773329 www.hotel-nives.com

SESTO-SEXTEN

Family Resort Rainer
Via S. Giuseppe, 40
hotel, restaurant, pizzeria — AIC
tel. 474.710366 www.familyresort-rainer.com

SIUSI ALLO SCILIAR

Hotel Villa Madonna
Via Ibsen, 29
hotel, restaurant — AIC
tel. 471.70886 www.villamadonna.it

SMARANO

Ostaria Del Filò
Viale Merlonga, 48/A
osteria — €€€, AIC
tel. 463.538057 www.ostariadelfilo.it

SOPRAMONTE

Alpino
Strada di Spineda 6
pizzeria — €-€€, AIC
tel. 461.866115

SOVER

Maso Sveseri
Loc. Sveseri 22
restaurant — AIC
tel. 461.698106 www.maso-sveseri.it

STENICO

Grand Hotel Terme
Loc. Terme di Comano
hotel, restaurant — AIC
tel. 465.701421 www.ghtcomano.it

TESERO

Agritur Maso Zanon
Via Cerin 15
agritourism — AIC
tel. 462.814215 www.agriturdarial.it

Hotel Scoiattolo
Loc.Pampe ago 1
hotel, restaurant — AIC
tel. 462.813244 www.scoiattolo.it

La Trattoria
Via Stazione - fraz.Lago
restaurant, pizzeria — €€€-€€€€, AIC
tel. 462.810203

Mair am Turm
Via Principale, 3

TIROLO
hotel, restaurant
tel. 473.923307

AIC
www.mairamturm.it

TONADICO

Hotel Tressane
Via Roma, 30

hotel
tel. 439.762205

AIC
www.brunethotels.it

Park Hotel Iris
Via Roma 26

hotel
tel. 439.762

AIC
www.brunethotels.it

TRAMBILENO
Rifugio Alpe Pozza "Vincenzo Lancia" (m. 1.802) restaurant
Loc. Alpe Pozza
tel. 464.868068

AIC

TRANSACQUA

Il Caminetto
Via Lungo Canali, 29

pizzeria
tel. 439.762088

€-€€, AIC

TRENTO

Agritur al Vigneto
Loc.Mader no 16

B&B
tel. 461.822322

AIC
www.agrituralvigneto.it

America
Via Torre Verde, 50

inn, restaurant
tel. 0461983010

€€, AIC
www.hotelamerica.it

Bouganville
Via Petrarca, 1/4

restaurant, pizzeria
tel. 0461236666

€, AIC

Grom

gelato (€, AIC)

Piazza Duomo, 27

L'Angolo dei 33
Via Santi Cosma e Damiano, 66

pub, restaurant
tel. 392.0454593

AIC

Montana
Strada di Vason, 70 - Monte Bondone

restaurant, hotel
tel. 0461948200

€€, AIC
www.hotelmontana.it

Rebuffo
Via per Fontanasa nta 24

restaurant, pizzeria
tel. 461.265932

AIC

Uva & Menta
Via Dietro le Mura, A35

pizzeria
tel. 04611903162

€, AIC

VALLE AURINA

Sporthotel e Resid.Griesfeld
Via St. Johann,5/6

hotel
tel. 474.671172

AIC
www.sporthotel-griesfeld.com

VARENA

Hotel alla Rocca
Via Alpini, 10

hotel
tel. 0462340321

€, AIC
www.hotelallarocca.biz

VERMIGLIO

Milano
Via Borgonuovo, 44

hotel, restaurant
tel. 0463758124

€-€€, AIC
www.albergomilano-50629.ea29.com

VIGO CAVEDINE

Genzianella
Via Zurlon 1

pizzeria
Fraz.Masi di Vigo

€-€€, AIC
tel. 461.566084

VIGO DI FASSA

Family Hotel La Grotta
Strada de Soraporta 8

hotel
tel. 462.76445

AIC
www.hotellagrotta.it

Rifugio Roda di Vael (m.2.283)   restaurant   AIC
Loc.Sella del Ciampaz   tel. 462.76445

VIPITENO
Sterzingerhof K.G.   restaurant, pizzeria   AIC
Geizkofler, 15   tel. 472.765128

VOLANO
Alle Palme   pizzeria   €-€€, AIC
Via Panizza 56   tel. 464.411201

Statue (D. Kraushaar)

CODROIPO

Ai Gelsi	hotel/restaurant	€€€€, AIC
Via Circonvallazione Ovest, 12	tel. 0432907064	www.gelsi.com

COLLOREDO DI PRATO

Al Cercjeben	trattoria	€€-€€€, AIC
Via Udine, 60	tel. 0432652527	www.alcercjeben.it
Notes: Closed Mondays, and Tuesday night.		

CORDENONS

Osteria Al Curtif	osteria	€€€, AIC
Via Del Cristo, 3	tel. 0434931038	

FAGAGNA

Agrit. Casale Cjanor	agritourism	€€ - €€€, AIC
Via Casali Lini, 11	tel. 0432801810	www.casalecjanor.com
Al Castello	restaurant	€€€€, AIC
Via S. Bartolomeo, 18	tel. 0432800185	www.ristorantealcastello.com
Per Tutti i Gusti	bakery	€, AIC
Via San Giacomo, 5	tel. 338.9306793	www.pertuttiigusti.me
Road House Blu's	sandwich shop	€, AIC
Via Spilimbergo, 184	tel. 432.800132	

FIUMICELLO

La Catapecchia	restaurant, pizzeria	AIC
Via Trieste, 120	tel. 431.970869	
www.it-it.facebook.com/events/263918543664988		

FORNI AVOLTRI

Vill. Turistico M.no Ge.Tur.	resort	AIC
Loc. Piani di Luzza	tel. 043372041	www.getur.com

FORNI DI SOPRA

Davost	hotel, restaurant	€€, AIC
Via Tagliamento, 26	tel. 043388103	www.hoteldavost.it

GORIZIA

Al Lampione	pizzeria	€, AIC
Via Silvio Pellico, 7	tel. 048132780	www.pizzerialampione.it

GRADISCA D'ISONZO

Al Pellegrino	restaurant, pizzeria	€-€€€€, AIC
P.zza G. Marconi, 5	tel. 048199918	

LATISANA

La Fattoria dei Gelsi	restaurant	€€€€, AIC
Via Lignano Sud, 55	tel. 043153100	www.gelsigroup.com

LAUCO

Barbavigi	B&B	AIC
Via Capoluogo, 146	tel. 0433747721	www.barbavigi.it

LIGNANO PINETA

Hotel Bella Venezia Mare	hotel, restaurant	€€, AIC
Via Arco del Grecale, 18/a	tel. 0431422184	www.bellaveneziamare.it

LIGNANO SABBIADORO

Al Mirelia	restaurant	€€, AIC
Via dell'Acquedotto, 6	tel. 043173064	www.alsoreli.com

Al Soreli
Raggio dell'Ostro, 14
restaurant
tel. 0431422766
€€, AIC

Atlantic
Lungomare Trieste, 160
hotel, restaurant
tel. 043171101
€€€, AIC
www.hotelatlantic.it

Désirée
Via Aquileia, 47
hotel, restaurant
www.hoteldesiree.it
€€, AIC

La Pigna
Via dei Pini, 9
hotel, restaurant, wine bar
tel. 431.428991
AIC
www.hotelapigna.it

Vill. Ge.Tur - Santa Maria del Mare resort
Viale Centrale, 29
tel. 431.409511
AIC
www.getur.com

MANZANO

Elliot
Via Orsaria, 50
restaurant
tel. 0432751383
€€-€€€€, AIC
www.elliotenoteca.com

MORTEGLIANO

Da Nando
Via Divisione Julia , 14
trattoria, inn
tel. 0432760187
€€€€, AIC
www.danando.it

PALAZZOLO DELLO STELLA

Gelateria Carapina
gelato (€, AIC)
Via Nazionale 45/1

PORDENONE

Alle Grazie
Via Dogana, 11
restaurant
tel. 0434573197
€€€, AIC

B&B E.B.Camere in Villa
Via S. Quirino, 60
B&B
tel. 345.6089089
AIC

B&B Il Vicolo
Vicolo Roggiuzzol e, 5
B&B
tel. 345.6089089
AIC
www.ilvicolobeb.it

Gelateria Montereale
Via Montereale, 23
gelato, bar
tel. 434.365107
€, AIC
www.biscottopordenone.it

Il Principato del Gelato
gelato (€, AIC)
Via San Quirino, 11

Mamey Cafè Pordenone
Via Udine, 80
bar
tel. 434.28796
€, AIC
www.mamey.it

Ristorante Pizzeria Alla Catina restaurant, pizzeria
Piazza Cavour, 3
tel. 434.520358
€-€€, AIC
www.allacatina.it

REMANZACCO

Al Cardinale
S.S. 54,55
restaurant, pizzeria
tel. 432.649021
€-€€, AIC
www.ristorantealcardinale.it

ROVEREDO IN PIANO

Tepepa Ale House Country Bar
Via Brentella 53/5
bakery
tel. 328.3986436
€, AIC

S. DANIELE DEL FRIULI

Al Picaron
Via S. Andrat, 3
hotel/restaurant
tel. 0432940688
€€€€, AIC
www.alpicaron.it

Al Portonat
Piazza Dante Alighieri, 7/9
osteria
tel. 0432940880
€€, AIC
www.alportonat.it

S. FLORIANO DEL COLLIO

Osteria Gostilna Gorsic restaurant €€€€, AIC
Loc.tà Sovenza, 7 tel. 0481884248

S.DANIELE DEL FRIULI

Al Portonat osteria €-€€, AIC
Piazza Dante Alighieri, 7/9 tel. 432.94088 www.alportonat.it
Notes: Great prosciutto. Nice restaurant for celiacs.

S.FLORIANO DEL COLLIO

Osteria Gostilna Korsic restaurant €€€, AIC
Loc.tà Sovenza, 7 tel. 481.884248 www.korsic.it

S.GIORGIO DI NOGARO

Laguna Blu restaurant, pizzeria €-€€, AIC
Via Marittima 69/B tel. 431.621436

Pizzeria Ristorante Da Alfonso restaurant, pizzeria €-€€, AIC
Via Roma 73 tel. 431.65375 www.pizzeriadaalfonso.com

SAN CANZIAN D'ISONZO

Arcimboldo restaurant €-€€, AIC
Via Risiera San Sabba, 17 tel. 048176089 www.arcimboldo.go.it

SAVOGNA D'ISONZO

Locanda Devetak restaurant €€€€, AIC
Via Brezici, 22 tel. 0481882488 www.devetak.com

SISTIANA MARE

Chiosco Verde restaurant €-€€€, AIC
Baia di Sistiana tel. 339.4783591 www.chioscoverde.com

SPESSA DI CIVIDALE

Agrit. Borgo dei Sapori agritourism €, AIC
Str. di Planez, 60 tel. 0432732477 www.borgodeisapori.net

TARCENTO

Costantini restaurant, inn €€€€, AIC
Via Pontebbana, 12 tel. 0432792372

TERENZANO

Gelateria Vanillà gelato (€, AIC) Piazza Terenzio, 27/c

TERZO DI AQUILEIA

Ristorante Pizzeria All'Anfora restaurant, pizzeria €, AIC
Via Julia Augusta, 3 tel. 431.31188 www.allanfora.it

TRICESIMO

Al Glicine gelato (€, AIC) P.zza Garibaldi, 3

Da Miculan trattoria AIC
P. Libertà, 16 tel. 0432851504 www.trattoriamiculan.com

Moby Dick restaurant, pizzeria €€, AIC
Via Michelangelo 30 - loc. Morena tel. 0432851711

TRIESTE

Ainoa La Cucina delle 4 Stagioni restaurant €€, AIC
Via Rossetti, 75 tel. 0402601283 www.ainoa.it

Bora di Trieste	B&B	AIC
Via della Raffineria, 8	tel. 40.661988	www.boraditrieste.freshcreator.com
Grom	gelato (€, AIC)	Via S. Nicolò, 18/b
Hotel Savoy Excelsior Palace	hotel, restaurant	€€€€, AIC
Riva del Mandracchio, 4	tel. 0407794730	www.savoytrieste.it
Pasticceria Rosa	bakery	€, AIC
Via Giulia 25	tel. 40.573079	www.pasticceriarosa.com
Notes: 100% GF!		
Pepenero Pepebianco	restaurant	€€€€, AIC
Via Rittmeyer, 14/a	tel. 0407600716	www.pepeneropepebianco.it

UDINE

Accademia del Gelato	gelato (€, AIC)	Via Crispi, 13
Alle Due Palme	hotel, pizzeria	€€-€€€, AIC
Via Leonardo da Vinci 5	tel. 432.481807	www.alleduepalme.it
Ancona 2	restaurant, pizzeria	€€, AIC
V.le Tricesimo, 101	tel. 0432545262	
Astoria Hotel Italia	hotel	AIC
Piazza XX Settembre, 24	tel. 432.505091	www.hotelastoria.udine.it
Da Guido	restaurant, pizzeria	€-€€, AIC
Via Po, 82	tel. 0432282812	
Damadolce Senza Glutine	bakery, gastropub	€, AIC
Via Veneto, 65 -Cussignacco	tel. 366.4368479	www.damadolce.it
Gelateria da Nonno Carletto	gelato (€, AIC)	Piazzale Cella, 20
Gelateria Gusto Antico	gelato (€, AIC)	Via Cividale 524
Grom	gelato (€, AIC)	Via Rialto, 12/c
Hotel Friuli	hotel	AIC
Viale Ledra, 24	tel. 432.234351	
Hotel Suite Inn	hotel	€€€€, AIC
Via F. di Toppo, 25	tel. 0432501683	www.hotelsuiteinn-udine.com
Il Ristorantino da Maria	restaurant	€€€€, AIC
Via Bertaldia, 25	tel. 432.504545	
Vitello d'Oro	restaurant	€€€€, AIC
Via Valvason, 4	tel. 0432508982	www.vitellodoro.com
Notes: Closed Monday at lunch, Wednesdays.		

VILLA VICENTINA

Al Ragno d'Oro	inn, restaurant	AIC
Via Trieste, 18	tel. 043196058	

Scale (D. Kraushaar)

THE MARCHES

(AIC = participates in the Associazione Italiana Celiachia program)

. ACQUAVIVA PICENA

Azzurro restaurant €€, AIC
Via Fontepezzana, 1 tel. 0735764175

ANCONA

Dolce e Amaro bar, tavola calda €, AIC
Via Piave, 17/b tel. 71.20021 polidorigianni@alice.it

Gelateria La Golosa gelato €, AIC
Via delle Grazie, 140 tel. 71.2804218 www.gelaterialagolosa.it

Il Lazzaretto restaurant, pizzeria €€, AIC
Largo Fiera della Pesca Molo Sud tel. 71.55368 www.ristoranteillazzaretto.it

La Botte restaurant, pizzeria AIC
Via Tavernelle, 14 tel. 07185325 www.labotte1986.it
Notes: Closed at lunch.

Opera Nova della Marca restaurant €€-€€€€, AIC
Fr.ne Varano, 127 tel. 71.2861093 www.operanovadellamarca.it

Osteria Teatro Strabacco restaurant Ost €€€, AIC
Via Oberdan, 2 tel. 07156748 www.strabacco.it

Rossopomodoro pizzeria €€, AIC
Via P. Filonzi, 4 tel. 71.2916363

ASCOLI PICENO

Al Teatro
Via del Teatro, 1
restaurant, pizzeria
tel. 736.253549
€€-€€€€, AIC
www.ristorantealteatro.com

Bella Napoli
Via Bonaparte, 18/20
Notes: Closed Thursdays.
pizzeria
tel. 0736257030
€, AIC

Il Viaggio
Via Cino del Duca, 10
restaurant
tel. 736.252119
€€, AIC
www.ilviaggioristorante.it

La Cittadella
Via Napoli, 106/112
Notes: Closed Tuesdays.
restaurant, pizzeria
tel. 0736343088
€, AIC
www.lacittadella.it

Mister O.K.
Via G. Spalvieri, 20
restaurant, pizzeria
tel. 073643483
€-€€, AIC

BELFORTE DEL CHIENTI

Chiaroscuro
Via Nazionale, 27
pizzeria
tel. 733.905499
€€, AIC
www.ristorantechiaroscuro.it

CAGLI

Le Fontane
Strada Cagli-Pergola, 126/a
restaurant, pizzeria
tel. 0721790148
€€€-€€€€, AIC

CAMERINO

Etoile
Via Le Mosse, 69
restaurant, pizzeria
tel. 0737630238
€, AIC

CAMPOCAVALLO DI OSIMO

Il Villino
Via Cagiata, 135
restaurant
tel. 71.717014
€€-€€€, AIC
www.ilvillino-osimo.it

CASTELRAIMONDO

Gelateria Bar Carnevali
gelato (€, AIC)
Corso Italia, 57

CIVITANOVA MARCHE

Bar Caffetteria Romoli
V.le Vittorio Veneto, 187
bar-cafe
tel. 0733771990
€, AIC

Hotel Cosmopolitan
Via Alcide De Gasperi, 2
hotel, restaurant
tel. 733.771682
AIC
www.cosmobusinesshotel.it

Mangia Centro Degustazione
Via Pitignano, 50
agritourism
tel. 0733890053
€€-€€€, AIC

Verde e Azzurro
Via B. Brin
B&B
tel. 0733709397
AIC
www.bbverdeazzurro.it

COLDELCE

La Celletta Country House
Via Serra di Genga, 7
Notes: Closed Mondays and Tuesdays.
restaurant
tel. 0721495130
€€€, AIC

CORRIDONIA

Gelatomania
gelato (€, AIC)
Via Trento, 8

Itaca
Via L. Lotto, 66/68
Notes: Closed Tuesdays.
restaurant, pizzeria
tel. 0733433935
€, AIC

CUPRAMONTANA

Ristorante Gina
Parco E. Amatori
restaurant, pizzeria
tel. 731.780157
AIC

ESANATOGLIA

Sibylla
Loc. Bresciano s.n.c.
restaurant
tel. 0737889140
€, AIC

FABRIANO

Bynice Gelateria Naturale
gelato (€, AIC)
Via Cialdini, 1

Gentile da Fabriano
Via Pontemagno, snc
Notes: Closed Fridays.
hotel, restaurant
tel. 0732627190
€€€, AIC

Marchese del Grillo
Via Rocchetta Bassa,73
hotel, restaurant
tel. 0732625650
€€€€, AIC
www.marchesedelgrillo.com
Notes: Closed Sunday night and Mondays.

FALCONARA

Oasi Paese dei Bimbi
Via Castello di Barcaglione, 10
Notes: Closed Tuesdays.
restaurant
tel. 071910849
€€-€€€, AIC

Ristorante Il Cantuccio
Via dei Mille, 10
restaurant
tel. 71.911596
€, AIC

Strabaccoamare
Via Flaminia, 480 (bagni 13)
restaurant
tel. 71.911037
€€€€, AIC
www.strabacco.it

FANO

Il Barone Rosso
Via E. Mattei, 50
restaurant, bar
tel. 0721865835
€€-€€€, AIC

Kalaverde
Via Fratelli Zuccari, 43
restaurant, pizzeria
tel. 721.84008
€€-€€€, AIC
www.kalaverde.it

Osteria dalla Peppa
Via Vecchia, 8
restaurant
tel. 721.823904
€€-€€€, AIC
www.osteriadallapeppa.it

FERMO

Gelateria Caffetteria Antonini
P.le Azzolino, 21
gelato, bar
tel. 743.221705
€, AIC

FOLIGNANO

Best Western Hotel Villa Pigna
V.le Assisi, 33
hotel, restaurant
tel. 0736491868
€€-€€€, AIC
www.hotelvillapigna.it

FOSSOMBRO NE

Nuovo Giardino
Viale Martiri della Resistenza, 1
restaurant, pizzeria
tel. 721.715198
€€€, AIC
www.nuovogiardino.net

FRAZ. RONCITELLI-SENIGALLIA

Degli Ulivi
Via Gioco del Pallone, 2
restaurant
tel. 0717919670
€€-€€€, AIC

GABICCE MARE

Grand H. Michelacci
P.zza Giardini, 1
hotel, restaurant
tel. 0541954361
AIC
www.michelacci.com

Hotel Alexander
Via Panoramica, 35
hotel
tel. 0541954166
€€€-€€€€, AIC

Hotel Perla
Via Trento, 5

hotel, restaurant
tel. 541.954672

AIC
www.hotel-perla.it

Mastin Vecchio
Via D. Alighieri, 5

GRADARA
restaurant, osteria
tel. 541.964024

€€-€€€, AIC
www.mastinvecchio.com

Chalet Ciaschì
Via C. Colombo, 18
Notes: Closed Mondays.

GROTTAMMARE
restaurant
tel. 0735735570

€€-€€€€, AIC

Aesis La Dolce Collina
Via Maccarata, 2

JESI
B&B
tel. 0731245854

AIC

Bar Il Tasso Alcolico
Via Marche, 14/D

bar
tel. 731.53785

€, AIC

Ciro & Pio Gelato Mio

gelato (€, AIC)

Via Don Sturzo, 7

Federico II
Via Ancona, 100

hotel, restaurant
tel. 0731211079

€€€, AIC

Mezzometro da Ale
Via Leopardi, 1

restaurant, pizzeria
tel. 0731213290

AIC

Paoloni La Brusca
Via Mazzangrugno, 78
Notes: Closed Mondays.

restaurant, pizzeria
tel. 0731246237

€-€€€, AIC
www.labrusca.it

Osteria dei Fiori
Via Lauro Rossi, 61

MACERATA
osteria
tel. 0733260142

€€€, AIC

Tuttogelato

gelato (€, AIC)

Via Spalato, 124 c/d

Maison del Celiaco
Via Verga 33

MARINA DI MONTEMARCIANO
bakery, sandwich shop
www.maisondelceliaco.it

€

Ristorante Delle Rose
Via delle Querce, 1

restaurant
tel. 0719198668

€€€€, AIC
www.ristorantedellerose.it

Il Girasole
Via Media, 11

MARINA MONTEMARCIANO
restaurant, pizzeria
tel. 0719198408

€-€€€, AIC

La Riva
L.mare Cristoforo Colombo, 180

MAROTTA
restaurant, pizzeria
tel. 0721960816

€€€-€€€€, AIC

Ca' Montioni
Loc. Montioni, 23

MERCATELLO SUL METAURO
agritourism, B&B
tel. 072289706

€€€, AIC
www.camontioni.it

Maria
Via Cavallara, 3

MONDAVIO
restaurant
tel. 0721976220

€€€, AIC

Chiostro dell'Avis
Via Fermi, 4

MONDOLFO
restaurant, pizzeria

€€-€€€, AIC

Gluten-Free Italy by Region

Albergo Vettore
Via Piane Ascolane, 8
Notes: Closed March-November.

B&B Il Sentiero
Via Media, 11

Cantarini
Via Litoranea, 90
Notes: Closed October-March.

Agriturismo Vecchio Gelso
C.da Casali,11

Ada
Via Molino Mensa, 37
Notes: Closed Tuesdays.

Bar Le Café
Via Mario del Monaco, 12

Chiccoteca
Via Buozzi, 20

G.H. Vittoria/Rist.Agorà
P.le della Libertà, 2
Notes: Closed Mondays.

Gelateria del Corso

H. Savoy/Rist. Ariston
V.le della Repubblica, 22

Hotel Nautilus
V.le Trieste, 26

La Testa del Re
Via delle Galligarie, 22/24

Lo Squero
Strada delle Marche, 60
Notes: Closed Mondays.

Polo Pasta e Pizza
V.le Trieste, 231

Ristò Vera
Via Yuri Gagarin, sn
Notes: Closed Sundays.

Da Lorenzo
Via Ponte Armellina, 68

La Locanda del Torrione
Via Montefeltresca, 193
Notes: Very highly rated.

MONTEGALLO
inn
tel. 0736806116   €€-€€€, AIC   www.albergovettore.it

MONTEMARCIANO
B&B
tel. 71.9198408   AIC   www.lacasasulsentiero.net

NUMANA
inn
tel. 0717390170   AIC

ORTEZZANO
agritourism
tel. 734.779348   AIC   www.vecchiogelso.com

OSIMO
restaurant, pizzeria
tel. 071715666   €-€€, AIC

PESARO
bar
tel. 721.23391   €, AIC

restaurant, pizzeria, bar
tel. 721.34324   AIC

hotel, restaurant
tel. 072134343   AIC

gelato (€, AIC)   C.so 11 Settembre, 168

inn, restaurant
tel. 072133133   AIC

hotel, restaurant
tel. 721.30275   AIC   www.nautiluspesaro.edenhotels.it

restaurant, pizzeria
tel. 072167609   €, AIC

restaurant
tel. 072165405   €-€€€€, AIC   www.ristorantelosquero.it

restaurant
tel. 0721375902   AIC

restaurant
tel. 0383813135   €, AIC

PETRIANO
restaurant, pizzeria
tel. 722.52093   AIC

PIETRARUBBIA
restaurant, pizzeria   €-€€€€, AIC
tel. 722.75387   www.ristorantelalocandadeltorrione.it

La Terrazza del Sole
L.go Giovanni Verga, 15

POLLENZA
pizzeria
tel. 0733549948

€, AIC

Artigiangel

PONZANO DI FERMO
gelato (€, AIC)

V.le Trieste, 30

Gelateria del Corso

PORTO RECANATI
gelato (€, AIC)

C.so Matteotti, 269

Giannino
Via C. Colombo, 25

hotel, restaurant
tel. 0719799141

AIC
info@conerohotel.com

Ciak Brasserie dal 1983
Via Canada, 16

PORTO SAN ELPIDIO
restaurant, pizzeria
tel.. 734.99577

€€, AIC
www.pizzeriaciakbrasserie.it

Chalet Duilio
L.re Gramsci Sud

PORTO SAN GIORGIO
restaurant, pizzeria
tel. 0734678731

€€-€€€, AIC
www.chaletduilio.it

Gelateria Pelacani di Giacomozzi A. gelato (€, AIC)

P.zza Mentana, 5

Happy Days
Via Verdi, 24
Notes: DS pizza point. Closed Tuesdays.

restaurant, pizzeria
tel. 0734673900

€, AIC

Vela
L.re Gramsci Nord

restaurant
tel. 734.676482

AIC
www.chaletvela.com

La Cantina di Ale
Via Le Grazie

RECANATI
restaurant, pizzeria
tel. 071977101

€€, AIC

Az. Agrit. Frattini Laura
Contrada Canali, 33

RIPATRANSONE
B&B
tel. 3282732083

AIC
www.agriturismopiceno.com

L'Oasi
Via Clementina, 9
Notes: DS pizza point. Closed Mondays.

ROSORA
restaurant, pizzeria
tel. 0731814308

AIC

La Vecchia Fattoria
Via Fiorenzuola, 32

S. ANGELO IN VADO
pizzeria
tel. 722.88667

€, AIC
www.misterimprese.it

La Sfinge
Via S. Giacomo, 48
Notes: Closed October-March.

S. BENEDETTO DEL TRONTO
hotel
tel. 0735655555

€€€€, AIC

Pizza Leggera Picena
P.za Sacra Famiglia, 1
Notes: DS pizza point.

restaurant, pizzeria
tel. 0735656645

€, AIC

Playa Marconi
Viale Europa, 3

pizzeria bar
tel. 03402206499

€, AIC

Le Stagioni
Via Montelatiere 17/a

S. MARCELLO
restaurant
tel. 731.267926

AIC
www.le-stagioni.it

	S. SEVERINO MARCHE	
Caffetteria Gelateria Dignani	bar, gelato (€, AIC)	Via Eustachio, 12/14
Il Taccolito Loc. Taccoli, 41	agritourism tel. 0733637257	€, AIC
La Lucciola C.da Colleluce, 55	restaurant, pizzeria tel. 733.638777	€€€, AIC www.ristorantelalucciola.com
	S.BENEDETTO DEL TRONTO	
Dal Gelataio	gelato (€, AIC)	Via Monfalcone, 17
Hotel Canguro Via S. Giacomo, 52	hotel tel. 735.650977	AIC www.hotelcanguro.it
	S.COSTANZO	
Locanda La Cerasa Strada Piagge, 1 Notes: Closed Mondays.	restaurant tel. 0721935117	€€€, AIC
Mary Sierra Via delle Grazie, 22	restaurant, pizzeria tel. 721.930515	€€, AIC www.pizzeriamarysierra.it
	SAN SEVERINO MARCHE	
La Lucciola C.da Colleluce, 55	restaurant, pizzeria tel. 0733638777	€, AIC
	SANT'IPPOLITO	
Cascina delle Rose Via delle Industrie, 9	restaurant tel. 0721728197	€€€, AIC www.cascinadellerose.com
	SENIGALLIA	
Bano Ristorante L.re Leonardo da Vinci	restaurant, pizzeria tel. 07160643	€€-€€€, AIC
Eden Via Marzi, 4	restaurant, pizzeria tel. 071659165	€-€€€, AIC www.ristoranteden.it
Gelogiallo	gelato (€, AIC)	Via L. da Vinci, 52
Hotel Sirena L.re Dante Alighieri, 78 Notes: Closed October-March.	hotel tel. 0717920605	AIC www.hotelsirena.com
Hotel Trieste Via Trieste, 27	hotel, restaurant tel. 71.659057	AIC www.hotelpensionetrieste.com
Il Casale Str. Prov.le S. Angelo, 20	restaurant tel. 071665003	€-€€€, AIC www.ilcasaleristorante.it
Michele da Ale L.mare L. Da Vinci, 33	restaurant, pizzeria tel. 07160578	€€€, AIC www.micheledaale.it
Universal Lungomare Mameli, 47	hotel tel. 0717927474	AIC www.hoteluniversal.it
	STAFFOLO	
Belvedere Via Redipuglia, 1/3	inn restaurant bar tel. 0731779261	€€€-€€€€, AIC
	TAVULLIA	
Brezza di Mare Via Ofanto, 4/a	restaurant tel. 721.49175	€€€-€€€€, AIC www.brezzadimare.it

La Nuova Briciola
P.zza Togliatti, 3
Notes: DS pizza point.

restaurant, pizzeria
tel. 0733974504

€, AIC

San Nicola
Via Flaminia, 6

restaurant, pizzeria
tel. 0733967448

€€, AIC

Antiche Mura
Via Don Minzoni, 11
Notes: Closed Tuesdays.

TREIA
restaurant, pizzeria
tel. 0733217053

€€, AIC

Da Otello
Via S. Lorenzo, 60
Notes: Closed Wednesdays.

restaurant, pizzeria
tel. 0733215710

€€, AIC

Villa Cortese
C.da Sterpare, 32

restaurant
tel. 0733216891

€€€€, AIC
www.villa-cortese.it

Zì Marì
Via Bocca Trabaria ovest, 145

URBINO
pizzeria
tel. 722.57105

€€, AIC
www.zimari.it

La Nuova Fazenda
Via Nazionale Urbinate, 201

VALLEFOGLIA
restaurant, pizzeria
tel. 721.496154

€, AIC
www.lanuovafazenda.it

Locanda Montelippo
Via Canarecchia, 31

agritourism, restaurant, B&B
tel. 721.416735

€€, AIC
www.montelippo.it

A Beautiful Grave (D. Kraushaar)

Vasto Marina (E. DiFabio)

ABRUZZO

(AIC = participates in the Associazione Italiana Celiachia program)

ALBA ADRIATICA

Me Gusta	gelato (€, AIC)	L.re Marconi, 80
Me Gusta Mas	gelato (€, AIC)	Lungomare Marconi 166

ATESSA

Royal Garden — restaurant, pizzeria — €-€€, AIC
Via Piana La Fara, 157 — tel. 0872895301

AVEZZANO

Attacchi di Pane — bakery — €, AIC
Via Mercato 6 — tel. 335.6301244 — www.attacchidipane.it/1

Barone Rosso — pizzeria — €-€€, AIC
Via Don Minzoni, 5 — tel. 0863453155
Notes: Closed Mondays.

Cozzolino — pizzeria — €-€€, AIC
Via Sandro Pertini 116 — tel. 863.22199
https://it-it.facebook.com/pages/Ristorante-Pizzeria-Cozzolino/165288806824839

Piadiland — restaurant — €, AIC
Via Trieste, 15 — tel. 3285964047 — www.piadiland.com

Umami — restaurant — 2, AIC
Via Antonio Gramsci 6/B — tel. 0863.33372/347.2632555

BUGNARA

H.Sagittario/Rist.Tre Archi — hotel, restaurant — €-€€€, AIC
Via Nolfese, 2 — tel. 086446463

La taverna di Pop's
Via Orientale 15

CASALINCONTRADA
pizzera, trattoria
tel. 871.371051

€-€€, AIC

Biocasa Quarto a Monte
Via Roma 12

CASOLI
B&B
tel. 347.6071674

AIC
www.quartoamonte.it

Il Sorriso
Via Pontenuovo, 45

CASTEL DI SANGRO
restaurant
tel. 0864840922

€, AIC
www.pizzeriailsorriso.com

La Rustica
C.da Astignano, 13
Notes: Must reserve in advance.

CASTELLANA DI PIANELLA
agritourism
tel. 0859771650

€€€-€€€€, AIC
www.agriturismolarustica.com

Alle Coste Gluten Free
Via Aterno 33

CELANO
B&B
tel. 863.791457

AIC
www.allecosteglutenfree.it

Bar Gelateria Castello

gelato (€, AIC)

Via L. Giuliani, 20/22

La Cittadella
Via Tiburtina Km.6930

trattoria
tel. 0863791293

€-€€, AIC

Le Mirage
Via Ranelletti, 278-280
Notes: Closed Tuesdays.

pizzeria
tel. 0863790830

€€, AIC

I Due Leoni
Via Nazionale, 58/c
Notes: Closed Mondays, Tuesdays and at lunch.

CEPAGATTI
trattoria
tel. 0859772685

€€€€, AIC

Il Girasole
Via Sant'Anna

CESE DI PRETURO
restaurant, pizzeria
tel. 0862461290

€€, AIC

Alternativa al Grano
Strada per Popoli

CHIETI
bakery, gelato
tel. 347.896864

€, AIC
www.alternativaalgrano.it

Gelat. Sigismondi

gelato (€, AIC)

P.zza Trento e Trieste, 6/8

Nino
Via P.ssa di Piemonte, 6

restaurant
tel. 087163781

€€, AIC

Bar Gelat. Ariston

CHIETI SCALO
gelato (€, AIC)

Via De Meis, 36

La Rusticana
C.da Madonna della Pace, 100
Notes: Closed Tuesdays.

CITTÀ S. ANGELO
restaurant, pizzeria
tel. 085959434

€-€€€, AIC

Miramare
Via T. De Caesaris, 8

hotel, restaurant, pizzeria
tel. 08595321

€-€€€€, AIC
www.miramarehotel.it

L'Isola Che Non C'era
Via Vetoio

COPPITO-L'AQUILA
pizzeria
tel. 0862319930

€, AIC

FARA FILIORUM PETRI

S. Eufemia
Via Aterno, 435
Notes: Closed Fridays.

inn, restaurant €€, AIC
tel. 087170154   www.hotelsanteufemia.altervista.org

FARA SAN MARTINO

La Villetta
c/o Villa Comunale

pizzeria €-€€, AIC
tel. 872.980452

FRANCAVILLA

La Nave
Viale Kennedy, 2
Notes: Closed Wednesdays.

restaurant €€€€, AIC
tel. 085817115

GIULIANOVA

Compagnia della Pizza
Via Trieste, 181/183

pizzeria €, AIC
tel. 3205569797   www.compagniadellapizza.com

Gelateria Magrini Ice
Piazza Dalmazia, 8/9

gelato €, AIC
tel. 349.1376404   www.magrinigelati.it

Hotel Clipper
Via Quinto, 5

hotel AIC
tel. 0858028579   www.hotelclipper.com

LANCIANO

Evergreen
C.da Iconicella 332

pizzeria, restaurant €-€€, AIC
tel. 872.43767   www.evergreenristorante.com

Pizzangelo
Via del Pescara, 7/a
Notes: DS pizza point. Closed Tuesdays.

pizzeria €, AIC
tel. 3383151900   www.pizzangelo.it

Ruhental
Via Follani, 138
Notes: Closed Tuesdays and lunch.

pizzeria, trattoria €, AIC
tel. 087244101

LORETO APRUTINO

Carmine
C.da Remartello, 52

restaurant €€€€, AIC
tel. 0858208553   www.ristorantecarmine.it

Le Magnolie
C.da Fiorano, 83
Notes: Closed Wednesdays, Sundays.

agritourism €€-€€€, AIC
tel. 0858289534

Rychot's

gelato (€, AIC)   Via Vittorio Veneto, 67

MAGLIANO DE' MARSI

Peter Pan
P.zza Della Repubblica 6

pizzeria €-€€, AIC
tel. 863.515032

MONTESILVANO

B&B La Palma
Via Aremonga, 14

B&B AIC
tel. 3396035640   www.beblapalma.it

Bella Notte
Via Orsini 20/B

B&B AIC
tel. 388.191494   www.bellanottemontesilvano.it

Dolce Capriccio

gelato (€, AIC)   V.le Abruzzo, 46

Hotel d'Atri
Via Calabria, 14/1

hotel, restaurant AIC
tel. 0854450112   www.hoteldatri.it

Zelig
Via Vestina, 415

restaurant, pizzeria
tel. 0854680673

€, AIC

MONTORIO AL VOMANO

Hotel Vomano
V.le Risorgimento, 113

hotel, restaurant, pizzeria
tel. 0861598498

€-€€, AIC
www.hotelvomano.it

MOSCIANO S. ANGELO

Borgo Spoltino
Str. Selva Alta
Notes: Closed Mondays, Tuesdays.

restaurant
tel. 0858071021

€€€-€€€€, AIC
www.borgospoltino.it

Via Veneto
Via V.Veneto, 8
Notes: Closed Mondays and at lunch.

pizzeria
tel. 0858062259

€, AIC

NOCCIANO

Le Nostre Radici
C.da Prato S. Lorenzo, 36
Notes: Closed Monday-Thursday

agritourism
tel. 085847644

€€€, AIC

ORTONA

La Magnolia
C.da Cucullo 28
www.bedandbreakfastlamagnolia.com

B&B
tel. 085.9031289/328.6761836

AIC

Novecento

gelato (€, AIC)

C.so Vittorio Emanuele, 94

PESCARA

Bibò

gelato(€, AIC)

Via Pepe, 105

Buffalo Bill
Via T. Da Celano, 22

restaurant, pizzeria
tel. 08563355

€-€€, AIC

Caprice Fabrizio Camplone
P.zza Garibaldi, 29

gelato, bar, bakery
tel. 85.691633

€, AIC
www.fabriziocamplone.com

De Marco
P.zza Duca Deli Abruzzi 63/65

gelato, bar
tel. 393.0736235

€, AIC

Grotta del Marinaio
Via Bardet, 6
Notes: Closed Mondays and at lunch.

restaurant
tel. 085690454

€€-€€€€, AIC

La Scuderia
c/o Parco Sabucchi

restaurant, pizzeria
tel. 85.4711492

€-, AIC
https://it-it.facebook.com/scuderiasabucchi

Maison del Celiaco
Via del Santuario 139 - Zona Gesuiti

bakery, sandwich shop

€
www.maisondelceliaco.it

Parc H. Villa Immacolata
Str. c.le S. Silvestro, 340

hotel
tel. 0854980031

€-€€, AIC

Pipè
V.le della Riviera 249

restaurant, pizzeriaizzeria
tel. 85.75178

€-€€, AIC
www.ristorantepipe.it

PESCASSEROLI

Pagnani
V.le Colli dell'Oro 5

hotel
tel. 349.2338659

AIC
www.hotelpagnani.it

PETTORANO SUL GIZIO

La Quercia
S.S. 17 km.107

restaurant, pizzeria
tel. 086448202

€, AIC

La Pineta
V.le G.D'Annunzi o 193

PINETO
hotel   AIC
tel. 085.9491406/338.8150994 www.hotellapineta.eu/en

Star Bene Senza Glutine
Vicolo del Voltone 2/4

RIMINI
bar, desserts   €
tel. 0541.1736666 www.starbenesenzaglutine.it

Brancaleone
Via Corsi, 36

ROCCAMONTEPIANO
restaurant (0)   €€€, AIC
tel. 087177571   www.ristorantebrancaleone.it

La Fattoria
S.S. 17 km.139
Notes: DS pizza point. Closed Tuesdays.

ROCCARASO
pizzeria   €, AIC
tel. 086462980

Gelat. Mario Magrini

ROSETO DEGLI ABRUZZI
gelato(€, AIC)   L.re Roma, 22

L'Angolo dello Spuntino
Largo Stazione
Notes: DS pizza point. Closed Tuesdays.

S. DEMETRIO NE' VESTINI
pizzeria   €, AIC
tel. 0862810200

Raggio Verde

gelato (€, AIC)   Via Nazionale, 29

S. SALVO MARINA

Cioccolat Gelateria ai 3 Scalini   gelato (€, AIC)   Via Magellano, 287

La Massaia
Via Montegrappa 4

pizzeria   €-€€, AIC
tel. 873.520496

Il Fienile
C.da Murata Alta, 50
Notes: DS pizza point. Closed Wednesdays.

S. VITO CHIETINO
restaurant, pizzeria   €-€€, AIC
tel. 0872618288

Gelateria Franca

S.TER. DI SPOLTORE
gelato (€, AIC)   Via M. Adriatico, 46

O' Sole Mio
Via M. Buonarotti 53

SANT'EGIDIO ALLA VIBRATA
restaurant, pizzeria   €-€€, AIC
tel. 861.842408   www.pizzeriaosolemio.eu

Az Agr. Fontemaggio
C.da Caltrucci, 33

SCERNI
restaurant   €€, AIC
tel. 0873914525

Di Silvio

SULMONA
gelato (€, AIC)   Via Solino, 2

La Tana di Lucifero
Via R. Campana, 6

TERAMO
restaurant, pizzeria   AIC
tel. 086243915

Il Ristoro dei Paladini
Parco Monte Pallano

TORNARECCIO
restaurant   €€-€€€, AIC
tel. 0872866621

A Casa di Ludo

Rist. Zafferano/H. Aurea
Via Leonardo da Vinci, 46

Ulivo Mare/H.CIVI
Via Milano, 23, 32

Il Tucano
Via Sterpara, 55

Poemi
Piazza ex Mercato Coperto

Caffè de Parma
C.so de Parma, 13/15

Dolce Brivido
Via S. Caterina da Siena, 16/18

Il Giardino dei Sogni
Via Colli, 1

Peste e Corna
Via G. Leopardi, 6/8
Notes: Closed Tuesdays.

Terzo Tempo Food & Fun
Via Conti Ricci, 1

Vecchia Vasto
L.go Siena, 14

Lucky Star
Via Val di Foro SS 263

TORTORETO LIDO
gelato (€, AIC)

hotel, restaurant
tel. 0861786430

restaurant, pizzeria, hotel
tel. 0861788026

VACRI
restaurant, pizzeria
tel. 0871720024

VAL VOMANO
restaurant, pizzeria
tel. 389.6815179

VASTO
bar
tel. 873366919

gelato
tel. 348.872193

B&B
tel. 0873361663

pizzeria
tel. 0873370808

sandwich shop, bar
tel. 0873378795

B&B, restaurant, pizzeria
tel. 0873363420

VILLAMAGNA
restaurant
tel. 0871300283

Via Trieste 141

€€, AIC
www.aureahoteltortoreto.it

€€€, AIC
www.ristoranteulivomare.it

€-€€€, AIC

AIC
www.pizzeriadeipoemi.it

€, AIC

€, AIC

AIC
www.ilgiardinodeisogni.net

€, AIC

€, AIC

€ - €€€, AIC
www.vecchiavasto.com

€€€€, AIC
www.ristoranteluckystar.it

The Grapevine (E. DiFabio)

Santa Maria della Grazia (M. Roglieri)

MOLISE

AGNONE
Staffoli Horses   agritourism   AIC
S.P. Montesangrin a, km.1
tel. 0865.771775
www.staffoli.it

BOJANO
Da Tonino   restaurant, pizzeria €€, AIC
Via S. Antonio Abate sn
tel. 0874.773031
www.pizzeriadatonino.it

CAMPOBASSO
Al Camaleonte   bar   €, AIC
Via Elena, 8   tel. 339.8917846

da Sasà e Barbara   gastropub, rotisserie   €€, AIC
Via Mazzini, 111   tel. 874.62081

Flower B&B   B&B   AIC
Via Novelli, 3   tel. 338.3030338
www.bed-and-breakfast.it/pagina.cfm?id=32915&idregione=11

Hotel Donguglielmo   hotel, restaurant   AIC
C.da S. Vito, 15/b   tel. 0874.418178   www.donguglielmo.it

Il Capriccio   gelato (€, AIC)   Via XXIV Maggio, 40

La Regina   pizzeria   €€, AIC
Via nicola Neri, 1 9   tel. 0874.1961290   www.pizzerialaregina.it

Ristorante Pizzeria Castello restaurant, pizzeria   €€, AIC
Via De Pretis, 27/a   tel. 0874.415845

CAPRACOTTA
L'Elfo   restaurant   €€, AIC
Via Campanelli, sn   tel. 0865.949131   www.ristorantelelfo.it

CAROVILLI
La Bacca Rara   restaurant, pizzeria   €€€, AIC
Via Fonte Curelli   tel. 339.3348900   www.labaccarara.it

CASTELMAURO
Parco delle Stelle   hotel, restaurant   €€, AIC
C.da Codarda   tel. 0874.744622   www.ricevimentiparcodellestelle.com

FORNELLI
Il Parco degli Ulivi   restaurant   €€€, AIC
Bivio Fornelli   tel. 0865.956662   www.ilparcodegliulivi.com

Le Terre del Sacramento C.da Collefalcone	**GUARDIALFIERA** agritourism tel. 0874.1865813	€€€, AIC www.leterredelsacramento.com
Solelago C,da Difese delle Camerelle	restaurant, hotel tel. 0874.840198	€€€, AIC www.solelago.com
Grand H. Europa V.le dei Pentri, 76	**ISERNIA** hotel, restaurant tel. 865.2126	€€€, AIC www.grandhotel-europa.it
Il Forno di Chiara Via Laurelli, 6	bakery tel. 339.5703166	€, AIC
L'Affresco C.so Marcelli	restaurant tel. 0865.413836	€€€, AIC www.ristoranteaffresco.com
Pasta & Pizza Via XXIV Maggio II° Trav. 6	pizzeria tel. 0865414549	€, AIC
Agriturismo La Collinetta C.da Colle di Lauro, 16	**LARINO** agritourism tel. 348.9582862	AIC www.agriturismocollinetta.com
Bar Biferno C.da Giardini, 8	**LUCITO** bar tel. 340.6851424	€, AIC
Vecchia Taverna Via G. Marconi	**MACCHIA D'ISERNIA** restaurant, pizzeria tel. 865.5566	€€-€€€, AIC www.vecchiataverna.eu
Il Giardinetto del Volturno C.so 25 Archi, 13	**MONTAQUILA** restaurant, pizzeria tel. 865.96504	€€-€€€, AIC
Ristorante Olmicello Via Regina Margherita, 48	**ORATINO** restaurant tel. 874.38285	€€-€€€, AIC www.ristoranteolmicello.com
Parco Attrezzato l'Abete Bianco Via Turistica snc	**PESCOPENNATARO** restaurant tel. 0865.941180	€€, AIC www.parcoabetebianco.com
Hotel Dora S.S. 85 Venafrana, km 24,600	**POZZILLI** hotel tel. 0865.908006	AIC www.hoteldora.it
Celiaco.M SRL c.da Selva, snc	**RIPALIMOSANI** sandwich shop, bakery tel. 0874.701842	€, AIC
Cinecittà via Madonna della Neve, 3	restaurant, pizzeria tel. 328.4990465	AIC
Masseria La Curea C.da Curea s.n.	**ROCCAMANDOLFI** agritourism tel. 340.0868596	AIC www.agriturismolacurea.it
Pizzeria Da Paride Via Cortina, 16	restaurant, pizzeria tel. 0865.814517	€, AIC

TERMOLI

Basilico	pizzeria	€, AIC
Via Madonna delle Grazie, 48	tel. 3396514595	
Il Binario dei Sapori	restaurant	AIC
Via XXIV Maggio, 12	tel. 0875.705645	lucaracano@libero.it
La Corte della Contessa di Porticone agritourism		€-€€, AIC
via del Mare,1	tel. 0875.705248	www.agriturismoporticone.it
La Quercia	pizzeria	€ - €€€, AIC
Via Elba, 1	tel. 0875.707211	www.pizzerialaquercia.it
Sognadoro	restaurant/pizzeria	€€ - €€€€, AIC
Via Mugnano Rocco, 3/a	tel. 0875706442	

VASTOGIRARDI

Agrit. S. Mauro	agritourism	€€ - €€€€, AIC
Loc. San Mauro	tel. 0865.836744	www.agriturismosanmauro.it
Rifugio dei Briganti	B&B	AIC
Via San Felice	tel. 3343759773	www.ilrifugiodeibriganti.com

VENAFRO

Al Ghiottone	restaurant, pizzeria	€€-€€€, AIC
Via Acluzio Gallo, 3/a	tel. 0865.909556	
Ristorante La Viuzza	restaurant	€€-€€€, AIC
Via Duomo, 13 zona laghetto	tel. 0865.909190	

Ovid in Sulmona (D. Frost)

Angel and cross (D. Krauschar)

BASILICATA
(AIC = participates in the Associazione Italiana Celiachia program)

GRUMENTO NOVA

H. Park Grumentum
Contrada Traversiti

hotel, restaurant
tel. 97565592

€€, AIC
www.hotelparkgrumentum.com

MATERA

Alle Fornaci
P.zza Cesare Firrao, 7

restaurant
tel. 0835335037

€€, AIC
www.ristoranteallefornaci.it

Casa Vacanze del Corso
Via del Corso, 46

B&B
tel. 3934939569

AIC
www.bedandbreakfast.it

Sapere e Sapori
Via Dante, 54/56

restaurant
tel. 0835256548

€€€-€€€€, AIC

MELFI

Sole di Mezzanotte
Via Cittadinanza Attiva

restaurant, pizzeria
tel. 0972236819

€€, AIC

MONTICCHIO LAGHI

Lago Grande
Via Lago Grande

restaurant, pizzeria
tel. 0972731181

€€, AIC

MURO LUCANO

Miramonti
C.da Fontanelle

hotel, restaurant
tel. 09762657

€-€€, AIC

NOVA SIRI

Villaggio Giardini d'Oriente resort, hotel, restaurant
Via Luci del Varietà   tel. 835.877684

AIC
www.giardinidoriente.com

La Sosta dei Cavalieri
C.da Serralta, 12

Hurricane
Contrada Tora, c/o Lago Pantano

Il Gazebo
C.da Tora, 17/bis

Blue Lion
C/da Varco d'Izzo snc

Caffetteria Garibaldi
C.so Garibaldi, 22

Gambero Rosso
V.le Dell'Unicef cc Galassia

Pasticceria La Delizia
Via del Gallitello, 265-267

Pasticceria La Terrazza
Via Umberto I°, 143

Locanda al Giglio D'Oro
C.da Serre S. Andrea

Tropical
Via Medaglia d'Oro

Agriturismo Tenuta Fortunato
Contrada Serra della Pietra

PICERNO
agritourism   €€, AIC
tel. 0971990035

PIGNOLA
restaurant, pizzeria   €, AIC
tel. 0971486204

restaurant, pizzeria   €€, AIC
tel. 0971471471

POTENZA
pizzeria, pub   €-€€, AIC
tel. 971.576

café   €€, AIC
tel. 3398108051

restaurant, pizzeria   €, AIC
tel. 0971470989   www.gamberorosso.apotenza.it

bar, gelato   €, AIC
tel. 971.444209

RIONERO IN VULTURE
bakery, bar, gelato   €, AIC
tel. 972.724187

RUVO DEL MONTE
restaurant   €€, AIC
tel. 097697516

SAN CHIRICO NUOVO
restaurant, pizzeria   €, AIC
tel. 0971731472

SENISE
agritourism   AIC
tel. 3391825956   www.tenutafortunato.com

Bistecca (D. Frost)

CALABRIA

(AIC = participates in the Associazione
Italiana Celiachia program)

	ACRI	
Antico Rustico V.co I Montessori, 40/42	restaurant, pizzeria tel. 0984954432	€-€€, AIC
Il Carpaccio C.da Cocozzello, 197/a	restaurant tel. 0984949205	€€€, AIC www.ilcarpaccio.it
Lulù C.da Duglia, 226	restaurant, pizzeria tel. 0984950695	€€-€€€, AIC
Panoramik Via Alcide De Gasperi, 305	restaurant, pizzeria tel. 0984941809	€€, AIC www.residencepanoramik.com
	AMANTEA	
Hotel La Tonnara Via Tonnara, 13	hotel, restaurant tel. 0982424272	€€€€, AIC www.latonnara.it
Il Sombrero Via Lungomare	restaurant, pizzeria tel. 0982428469	€€-€€€, AIC www.ilsombrero.it
Mediterraneo Palace Hotel Via Stromboli 79	hotel, restaurant tel. 982.42209	AIC www.mediterraneohotel.net
	BADOLATO	
Euro Bar 2000	gelato (€, AIC)	Via Nazionale, 180
	BAGNARA CALABRA	
Al Vecchio Teatro Via Nastari 20	pizzeria tel. 966.37159	€, AIC
G.H. Victoria P.zza Marconi, 4	hotel tel. 0966376126	€€€, AIC www.victoriagrandhotel.it
Le Saie Corso Garibaldi, 200	hotel tel. 0966474412	€€€-€€€€, AIC www.lesaie.it

BELVEDERE M.MO

Gelateria Capotirone — gelato (€, AIC) — Via Capo Tirone, 7

BOCALE SECONDO

B&B Casa Per Ferie da Nonno Ciccillo B&B — AIC
Viale Paolo Renosto — tel. 328.3722888

BONIFATI

Baia Del Capo — restaurant, pizzeria — €-€€, AIC
Via Filippo Turati — tel. 3403722908

Pietrabianca — restaurant, pizzeria — €, AIC
C.da Sparvasile — tel. 098296322 — www.ristorantepietrabianca.com

BORGIA

Feudo degli Ulivi — inn, restaurant — €€€, AIC
Contrada Fiego — tel. 0961956435 — www.feudodegliulivi.com

BOTRICELLO

La Casa di Botro — agritourism — €€-€€€, AIC
Via Zaccagnini, 2 — tel. 0961966592

BOVA MARINA

Gelateria Ficara — gelato, bar (€, AIC) — Via Nazionale 51/53

La Perla Jonica — restaurant, pizzeria — €€-€€€, AIC
Loc. S. Pasquale — tel. 0965.764366

CAMIGLIATELLO

Hotel Tasso — hotel — €€, AIC
Via Tasso - Camigliatello Silano — tel. 0984578113 — www.hoteltasso.it

CAMPO CALABRO

Lido Dello Stretto — restaurant, pizzeria — €€-€€€, AIC
Via Risorgimento, 141 — tel. 347.8820260

CAMPORA S. GIOVANNI

La Principessa — village, reception hall — €€, AIC
SS 18 — tel. 098246903 — www.hotellaprincipessa.it

CANDIDONI

La Fattoria della Piana — agritourism — €, AIC
Contrada Sovereto — tel. 3481000710 — www.fattoriadellapiana.it

CARIATI

Pedro's — restaurant, pizzeria — €€, AIC
Via S. Patrizi — tel. 0983969311

CASTROLIBERO

Blade Runner — pizzeria — €, AIC
Via Papa Giovanni XXIII — tel. 0984852859

CASTROVILLARI

Antica Trattoria — restaurant, pizzeria — €-€€, AIC
Via Padre Francesco Russo — tel. 981.22604

La Falconara — hotel, restaurant — €€-€€€, AIC
Via Falconara - contr. Pietà — tel. 098144109 — www.lafalconarahotel.it

Mordi & Fuggi — restaurant, pizzeria — €-€€, AIC
Viale Umberto Caldora 23 — tel. 0981.48001 9

Palm Tavern Pub
P.zza Indipendenza, 8

sandwich shop
tel. 3342626695

€, AIC

Sottosopra/Bar Marilyn
Via Roma, 101

pub, bar
tel. 098121600

€, AIC

CATANZARO

Agriturismo Raffaella
Contrada Comunelle di Petrini

agritourism
tel. 0961761747

€€€, AIC
www.agriturismoraffaella.it

Ai Reduci
C.da Sangue di Cristo loc. Siano

agritourism
tel. 0961469771

€€, AIC

Bacchus
V.le dei Normanni, 57

restaurant
tel. 0961753013

€€, AIC

Il Gufo
Via V. Gattoleo, 5 loc. Pitera

sandwich shop
tel. 0961741650

€, AIC

Magic Pub
Via Fiume Busento 130/a

pizzeria
tel. 3397014532

€-€€, AIC

CATANZARO LIDO

Albatros
Via T. Gulli 33

restaurant/pizzeria
tel. 0961738316

€, AIC
www.ristorantealbatros.it

Bausan

gelato (€, AIC)

Via Bausan, 15/17

Happy Pizza
Via Caprera, 395

tavola calda, pizzeria
tel. 380.3641913

€-€€, AIC

Tortuga Pub
Via Lungomare, 289

restaurant, pizzeria sandwich shop
tel. 0961360008

€, AIC

CATONA-REGGIO CALABRIA

Regent Hotel della Cisca
Via Mercato, 9

hotel, restaurant, pizzeria catering
tel. 0965301067

€€, AIC
www.regenthotel.rc.it

CAULONIA

Agriturismo Feudo Gagliardi
C.da Stincuso

agritourism, restaurant
tel. 964.84621

AIC
www.feudogagliardi.it

CETRARO

Voglia di Pizza
Via Lungo Aron

pizzeria
tel. 098291960

€, AIC
www.vogliadipizzaglutenfree.com

CITTANOVA

Il RE Leone
Via Bruzio, 19

pizzeria
tel. 0966.655583

€-€€, AIC

COLOSIMI

Blue Moon
Via Stazione, 1

pizzeria
tel. 0984963198

€, AIC

CORIGLIANO CALABRO

Il Sombrero
Via Berlinguer

restaurant, pizzeria
tel. 3392850724

€, AIC

La Corte
via S. Giovanni Evangelista

restaurant, pizzeria
tel. 0983.887305

€€-€€€, AIC

Villaggio Airone Resort Località Scavolino	CORIGLIANO SCALO resort tel. 0983547140	AIC
A Cannarutia C.da S. Pietro - Donnici Superiore	COSENZA restaurant, pizzeria tel. 0984781856	€€, AIC
Al Vicoletto Via Simonetta, 7-9-11	restaurant tel. 0984791609	€-€€€€, AIC
Da Tonino Via Alimena, 125	tavola calda, catering tel. 09841811285	€, AIC
Italy srl	gelato (€, AIC)	Via Caloprese 123
Prima o Poi L.tà Sena Vill. Mimosa	CROPANI MARINA restaurant, pizzeria tel. 0961960944	€€€-€€€€, AIC
San Marco V.le Venezia, sn	restaurant, pizzeria tel. 0961962127	€€-€€€, AIC
B&B Villa Ermenegilda Via dei Gelsomini 74	CROTONE restaurant, B&B tel. 0962.930209	AIC www.villaermenegilda.it
Bar - Pizzeria Degli Amici Via Nazioni Unite, 47	pizzeria bar tel. 0962962330	€, AIC
Capriccio Via Mario Nicoletta, 176-178	restaurant, pizzeria tel. 3289164833	€, AIC
Il Convivio di Hera Via Capo Colonna, 103	hotel, restaurant tel. 0962934153	€€€€, AIC www.conviviodihera.it
Le Lanterne S.S. 106 Km.247	restaurant, pizzeria tel. 347.2224840	€-€€, AIC
Lido degli Scogli V.le Magna Grecia	inn, pizzeria, restaurant tel. 096228625	€€€€, AIC www.albergolidodegliscogli.com
Pepe Nero via Regina Margherita 23/25	restaurant, pizzeria tel. 962.24847	€-€€, AIC
Zzà Rosì Via A. Tedeschi, 81	restaurant, pizzeria tel. 0962900422	€€, AIC
Blob Il Gelato **Ice Cream**	gelato (€, AIC) gelato (€, AIC)	Via Napoli, 30 V.le Gramsci, 96
Cardel Villaggio Cesariello	DECOLLATURA hotel, restaurant tel. 096861334	€€-€€€, AIC www.hotelcardel.com
La Vecchia Fattoria Loc. Sorbello	agritourism tel. 096861815	€€-€€€, AIC www.agriturismolavecchiafattoria.it
Gel. Come Una Volta	DIAMANTE gelato (€, AIC)	Via Mazzini
Hotel Cristina c/da Pietrarossa, 24	hotel, restaurant tel. 098581210	€€, AIC www.cristinahotel.com

Hotel Torino
S.S. 18

Ristorante Hotel Sagapò
Via Vittoria 8

Il Casale Osteria Tipica
Contrada Malaspina

L'Etoile

Solero Beach
C.da Valle Santa Maria

Bar Gardenia Gelateria

La Madonnina
Via Marina, 37

Royal Garden
Via Provinciale 218

Windy Hill
P.zza S. Francesco di Sales

Paladina
Via Sandro Pertini

Park H. Mirabeau
C.da Pilinga

L'antica Ciambra
Via Lungomare

Golosia

Parco Attrez. Monte Covello
Via Montecovello

Re Artù Pizzeria
Via 3° Vico Fratelli Bandiera 5

L'Oasi
Contrada Mortella

Baia degli Dei
loc. Annunziata Le Castella

Bram Hotel
Via Del Mare

FALERNA
hotel, restaurant
tel. 096893053 — €, AIC — www.hotel-torino.org

hotel, restaurant
tel. 968.97124 — AIC — www.ristorantehotelsagapo.it

FEROLETO ANTICO
restaurant, pizzeria
tel. 0968455023 — €€-€€€, AIC

FUSCALDO
gelato (€, AIC) — Piazza Marconi, 18

pizzeria
tel. 0982618200 — €, AIC

GALLICO MARINA
gelato (€, AIC) — Via Quarnaro 1,traversa,Mar ra 17/e

restaurant, pizzeria
tel. 0965370023 — €, AIC

GALLINA R.C.
restaurant
tel. 0965682703 — €€€-€€€€, AIC — www.royalgarden.it

restaurant, pizzeria
tel. 0965682656 — €-€€€, AIC — www.ristorantewindyhill.it

GASPERINA
restaurant, pizzeria
tel. 096748094 — €, AIC — www.ristorantelapaladina.it

hotel, restaurant
tel. 0967577656 — €€€, AIC

GIOIA TAURO
restaurant, pizzeria
tel. 3476207978 — €, AIC

GIOIOSA JONICA MARINA
gelato (€, AIC) — Piazza Zaleuco

GIRIFALCO
restaurant, pizzeria
tel. 0968749515 — €€€, AIC

pizzeria
tel. 0968.748811 — €, AIC

GIZZERIA LIDO
restaurant
tel. 0968466181 — €€€-€€€€, AIC

ISOLA CAPO RIZZUTO
hotel
tel. 0962.795235 — AIC — www.baiadeglidei.com

LAMETIA TERME
hotel, restaurant
tel. 968.51598 — AIC — www.bramhotel.it

Parva Domus Via D'Audino 19	B&B tel. 0968.436352	AIC www.bebparvadomus.com
Sapori senza glutine Via Della Vittoria	sandwich shop, bakery tel. 3895682260	€€, AIC

LAMEZIA TERME

A Ruga Via S. Giovanni	restaurant tel. 096825486	€€-€€€, AIC

Associazione Accademia Della Pizza Italiana La Brace restaurant, pizzeria		€€, AIC
Via G. Murat	tel. 0968.453610	

LAUROPOLI DI CASSANO

Arnold's Via Paolino Chidichimo	pizzeria tel. 3336801558	€ - €€, AIC

LAZZARO

La Cascina Calipso Via Nazionale Fornaci	restaurant, pizzeria tel. 0965.676017	€-€€, AIC
L'Antico Casale S.S. 106, 261	restaurant, pizzeria tel. 0965714146	€-€€€, AIC

LOCRI

Winter Cactus C.so Vitt. Emanuele, 87	restaurant, pizzeria tel. 3384396246	€, AIC

LONGOBARDI

La Collina Verde S.S.182	restaurant, pizzeria tel. 348.1225026	€-€€, AIC

MAIDA

La Coccinella	gelato (€, AIC)	Via Nazionale, 8

MAIERATO

Popilia country resort Località Cutà s.s. 110 km 1	hotel, restaurant tel. 0963.264252	€€-€€€, AIC www.popiliaresort.it

MALVITO

La Cambusa C.da Peiorata 9	pizzeria tel. 347.7849567	€-€€, AIC

MANDATORICCIO

Castello Flotta Località Procello	restaurant tel. 983.90889	€€-€€€, AIC

MARINA DI GIOIOSA JONICA

Gambero Rosso Via Montezemolo, 65/67	restaurant tel. 0964415806	€€€€, AIC

MELIA DI S. ROBERTO

La Locanda di Marcello Via Purgatorio	hotel, restaurant tel. 0965755407	€€-€€€, AIC www.lalocandadimarcello.it

MELITO PORTO SALVO

L'Angelo Biondo Via Madonnuzza, 5	restaurant, pizzeria tel. 3450661905	€€, AIC

Black Bar Rist. Pizz.
Via Spadolini

MIRTO CROSIA
restaurant, pizzeria   €-€€, AIC
tel. 983.42798

Villa Santa Caterina
Via Garigliano

MONTALTO UFFUGO
agritourism, restaurant   €€-€€€, AIC
tel. 0984934433   www.agriturismovillasantacaterina.it

Costaraba
Via delle Mandrelle

MONTAURO SCALO
restaurant, pizzeria   € - €€, AIC
tel. 0961578800   ristorantecostaraba@gmail.com

Lido On The Beach
Calalunga

restaurant, pizzeria bar   €€, AIC
tel. 567577351

Il Capriccio
Via Nazionale, 229

MONTEPAONE LIDO
restaurant, pizzeria   €, AIC
tel. 0967576654

Il Ghiottone
Via Mazzini, 38

restaurant, pizzeria   €, AIC
tel. 0967576837

Al Convento
Via Vincenzo Severini, 1

MORANO CALABRO
restaurant, pizzeria   €, AIC
tel. 09811896138

Chalet Rocco
Località Campotenese

B&B   AIC
tel. 098133992   www.chaletrocco.com

Green House
Contrada Barbalonga

B&B   AIC
tel. 3493536413   www.greenhousebb.it

Hotel Regina
C.da Campotenese

hotel, restaurant, pizzeria   €-€€, AIC
tel. 098133768   www.reginahotel.calabria.it

L'Accademia
L.re Cicerone - Lazzaro

MOTTA SAN GIOVANNI
restaurant   €-€€, AIC
tel. 0965714132

Brivido Gelat. Artigianale

PAOLA
gelato (€, AIC)   C.so Garibaldi, 35

Il Pavone
Via della Libertà, 8

pizzeria   €, AIC
tel. 0982583661

Pa Pla
P.zza del Popolo, 2

sandwich shop   €, AIC
tel. 0982611080

Sancho Panza
Via Sant'Agata, 38

restaurant, pizzeria   €€, AIC
tel. 0982612155

La Collina degli Ulivi
Via Martorara, 2

PELLARO
trattoria   €€-€€€, AIC
tel. 3336292558

Mamas
Via Quattronari, 14

pizzeria   €, AIC
tel. 0965.35838

Tahiti
Via Nazionale Trav.H 20

pizzeria, ice cream   €, AIC
tel. 0965350342

PIANETTE DI ROVITO

New Number One	pizzeria	€-€€, AIC
Via A. Gramsci 10	tel. 0984.433653	

PIZZO CALABRO

Hale Bopp	restaurant	€€, AIC
Via A. Anile, 8	tel. 0963532259	
Corallini	gelato (€, AIC)	Via Lung.re C. Colombo
Gelateria Enrico	gelato (€, AIC)	Via Prangi 104 Loc. Marinella
Gelateria Ercole	gelato (€, AIC)	P.zza Della Repubblica, 18
Il Tartufo Domenico Penna	gelato (€, AIC)	Via S. Sebastiano

POLISTENA

Il Gusto	restaurant, pizzeria	€, AIC
Via On. Luigi Longo 81	tel. 0966932999	
Miaglut	bakery, rotisserie	€, AIC
Via Perugia 12	tel. 0966.935210	

PRAIA A MARE

Escopocodise ra	pizzeria	€, AIC
Via Leonardo Da Vinci 20	tel. 3406523131	

REGGIO CALABRIA

Armacà	restaurant, pizzeria	€€, AIC
contradà armacà	tel. 965.48765	
Baylik	restaurant	€€€, AIC
Via Vico Leone, 1-3-5	tel. 096548624	
Bridge Lounge Pub	pub	€, AIC
Via Sbarre C.li, 775 (Ponte S. Agata)	tel. 0965025504	
Caffetteria Biesse	tavola calda	€, AIC
c/o la Fac. di Archit.-salita Melissari	tel. 0965800213	
E' Hotel	hotel, restaurant	€€€, AIC
Via Giunchi, 6	tel. 0965893000	www.ehotelreggiocalabria.it
El Puente	pizzeria	€, AIC
Via Sbarre Centrali, 765	tel. 0965594465	

Gelateria Bar Mckenzye gelato (€, AIC) Via Giudecca 15, 1° tratto Tapis Roulant

Il Rusticone	pizzeria	€, AIC
Via S. Caterina, 29	tel. 096544433	
Le Specialità Senza Glutine	restaurant, pizzeria	€, AIC
Via Antonio Cimino, 54	tel. 0965324461	
Mamas	pizzeria	€, AIC
Viale Calabria 349	tel. 0965626000	wwwpizzeriamamas.it
Pizza New	restaurant, pizzeria	€, AIC
Via Guglielmo Pepe 12/a	tel. 0965324461	
Pizza Roma	pizzeria	€, AIC
Via San Francesco Da Paola 24	tel. 0965.951278	
Pizzeria Spaccanapoli	pizzeria	€, AIC
Via Fata Morgana 3/5	tel. 0965.312276	

Zero Glut
Via Ipponio 99

bakery, pizza, rotisserie
tel. 3480127619

€, AIC

Giòpasticceria
Via Leonardo Da Vinci 80

bakery, pizza, rotisserie
tel. 331.9026612

€, AIC

La Cantina del Contadino
Via Rocchi, 3

agritourism
tel. 0984403679   www.agriturismoquercia.com

€, AIC

La Conca d'Oro

gelato (€, AIC)   Via Modigliani-S. Agostino

Nonsolopizza
Via G. Dechirico 121

pizzeria
tel. 0984.466579

€, AIC

Palagarden
C.da Marchesino - Parco Robinson

restaurant, pizzeria
tel. 0984464529

€, AIC

S. Francesco
Via Ungaretti, 2

hotel
tel. 0984461721

€€, AIC
www.hsf.it

Hotel Incoronato
Via Grotticello Loc. S. Nicolò

hotel, restaurant
tel. 0963663428

€€-€€€, AIC
www.hotelgrotticelle.it

Villaggio Hotel Tonicello
Contrada Capo Vaticano

hotel
tel. 0963663724

AIC
wwwtonicello.com

Villaggio Pineta Petto Bianco hotel, restaurant
Contrada Campia

tel. 0963665768

€€, AIC
www.villaggiopettobianco.it

Borgo Cariati
Via Risorgimento S.S, 111

bakery
tel. 0966.046258

€, AIC

Al Favaloro
Via dei Bizantini, 13

restaurant, pizzeria
tel. 096256551

€€-€€€€, AIC

Fish market (J. Kelly)

ROCCELLA JONICA

La Cascina
S.S. 106

restaurant, pizzeria
tel. 0964866675

€€€, AIC

La Taverna di Bacco
Via Orlando, 5

restaurant, pizzeria
tel. 096485666

€, AIC

L'Angelo Dolce

gelato (€, AIC)

Via Roma, 55

Parco dei Principi
C.da Badessa

hotel
tel. 0964860201   www.parcodeiprincipi-roccella.com

AIC

Ranch Sound
C.da Canne

restaurant, pizzeria
tel. 0964863389

€€, AIC

ROGLIANO

Il Girasole
Viale Stazione 16

B&B
tel. 0984.982025

AIC

ROMBIOLO

Il Casolare
Loc. Romanò str.prov. Nicotera

agritourism
tel. 3401512890   www.agriturismo-ilcasolare.com

€€-€€€, AIC

ROSE

Caravaggio
C/da Petraro

pizzeria, restaurant
tel. 0984993327

€, AIC

ROSSANO SCALO

Il Drago
Via Ippocrate, 24

restaurant, pizzeria
tel. 0983512189

€, AIC

Pascia'
Contrada Cutura

restaurant, pizzeria
tel. 0983565493

€€€, AIC

SALINE JONICHE

Le Agavi
Via Fucidà 2

agritourism, restaurant, pizzeria
tel. 0965782371

€, AIC
www.leagavi.net

Naif
Via Nazionale, 195

restaurant, pizzeria
tel. 0965772968

€, AIC

SAN FERDINANDO

Le Dune Blu
Località Baia dei Pini

resort
tel. 0966.766649

AIC

SAN FILI

Il Carro
Via Gramsci

agritourism
tel. 3492439940

€, AIC
www.agriturismo-ilcarro.it

SAN GIOVANNI IN FIORE

Brillo Parlante
Via Lungo Lago Lorica

restaurant
tel. 984537282

€, AIC

Da Paura
Via Fiume Lese 36

restaurant, pizzeria
tel. 0984.970025

€€, AIC

Hotel Biafora
Contrada Garga, 9

hotel, restaurant
tel. 0984970014

€€-€€€, AIC
www.hotelbiafora.it

Hotel Duchessa Della Sila
Viale della Republica 461

hotel, restaurant, pizzeria
tel. 0984.915522

AIC
www.duchessadellasila.it

La Pirainella Via G.A. Lopez	restaurant, pizzeria tel. 0984.970579	€€, AIC
L'angolo Del Gusto Via Roma	pizzeria tel. 984913038	€, AIC

SAN LUCIDO

Eat and Drink Corso Umberto, I	pizzeria, sandwich shop tel. 098284705	€, AIC
Rist.Dragut/H. La Fortezza Via Marina Taverna, 22	hotel, restaurant tel. 0982848784	€€€, AIC www.residencelafortezza.it

SAN MARCO ARGENTANO

L'Etoile	gelato (€, AIC)	P.zza Selvaggi
L'Europa C.da Iotta	restaurant, pizzeria tel. 0984522028	€, AIC

SAN NICOLA ARCELLA

Il Furano C.da Marinella	restaurant tel. 0985300644	€€, AIC

SAN SOSTENE

Residence Paradise Via delle Magnolie	restaurant, pizzeria tel. 096771648	€€€, AIC

SAN VINCENZO LA COSTA

La Locanda del Greco C.da Greco Battista, 15	agritourism tel. 0984936615	€€, AIC

SANGINETO

Sachsenhausen S.S. 18 n° 41	restaurant, pizzeria tel. 098296378	€€, AIC

SAN STEFANO D'ASPROMONTE

B&B Musolino-La Civetta Via Nazionale Cucullaro	restaurant tel. 0965740304	€, AIC
Le Fate dei Fiori Via Nazionale, 53	hotel, restaurant tel. 0965749015	AIC www.lefatedeifiori.it
Rifugio Husky Via degli Abeti - Gambarie	restaurant, pizzeria tel. 3492351243	€€, AIC

SANTA CATERINA DELLO JONIO

Excalibur Via delle Serre, 21/23	restaurant, pizzeria tel. 096783407	€€-€€€, AIC

SATRIANO

Fuego Viale Europa, 196	pizzeria tel. 0967620148	€, AIC
La Villa Via S. Bruno da Colonia	B&B tel. 09674059193	AIC

SCALEA

Albergo Residence Villa Brazzano Via Foresta 11	hotel, restaurant tel. 0985.939895	AIC www.forestvillabrazzano.it
Hotel Talao C.so Mediterraneo, 66	hotel tel. 098520444	€, AIC www.hoteltalao.it

Krataiis	**SCILLA**	
Via G. Oriccioli, 26	restaurant	€€€€, AIC
	tel. 0965754022	
L'Orso Cattivo	**SETTINGIANO**	
Contrada Gambieri	restaurant, pizzeria	€€, AIC
	tel. 0961998149	
Hotel President	**SIDERNO**	
S.S. 106	hotel, restaurant	€€, AIC
	tel. 0964343191	www.grandhotelpresident.com
La Mimosa	restaurant, pizzeria	€-€€, AIC
Via Mediterraneo, 78	tel. 0964342303	
Il Faro	**SORBO SAN BASILE**	
Contrada Cutura	restaurant	€€, AIC
	tel. 0961921214	
Al Marinaio	**SOVERATO**	
Via Cristoforo Colombo, 16	pizzeria	€, AIC
	tel. 096721233	
Bar Morè	gelato (€, AIC)	Via Chiarello Poliporto
Braxtor	pizzeria	€, AIC
Via Marina, 24/30	tel. 0967528456	
La Tavola di Melusinda	restaurant	€€-€€€, AIC
Via della Vittoria, 1/3	tel. 3493766493	
Pizzeria Da Benito	pizzeria	€-€€, AIC
Via F. Cilea 64	tel. 3383959754	
La Fontanella Rist. Pizz.	**SPADOLA**	
Località Cannella ss 110	restaurant, pizzeria	€-€€, AIC
	tel. 963.70136	
	SPEZZANO DELLA SILA	
La Pignanella	restaurant	€€-€€€, AIC
C.da Molarotta- Camigliatello S.no	tel. 0984.578443	
	STALETTÌ	
Baia dell'Est	hotel, restaurant	€€€, AIC
Via Caminia	tel. 0961911352	www.baiadellest.it
Hotel Club Poseidon	hotel, reception hall	€€-€€€, AIC
Via Lido di Copanello, 12	tel. 0961911252	www.hotelresidenceposeidon.it
Ristorante la baia di Caminia	restaurant, pizzeria	€€-€€€, AIC
Via del Mare 2	tel. 0961.911093	
	STECCATO DI CUTRO	
Villaggio Serenè	resort	AIC
Loc. Marinella	tel. 962.77	www.bluserena.it
	TAURIANOVA	
La Cucciarda	restaurant, pizzeria	€€, AIC
Contrada Pegara	tel. 0966612766	
Metropolis' Pizza	restaurant, pizzeria	€€, AIC
C.da Crocicchia c/o Parco	tel. 0966645073	

Scionti Francesco Pasticceria   gelato (€, AIC)   Via Roma, 55

TAVERNA

Hotel Sila   hotel, restaurant   €€, AIC
Via Villaggio Mancuso   tel. 0961922032

TERRANOVA DA SIBARI

Hostaria Antico Borgo   restaurant, pizzeria   €€, AIC
Viale Castello 17   tel. 0981955964

TORTORA MARINA

La Locanda del Corso   B&B   AIC
C.so Aldo Moro, 87/91   tel. 0985766849   info@lalocandadelcorso.it

TREBISACCE

Capraro   pizzeria   €, AIC
Via 25 Aprile, 36   tel. 098158281

TRENTA

Lucignolo   pizzeria   €, AIC
Via F. Gullo 60   tel. 0984.439871

TROPEA

Da Nico e Lilly   restaurant, pizzeria   AIC
Via Orazio Toraldo Di Francia   tel. 3930037114   www.ristorantedanicoelillytropea.it

VIBO MARINA

Birreria Tato's   restaurant, pizzeria   €, AIC
Via Longobardi, 15   tel. 0963571530

La Rada   restaurant   AIC
Via A. Vespucci   tel. 0963.577030   www.ristorantelidolarada.com

VIBO VALENTIA

Glut Word   tavola calda   €, AIC
Via Dante Alighieri   tel. 330982495

Ristorante Pizzeria Terravecchia   restaurant, pizzeria   €-€€, AIC
Via Terravecchia 184   tel. 3283796701

VILLA S.GIOVANNI

De la Ville   hotel, restaurant   €€-€€€, AIC
Via Ammiraglio Curzon   tel. 0965795600   www.grandhoteldelaville.eu

Il Gallo D'Oro   restaurant, pizzeria   €€-€€€, AIC
Via Roma, 81   tel. 0965.752258

VILLAPIANA

Orto della Signora   restaurant, pizzeria   €€, AIC
C.da Orto della Signora   tel. 0981505688   www.ortodellasignora.it

ZAMBRONE

Hotel La Praia   hotel, restaurant   AIC
Via Del Mare   tel. 0963.392086   www.lapraia.it

Cioccolati di Pasqua (J.Kelly)

SAN MARINO
(AIC = participates in the Associazione Italiana Celiachia program)

DOGANA
Dell'Angelo   restaurant, pizzeria   €-€€€, AIC
Via 3 Settembre, 65   tel. 0549941292
Notes: Closed Fridays.

DOMAGNANO
Pizza Leggera   pizzeria   €, AIC
Str. Di Paderna, 2   tel. 0549909608
Notes: DS Pizza Point. Closed Mondays.

SAN GIOVANNI-BORGO MAGGIORE
Boschetto   restaurant, pizzeria   €-€€€, AIC
Strada San Gianno, 97   tel. 0549878450
Notes: DS Pizza Point. Closed Mondays.

SAN MARINO
H. La Rocca R. Il Beccafico   hotel, restaurant   €-€€€, AIC
Via Salita alla Rocca, 35   tel. 549991166

Index

Index

Index

Marina di Bibbona, 81
Marina di Camerota, 179
Marina di Campo-Isola d'Elba, 81
Marina di Carrara, 81
Marina di Gioiosa Jonica, 286
Marina di Grosseto, 81
Marina di Massa, 82
Marina di Montemarciano, 265
Marina di Pietrasanta, 82
Marina di Ragusa, 213
Marina di S. Nicola/Ladispoli, 54
Marina Montemarciano, 265
Marina Romea, 162
Marino, 54, 294
Marlia, 82
Marone, 127
Marostica, 106
Marotta, 265
Marsala, 213
Martellago, 106
Martina Franca, 200
Marzabotto, 162
Mason Vicentino, 106
Massa, 82, 83, 179
Massa e Cozzile, 83
Massa Lubrense, 179
Massafra, 200
Matera, 279
Mathi, 238
Matino, 200
Mattie, 238
Mattinata, 200
Mazara del Vallo, 213
Mazzarino, 213
Mazzo di Rho, 127
Meano, 252
Medicina, 162
Mele, 142
Melfi, 279
Melia di S. Roberto, 286
Melito Porto Salvo, 286
Meltina, 249, 252
Mentana, 54
Merano, 252
Merate, 127
Mercatale Val di Pesa, 83
Mercatello, 151, 265

Merì, 214
Merlengo Ponzano Veneto, 106
Messina, 214
Mestre, 106
Mestre-Zelarino, 106
Meta, 180
Mezzo Lombardo, 252
Milano, 162
Milazzo, 214
Milena, 214
Minervino, 200
Minervino Murge, 200
Mira, 107
Mirabella Eclano, 180
Mirabella Imbaccari, 214
Miramare, 163
Miramare di Rimini, 163
Mirandola, 163
Mirano, 107
Mirto Crosia, 287
Misano Adriatico, 163
Misilmeri, 214
Misterbianco, 214
Modena, 163
Modica, 214
Modugno, 200
Moena, 252
Mogliano Veneto, 107
Moiano, 180
Mola di Bari, 200
Molfetta, 200
Molinara, 180
Molini di Tures, 249, 252
Molveno, 252
Monastero Bormida, 238
Monastero di Lanzo, 238
Monastero di Vasco, 238
Moncalieri, 238
Moncucco Torinese, 238
Mondavio, 265
Mondolfo, 265
Mondovi, 238
Moneglia, 142
Monforte d'Alba, 238
Monopoli, 201
Monreale, 214

Monsummano Terme, 83
Montà d'Alba, 238
Montagnaga di Pinè, 252
Montalcino, 83
Montale, 83
Montalto di Castro, 54
Montalto Uffugo, 287
Montanaro di Francolise, 180
Montaquila, 277
Montauro Scalo, 287
Montavarchi, 83
Monte Colombo, 164
Monte Compatri, 54
Monte S. Savino, 83
Monte San Biagio, 54
Montebelluna, 107
Montecarlo, 83
Montecastrilli, 151
Montecatini Terme, 83
Montecchia di Crosara, 107
Montecchio Emilia, 164
Montecenere di Lama Mocogno, 164
Montefalco, 151
Monteforte d'Alpone, 107
Montegallo, 266
Montegrotto Terme, 107
Montelupo, 83
Montemarciano, 266
Montemezzo di Sovizzo, 107
Montemurlo, 84
Montepaone Lido, 287
Monteroni d'Arbia, 84
Monteroni di Lecce, 201
Monterosso al Mare, 142
Monterotondo, 54
Montesarchio, 180
Montescudaio, 84
Montesilvano, 272
Monteu Roero, 238
Montevaccino-Trento, 252
Montevarchi, 84
Monteverde, 180
Montiano, 84
Monticchio Laghi, 279
Montichiari, 127
Monticiano, 84

Index

Index